Schedule effects: drugs, drinking, and aggression

SCHEDULE EFFECTS

Drugs, drinking, and aggression

Edited by R.M. Gilbert and J.D. Keehn

Published for the Addiction Research Foundation by
University of Toronto Press

© University of Toronto Press 1972
Toronto and Buffalo
Printed in Canada
ISBN 0-8020-3286-9
Microfiche ISBN 0-8020-0200-5
LC 70-189607

Contents

The proximal events controlling adjunctive behaviour
Displacement activities as adjunctive behaviours
Adjunctive behaviour: adjustive, toxic, or creative
response?
On the nature of adjunctive behaviour

Methods
Behaviour production by aversive stimuli
Some differential effects of several drugs upon
different response classes
Discussion
Comment by N.K. Innis and J.D. Keehn

A functional definition of aggression
Unconditioned aggression
Respondent conditioning of pain-aggression
Operant conditioning of aggression
Interaction of unconditioned aggression with aversively
controlled operants
Punishment-aggression interactions
Side-effects of aversive control

Preface

In May 1970 the Addiction Research Foundation of Ontario sponsored a symposium on 'Schedule-induced and schedule-dependent phenomena,' partly to stress the Foundation's concern with the relationships between drugs, behaviour, and the environment, and partly to celebrate the completion of the Foundation's splendid new facilities in Toronto. The plans were premature in one sense. The building at 33 Russell Street was not ready until later in the year, and the symposium was held instead at the University of Toronto. The topic, nonetheless, was very timely.

The strange and unwieldy title of the symposium arose because we wished to bring together two hitherto unrelated kinds of phenomena, both involving reinforcement schedules and both of some importance in the analysis of drug use. Reinforcement refers to the strengthening, selection, or maintenance of an organism's behaviour by its consequences, known as reinforcers. A reinforcement schedule describes the rule for assigning reinforcers to particular forms of behaviour. Such rules are applied in experimental situations: they are assumed to apply, by analogy, in the 'real world.' Reinforcement schedules are important determiners of the effects of various procedures on behaviour. For example, one cannot make a general statement about the effect of a particular drug dosage on food-reinforced behaviour, only about the effect on behaviour controlled by a particular schedule of food reinforcement. Such procedures may be referred to as schedule-dependent, hence one of the adjectives in the title of the symposium. Many of the apparently paradoxical effects of behaviourally active drugs become clear if the controlling schedules are taken into account.

When the particular form of behaviour specified by a reinforcement schedule is brought under the control of the schedule, other behaviour is also affected. Trivially, this happens because the effect of the schedule is to promote the occurrence of the reinforced form at the expense of other forms of behaviour. Certain reinforcement schedules, however, cause an increase in behaviour that is not specified by the schedule.

Which kind of behaviour increases in frequency depends upon factors in the environment. If drinking is possible, the schedule may induce a metobolically excessive amount of drinking, even of a relatively unpalatable fluid such as a solution of ethyl alcohol. One of the earliest discoveries of the phenomenon of schedule-induced polydipsia involved the consumption of alcohol. The phenomenon is of more than historic interest, however. Much drinking of alcohol, still Ontario's major drug concern, occurs for reasons that are not obvious. One cause of the obscurity could be that the drinking is controlled not only by its consequences but also by schedules in the natural environment that specify other behaviour. Consumption of other drugs has been induced in this manner under laboratory conditions. Furthermore, behaviours involved in hyperactivity and aggression, both believed to be drug-related, have also been induced by schedules of reinforcement.

The link between the two kinds of phenomenon goes beyond the inclusion of the term 'schedule' in their descriptions. Each constitutes an extension of the simple reinforcement model of the control of behaviour. The simple model points to the hegemony of reinforcement contingencies in the determination of the behaviour of organisms. The extensions show, on the one hand, that reinforcement schedules may themselves determine the effects of other procedures and, on the other hand, that reinforcement schedules may maintain non-specified behaviour. It was hoped that the symposium would produce other grounds for synthesis. To this end a variety of speakers was invited whose interests ranged from the particular behaviour that, on occasion, happens to be schedule-induced, through the substantive topics of the meeting, to reinforcement processes themselves.

A synthesis was not forthcoming. Instead we had a fairly neat split of papers between the half that focused on reinforcement processes and the half that concentrated on schedule effects. Furthermore, the former group emphasized theoretical and procedural analysis whereas the latter group presented data. The split was beneficial to the organizers who might otherwise have been faced with the publication of an unwieldy volume of diverse contents. We had expected that many of the contributors would not want to write versions of their presentations for formal publication. As it happened, only two contributors withdrew. The remainder are featured in two volumes, published by different houses.

The present volume has its origin in the papers that emphasized schedule effects.* The nine chapters constitute generally an updating or com-

*The other volume is entitled *Reinforcement: Behavioral analyses*, edited by R.M. Gilbert and J.R. Millenson and published in 1972 by Academic Press (New York). It contains the following chapters:1. Induction and the provenance of operants, by

plete rewriting of material presented or discussed at the Toronto symposium. Chapters 1 and 2 are concerned specifically with schedule-dependent effects. McKearney, in Chapter 1, describes how the effect of a drug upon behaviour depends upon the schedule of reinforcement that is maintaining the behaviour, even when the 'reinforcer' is a stimulus that might be expected to punish. Blackman, in Chapter 2, reviews work on another schedule-dependent effect, that of the intrusion upon behaviour of a stimulus that predicts shock. He argues that 'anxiety' should be defined as an effect rather than as a cause. In Chapter 3, Thompson and Pickens consider schedule influences upon drug self-administration, noting that, given certain conditions, drug reinforcers are similar to other reinforcers. The remaining chapters are concerned, in one way or another, with schedule-induced behaviour. Keehn, in Chapter 4, considers that such behaviour, and many other phenomena, justifies restatement of the Law of Effect in dynamic, relative terms. Chapter 5 consists of a review by Hawkins and his associates of their work on schedule-induced drinking, including the drinking of alcohol solutions to intoxication. Wuttke and Innis, in Chapter 6, report experiments that show how schedule-induced drinking occurs when other behaviour is maintained by second order schedules of reinforcement. They describe the results in ethological terms. An ethological account is also provided by Falk in Chapter 7, where he emphasizes the functional properties of adjunctive behaviour, that is, behaviour that arises as a consequence of the control of other behaviour. The last two chapters are concerned with the effects of aversive stimuli. Hutchinson and Emley, in Chapter 8, present data on biting and manipulative responses of monkeys to electric shock, and the effects of various drugs on these kinds of behaviour. Finally, Ulrich and his associates, in Chapter 9, review work on the elicitation and induction of aggression, concluding with comments on the extrapolation of findings on animal aggression to human behaviour.

Noting recent allegations of dullness by reviewers of symposium compilations, we approached decisions about the format of this volume

---

E.F. Segal; 2. Constraints on the operant conditioning of drinking, by A.H. Black; and G.A. Young; 3. The effect on extinction of the preference relations between the instrumental and contingent events, by D. Premack; 4. Development and maintenance of responding under schedules of electric-shock presentation, by R. Stretch; 5. Motivational properties of conditioned anxiety, by J.R. Millenson and P. de Villiers 6. The Measurement of rate-dependent changes in responding, by S.E.G. Lea and M.J. Morgan; 7. Behavioral control by intermittent stimulation, by W.N. Schoenfeld and B.K. Cole; 8. Reinforcement schedules: Contingency or continuity, by T.M. Bloomfield; 9. Temporal control and the theory of reinforcement schedules, by J.E.R. Staddon; 10. Variation and selection of behavior, by R.M. Gilbert.

somewhat cautiously. Formal publication of the original contributions to the meeting would certainly have provided a dull compilation but this danger was averted by the authors' insistence upon thorough rewriting, for which we are grateful. At one point we were concerned about the coherence of the projected volume. Not liking the editorial profundities that often fill white spaces between chapters in books such as this, we suggested to authors that they provide conceptual connective tissue in the form of comments on the contributions of others. This suggestion was effective in the sense that comments were made, but unsuccessful inasmuch as few were suitable for inclusion, usually because the target chapter was changed in such a way as to render the comment inappropriate. We still have doubts as to the best way to present this kind of material, even though we are happier now that the present volume achieves some focus on the subject of its title. On the merit of compilations as such we are less in doubt. They provide a medium for reasonably short but discursive presentations of data and theory. Editors of journals that also provide this facility cannot devote three or four issues to one limited range of topics. Even if they wanted to they would, most probably, for various reasons, provide less licence to pontificate and speculate than the editors of a book.

We have been greatly helped by a number of people, mostly staff of the Addiction Research Foundation in Toronto. Our special thanks are due to June Shepperd and Mary Wildridge.

March 1972   RMG
                                                       JDK

Acknowledgments

The Society for the Experimental Analysis of Behavior, Inc., for permission to reproduce from the *Journal of the Experimental Analysis of Behavior* what appear here as Figures 6, 7, and 10 of Chapter 1, Figure 1 of Chapter 2, Figures 8 and 21 of Chapter 4, Figure 2 of Chapter 7, and Figure 4 of Chapter 9.

The American Association for the Advancement of Science for permission to reproduce from *Science* what appears here as Figure 5 of Chapter 1.

The Meredith Corporation, Inc., for permission to reproduce from *The theory of reinforcement schedules,* edited by W.N. Schoenfeld and published by Appleton-Century-Crofts, what appears here as Figure 1 of the reply to the comment on Chapter 1, and from *Stimulus properties of drugs,* edited by T. Thompson and R. Pickens and published by Appleton-Century-Crofts, what appear here as Figures 6, 7, 10, and 12 of Chapter 3.

Academic Press, Inc., for permission to reproduce from the *Quarterly Journal of Experimental Psychology* what appear here as Figures 2 and 3 of Chapter 3.

The Federation of American Societies for Experimental Biology for permission to reproduce from *Federation Proceedings* what appear here as Figures 2 and 3 of Chapter 1.

The Psychonomic Society, Inc., for permission to reproduce from *Psychonomic Science* what appear here as Figures 1, 16, and 22 of Chapter 4.

The Editor of *The Psychological Record* for permission to reproduce what appear here as Figures 17, 18, 19, and 20 of Chapter 4.

The Editors of *Psychological Reports* for permission to reproduce what appear here as Figures 9, 10, 11, 12, 13, abd 14 of Chapter 4.

The New York Academy of Sciences for permission to reproduce from the *Annals of the New York Academy of Sciences* what appears here as Figure 3 of Chapter 7.

G.E. Coulson for permission to reproduce from his Ph D Thesis what appear here as Figure 4, 5, 6, and 7 of Chapter 4;

Pergamon Press, Ltd., for permission to reproduce, with minor alterations, from Volume 6 of *Physiology and Behavior* what appears here as Chapter 7.

Schedule effects: drugs, drinking, and aggression

1 Schedule-dependent effects: effects of drugs, and maintenance of responding with response-produced electric shocks

JAMES W. McKEARNEY

The precise conditions under which certain environmental events, called reinforcers, are related to responding determine the rate of occurrence and the temporal pattern of the resulting behaviour. The rate of occurrence and temporal pattern of responding largely determine the effects that experimental interventions will have. Further, the effects of certain interventions or events depend jointly on the schedule under which they are presented and on the characteristics of the behaviour existing at the time they are presented. Existing behaviours, of course, have been critically shaped by the organism's history of reinforcement. Thus, characteristics of ongoing behaviour are jointly determined by the organism's history of reinforcement and by the schedule dependencies presently in operation; in turn, past and present behaviours influence the effects that new schedule conditions or other experimental interventions will have.

This paper will focus on certain of these co-dependencies. The general dependence of the effects of environmental events on the precise conditions under which they are presented will be illustrated primarily by experiments both on the effects of drugs on behaviour and on the varied effects of electric shocks.

EFFECTS OF DRUGS

By way of introduction, it is instructive to look at the effects of drugs

Experiments by the author, described herein, were conducted at Harvard Medical School and were supported by grants MH-02094, MH-07658, and 5 T1-MH-07084 from the US Public Health Service. Preparation of the manuscript was supported in part by grants 5 T01 MH-10625 and MH-18421 from the US Public Health Service.

on behaviour, because it is here that some of the clearest examples of the
importance of ongoing behaviour are seen. Traditional psychological
theories have emphasized the importance of motivational states in pre-
dicting and controlling behaviour. Responding maintained by the presentation of food or water is usually said to depend on a 'hunger' or 'thirst'
drive; behaviour maintained by the termination of a so-called noxious
stimulus, or behaviour suppressed by the presentation of such a stimulus,
is said to depend on a 'fear' or 'anxiety' drive. Because these ideas are so
widespread, the effects of drugs on behaviour are often interpreted in
terms of the effects drugs are supposed to have on the motivational
states thought to underly the behaviour. For example, a tranquillizing
drug such as chlorpromazine is often said to reduce avoidance responding because it reduces the anxiety or fear supposedly associated with the
delivery of electric shock. Decreases in responding under schedules of
food presentation after amphetamine administration are often attributed
to anorexic effects of the drug.

When we say that the effects of drugs depend crucially on the characteristics of the behaviour under study, this is, of course, only an extension of the general pharmacologic principle that the effects of a drug
depend on the circumstances under which it is administered. This general point should need little illustration. A classic example is the approximately tenfold increase in the lethality of amphetamine that results
when aggregated rather than singly-caged animals are studied (cf, Dews
and Morse, 1961).

Though it will not be possible to go into all the experimental evidence
in detail here, it can be summarized by saying that the notion cannot be
supported that drugs have their effects on behaviour because of effects
on motivational states.

If drug effects depended on the type of 'motivation' involved, then
two things should be true:* first, a drug's effects on similarly motivated
behaviours should be similar, and second, a drug's effects on differently
motivated behaviours should be different. Figure 1 shows cumulative
records of key-pecking of a pigeon under a multiple 10-minute fixed-
interval 31-response fixed-ratio schedule of food presentation: in the
presence of a red key-light, food was presented following the first
response to occur after ten minutes had elapsed; in the presence of a
blue key-light, food was presented following the thirty-first response.
These two components of the schedule alternated repeatedly throughout
the session. As Figure 1 (top record) shows, the food presentation maintained distinctly different patterns of responding depending on the

*This analysis is based on that of Kelleher and Morse (1968a).

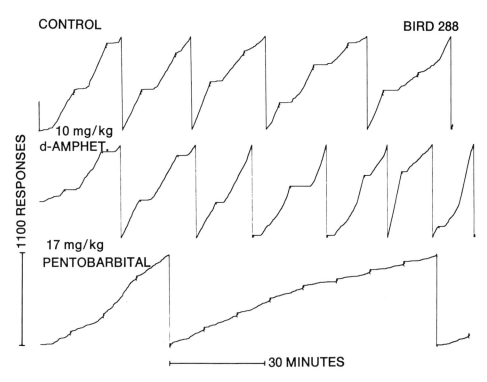

CONTROL   BIRD 288

1100 RESPONSES

10 mg/kg
d-AMPHET.

17 mg/kg
PENTOBARBITAL

├──────────────────┤ 30 MINUTES

Figure 1   Cumulative records of responding under a multiple 10-minute fixed-interval 31-response fixed-ratio schedule of food presentation in the pigeon. Ordinate: cumulative responses. Abscissa: time. FI and FR components alternated throughout the session. If no response was made within 60 seconds of the end of the FI, or if 31 responses were not emitted within 60 seconds during the FR, the alternate schedule component was presented (60-second limited-hold). Note that different patterns of responding were maintained under the two schedules: under the FI, there was a pause followed by an increasing rate until food presentation, whereas under the FR there was a high and steady rate until food was presented. Top record: control. Middle record: performance at about 3 1/2 hours after administration of 10.0 mg/kg d-amphetamine. Bottom record: performance at about 2 hours after administration of 17.0 mg/kg pentobarbital. Note that after d-amphetamine FI responding was increased, but FR responding was completely abolished (flat portions after FI food presentation); after pentobarbital, FI responding was markedly decreased, but FR responding continued to occur normally.

schedule. The second record in Figure 1 illustrates the effects of 10 mg/kg d-amphetamine on this performance. Responding during the fixed-interval component was markedly increased, but there was no responding during the fixed-ratio component. Though this is an extreme example, it has been well documented that the amphetamines tend to increase responding that normally occurs at relatively low rates – in this case, during the fixed-interval – at the same doses at which it decreases rates of responding that normally occur at higher rates – here, the fixed-ratio (Dews, 1958; see also the review by Kelleher and Morse, 1968a). The third record illustrates the effects of 17 mg/kg pentobarbital. In this case, responding during the fixed-interval was decreased markedly, while fixed-ratio responding continued to occur at a normal rate. In both of these examples responding was maintained by the same reinforcer, food, yet the drugs had entirely different effects depending on the rates of responding engendered by the particular schedule in effect. Clearly, the idea that similarly motivated behaviours are similarly affected by drugs is untenable.

Consider the second prediction: that differently motivated behaviours are differently affected by drugs. There are many studies in the literature that claim to have demonstrated a differential sensitivity to drugs of behaviours maintained with different reinforcers. For example, some have claimed that the tranquillizing drugs chlorpromazine and reserpine have more marked effects on avoidance behaviour than on behaviour maintained by food or water presentation. However, in none of these studies have the schedules under which food is presented and shock is avoided, or the resultant patterns of responding, been the same. For example, drug effects on continuous avoidance behaviour (in which each response postpones for a specified period an otherwise regularly occurring shock) might be compared with responding maintained under a fixed-interval or fixed-ratio schedule of food presentation. The patterns of responding engendered under these schedules, however, will not be comparable. In view of the well-documented dependence of drug effects on control patterns of responding (eg, Figure 1), it should come as no surprise that the different patterns should be differently affected by drugs, but is it reasonable to attribute these differences to the different motivations that are thought to underly the behaviours?

Recent experiments by Kelleher and Morse (1964) and Cook and Catania (1964) have compared the effects of drugs on similar patterns of responding maintained by food presentation or electric shock termination. Cook and Catania studied one group of monkeys responding under a 10-minute fixed-interval schedule of food presentation, and another group under a 10-minute fixed-interval schedule of electric shock termination (in which the first response after 10 minutes terminated a continuously delivered shock). Typical fixed-interval patterns of responding were engendered under both schedules, and the effects of graded doses of a variety of drugs (chlorpromazine, imipramine, meprobamate, chlordiazepoxide) were found to be the same regardless of whether responding was maintained by food presentation or by electric shock termination.

Kelleher and Morse (1964) studied responding under multiple fixed-interval fixed-ratio schedules of food presentation and under multiple fixed-interval fixed-ratio schedules of termination of stimuli associated with the periodic delivery of electric shocks. Figure 2 shows cumulative records of control performances under both multiple schedules. Kelleher and Morse found that the effects of amphetamine and chlorpromazine were the same irrespective of whether the performances were maintained by food presentation or stimulus-shock termination; d-amphetamine produced dose-dependent increases in responding under both FI schedules, except at the highest dose, but produced only decreases under both FR schedules, while chlorpromazine produced dose-dependent decreases in responding under both FI and both FR schedules (Figure 3). In each of these experiments the effects of drugs depended more on the schedules and resultant patterns of responding than on the type of reinforcing event maintaining the behaviour. When similar patterns of responding are generated, it makes little difference whether the behaviour is maintained by food presentation, electric shock termination, or, as we shall see later, by electric shock presentation. The effects of drugs depend more on the pattern of responding than upon the type of reinforcer.

The rate of occurrence of the behaviour is an important determinant of the effects of drugs. For example, in the experiments described earlier, d-amphetamine increased responding under schedules that engender lower rates of responding, while it either had no effect or decreased responding under schedules that normally generate higher rates of responding. Such a dependence on control rate is forcefully demonstrated by examining the effects of d-amphetamine on responding within a schedule-controlled performance. Responding under a fixed-interval schedule is characterized by a gradually increasing rate as the time elapses; thus, a wide variety of different rates, ranging from almost zero at the beginning of the interval to as many as one or more responses per second at the end of the interval, is available for study. Figure 4 presents an analysis of the effects of d-amphetamine on the responding of a pigeon during individual 1-minute segments of a 10-minute fixed-interval schedule of food presentation. The percentage increase in responding during individual 1-minute segments after d-amphetamine is plotted against the control response rates during the segments. The dose of amphetamine chosen for illustration is one that produced maximal increases in responding. As the figure shows, the change in responding after amphetamine was inversely related to the control rate. At rates of

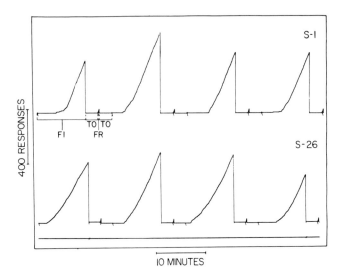

Figure 2   Multiple fixed-interval fixed-ratio performances controlled by different reinforcers in the squirrel monkey. Ordinate: cumulative responses. Abscissa: time. The recording pen reset with each reinforcement. Upper record: food presentation. Lower record: stimulus-shock termination. A 2.5-minute time-out period followed each reinforcement. Short diagonal strokes on the event record for the lower record indicate electric shock (6.2 mA) presentations. Note that the patterns of responding were the same regardless of the type of event maintaining the behaviour. From Kelleher and Morse (1964), with permission.

about 0.3 responses per second and lower there was a graded increase in rate, whereas at 1 response per second and higher there was a decrease in rate. Because all data points fall along the same regression line, the rate-decreasing effects of amphetamine, often attributed to supposed anorexic effects of the drug, appear to be simple quantitative extensions of the rate-increasing effects rather than indications of some qualitatively different process. Kelleher and Morse (1968a) recently summarized the evidence indicating that control rate of responding is of overwhelming importance in determining the effects of drugs.

Although the control rate of responding is an important determinant of the effects of drugs on schedule-controlled behaviour, it is not, of course, the sole determinant. For example, amphetamines do not increase rates of responding suppressed by presentation of electric shock (punished responding), but they do increase other low rates of responding (for example, at the beginning of the fixed-interval). Other experiments (Verhave, 1958; McMillan, 1968) have shown that, for drugs that normally increase low rates of responding to show their effects, there must exist some minimum tendency to respond.

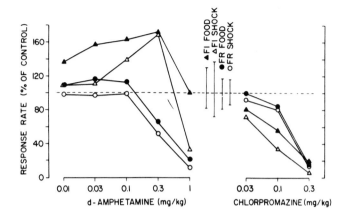

Figure 3 Effects of d-amphetamine and chlorpromazine on responding under multiple FI FR schedules of food presentation and stimulus-shock termination. Each point represents two or more observations in three monkeys under each multiple schedule. Sessions were 2 1/2 hours long. Vertical lines signify the range of control (non-drug) observations. Note the similarity of the pairs of dose-effect curves for FI and for FR components, regardless of the type of reinforcing event. From Kelleher and Morse (1964), with permission.

Another apparent exception to the dependence of drug effects on control rate of responding involves behaviour under the control of powerful discriminative stimuli. In one set of experiments (McKearney, 1970b), pigeons responded under a 10-minute fixed-interval schedule of food presentation. During odd-numbered minutes of the fixed-interval an S^Δ condition prevailed (S^Δ being defined as a stimulus in whose presence food was never presented). S^Δ was either a change in the key-light colour or a change in overhead illumination. Responding during even-numbered minutes in the presence of S^D (a stimulus in whose presence food was presented) showed the usual pattern of positive acceleration; responding during S^Δ was similarly graded, but rates were much lower. The response rate-increasing effects of amobarbital were inversely related to control rates of responding, regardless of whether S^Δ or S^D rates were considered. When S^Δ was a change in key-light colour or a change from a darkened to a brightly illuminated chamber, however, the increases in S^Δ responding were considerably less than would be predicted on the basis of the effects on S^D responding. That is, plotted in the manner of Figure 4, the points for S^Δ minutes were displaced downwards from those for S^D minutes, but still were related to control rate in an inverse linear fashion. When S^Δ was a change from a darkened to a dimly illuminated chamber (ie, when the change in stimulus intensity was less), increases in S^Δ responding after amobarbital were considerably greater, and of the

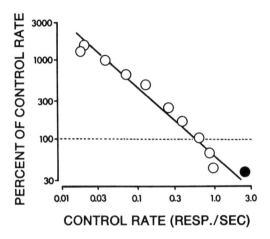

Figure 4   Effects of d-amphetamine on responding during individual 1-minute segments of the FI FR schedule of food presentation. Abscissa: control rate in 1-minute segments. Ordinate: rate in 1-minute segments after d-amphetamine, expressed as percent of control rate. Coordinates are logarithmic. Each point represents a single observation. Note that there is an inverse linear relation between control rate and amount of increase after d-amphetamine. Note that the point for fixed-ratio responding (filled circle) falls along the same regression line as the points for fixed-interval responding.

approximate order expected on the basis of control rate (ie, there was no displacement of S^Δ points from the S^D regression line). Such increases were systematically related to the intensity of the S^Δ stimulus; that is, the less intense the stimulus the greater the increase after amobarbital, even though control rates changed little as S^Δ intensity was decreased. These experiments suggest that the control rate of responding in the presence of a stimulus does not alone reflect the amount of control that will be exercised in the presence of a drug (drug effects changed as S^Δ intensity was decreased even though responding in the absence of the drug did not change), and that the dependence of the effects of drugs on control rates of responding can be modified when behaviour is under the control of powerful discriminative stimuli.

To summarize, the effects of many drugs on behaviour seem to depend importantly upon the control rate and pattern of responding, irrespective of supposed intervening states. Such results suggest that drugs modify behaviour patterns themselves rather than the motivational or emotional states that are thought to underly the behaviour.

MAINTENANCE OF RESPONDING WITH RESPONSE-PRODUCED
ELECTRIC SHOCKS

A given stimulus may affect behaviour in a variety of different ways
(Skinner, 1938). Under certain conditions the presentation of a stimulus
may elicit patterns of behaviour that are relatively stereotyped for a
given species. Under other circumstances the same event may serve as a
discriminative stimulus, setting the occasion for the occurrence or non-
occurrence of some behaviour. Under some conditions ongoing behaviour is suppressed by the presentation of a stimulus (punishment), and
under other conditions responding can be enhanced and maintained by
the presentation of a stimulus (reinforcement). Although one or another of these functions may dominate in the sense of being more obvious, careful experimental analysis often reveals the co-existence of
two or more.

Clearly, it is unreasonable to suppose that a particular environmental
event (stimulus) will have the same effects regardless of the conditions
under which it is imposed. For example, a loud noise will elicit a startle
reaction in a naive subject, but will not do so, or will do so to a lesser
extent, in a subject that has been exposed repeatedly to the noise. If
this same stimulus is frequently paired with the occurrence of another
event, for example, the delayed presentation of food, the presentation
of the noise may occasion a quite different behaviour – in this case,
approaching the food magazine. If the noise is sufficiently loud, its presentation following the occurrence of some response may reduce the
future probability of occurrence of that response. Under other conditions, for example, in a sensorally-deprived subject, a dependence of
noise presentation upon responding might enhance such responding.

In spite of the fact that the effects of a given environmental event are
not invariant, psychological theories have frequently assumed invariance
either tacitly or explicitly. Thus, stimuli such as food or water are, for
appropriately deprived subjects, often thought of as inherently 'positive'
stimuli whose presentation consequent to some behaviour is said to be
'rewarding,' whereas stimuli such as electric shock are thought to be
'negative' or 'fear-producing' events, whose termination or reduction
will maintain behaviour, or whose presentation will suppress behaviour.
Because the assignment of a given stimulus to the positive or negative
category is often based on *a priori*, hedonistic, and non-empirical criteria, exceptions to the usual effects of stimuli are often regarded as
anomalous or paradoxical.

In the classical experiments of Estes and Skinner (1941), responding was shown to be suppressed in the presence of a stimulus that regularly preceded an unavoidable electric shock. These results have been confirmed in many experiments since then, and varying interpretations of these results have been made (see, eg, Millenson, 1967; Blackman, Chapter 2). One hypothesis is that an 'emotional' state becomes conditioned to the pre-shock stimulus, and that this emotional state interferes with the ongoing behaviour, resulting in suppression. Another hypothesis is that the electric shock elicits competing skeletal responses that interfere with the performance of the ongoing behaviour, and that these competing responses become conditioned to the pre-shock stimulus.

A number of experiments, however, have shown that a pre-food (or pre-water) stimulus can have much the same effect as a pre-shock stimulus. Azrin and Hake (1969) used a procedure similar to the one used in experiments that have demonstrated suppression by a pre-shock stimulus, but substituted response-independent food or water presentations for the electric shock. Responding of rats was maintained under a variable-interval schedule of food or water presentation. A stimulus was presented occasionally and its termination was paired with the response-independent presentation of either food, water, or electrical brain stimulation. Azrin and Hake found a reduction in responding during the stimulus, just as earlier experiments had found a reduction in responding in the presence of a pre-shock stimulus. Herrnstein and Morse (1957) reported a slightly different result. In pigeons responding under a DRL schedule of food presentation, which engenders a relatively low rate of responding, presentation of a stimulus that had been paired with response-independent food presentation caused an increase in the rate of responding. Meltzer and Brahlek (1970) have shown recently that either suppression or enhancement can be obtained during a stimulus associated with the response-independent presentation of food. Their experiments indicated that stimulus duration is an important variable; responding was suppressed during a 12-second stimulus, less suppressed during a 40-second stimulus, and enhanced during a 120-second stimulus.

The most commonly reported effect of the presentation of a pre-shock stimulus on responding maintained by electric shock postponement is an increase in responding during the stimulus (Sidman, Herrnstein, and Conrad, 1957; Kelleher et al, 1963; Waller and Waller, 1963), but there is some recent evidence (Roberts and Hurwitz, 1970) that the stimulus duration is of importance here also; these investigators found that there was a suppression of responding under a continuous avoidance schedule with a relatively short duration (1 minute) pre-shock stimulus.

From even this brief review of the effects of response-independent events on ongoing behaviour, it can be seen that the effects depend on variables other than simply the nature of the stimuli involved. For example, depending on the ongoing rate of responding and the duration of the stimulus, a pre-food stimulus can lead to either increases or decreases in responding. Responding under a schedule of food presentation may be suppressed by a pre-shock stimulus while responding under an avoidance schedule may either be enhanced or suppressed in the presence of the stimulus, depending on its duration. Thus, what was once thought of as a simple 'classically conditioned emotional response' turns out to be a very complex phenomenon.

An exhaustive discussion of the suppressive effects of response-dependent presentation of electric shock is beyond the scope of the present paper. Comprehensive reviews on the subject (Azrin and Holz, 1966; Church, 1963) are available. Here I will review only the general effects of punishment as they specifically relate to present considerations.

The most commonly reported effect of presenting response-dependent electric shocks to animals performing under various schedules of food or water presentation is suppression of responding. The degree of suppression has been shown to depend on factors such as the intensity of electric shock, the amount of food or water deprivation, the period of time over which shock has been presented, the schedule under which the electric shock is presented, and the schedule controlling the reference behaviour (Azrin and Holz, 1966; Church, 1963). Though response suppression is commonly found, this need not be the effect of response-dependent electric shock. Response-dependent presentation of electric shocks may increase aggressive behaviours (Ulrich, Dulaney, Kucera and Colasacco, Chapter 9) and may increase rather than decrease certain instinctive behaviours, such as alert-posturing in the Mongolian gerbil (Walters and Glazer, 1971). If shock is delivered during periods in which food is also available for responding, and not in periods in which food is not available, the presence of shock may control a higher rate of responding than its absence (Holz and Azrin, 1961). That is, when shock can serve as a discriminative stimulus, its presentation need not necessarily produce response suppression.

In animals that have responded under schedules in which responding postpones delivery of electric shock, the periodic delivery of response-independent shocks can maintain responding, even when the shock postponement schedule is no longer in effect (Sidman, Herrnstein, and Conrad, 1957; Sidman, 1958; Kelleher, Riddle, and Cook, 1963; Waller and Waller, 1963). More recent experiments have shown that, under certain conditions, responding can be engendered and maintained under schedules of response-dependent electric shock presentation (McKearney, 1968, 1969; Kelleher and Morse, 1968b; Byrd, 1969; Stretch, 1972). In one set of experiments (McKearney, 1968) monkeys were first trained under a shock postponement schedule (Sidman, 1953). Shocks were programmed to occur every 10 seconds, but each depression of the response-key postponed delivery of shock for 30 seconds. After a number of sessions under this schedule, a 10-minute fixed-interval schedule of shock presentation was programmed concurrently with the shock postponement schedule. Under the 10-minute fixed-interval schedule, the first response occurring after 10 minutes produced a shock. After a number of sessions under the concurrent schedule, the shock postponement schedule was eliminated and for the remainder of the experiments the only schedule in effect was the 10-minute fixed-interval schedule of shock presentation. Figure 5 shows cumulative records of responding at various stages of this experiment. The shock postponement schedule engendered a low, relatively uniform rate of responding. When the 10-minute fixed-interval schedule was added there was no change in the temporal pattern of responding; that is, the distribution of responding within the 10-minute intervals did not change. Elimination of the shock postponement schedule, so that the only consequence of responding was delivery of shock under the fixed-interval schedule, increased rates and markedly changed the temporal pattern of responding. Response rate was low immediately after each shock and then gradually increased until the next shock was presented. When a 30-second time-out period followed each shock, this pattern of positively accelerated responding was accentuated, but subsequent removal and reinstatement of the time-out period had no substantial effect on the response pattern. As Figure 6 shows, characteristic patterns of positively accelerated responding were maintained under the fixed-interval schedule of shock presentation.

Kelleher and Morse (1968b) have also reported maintenance of responding under a fixed-interval schedule of electric shock presentation in squirrel monkeys. Monkeys were initially trained under a 2-minute variable-interval schedule of food presentation; then a 10-minute fixed-interval schedule of shock presentation was arranged concurrently. In addition, each response during the eleventh minute of each cycle produced a shock (that is for a 1-minute period after the delivery of shock under the fixed-interval schedule). After extended exposure to these concurrently arranged schedules, food presentations were eliminated and a pattern of positively accelerated responding was maintained under the 10-minute fixed-interval schedule. Responding was suppressed during the period in which each response produced a shock. These experiments show that fixed-interval schedules of electric shock presentation can maintain positively accelerated responding in monkeys with no prior experience under avoidance schedules. They also show that the effects

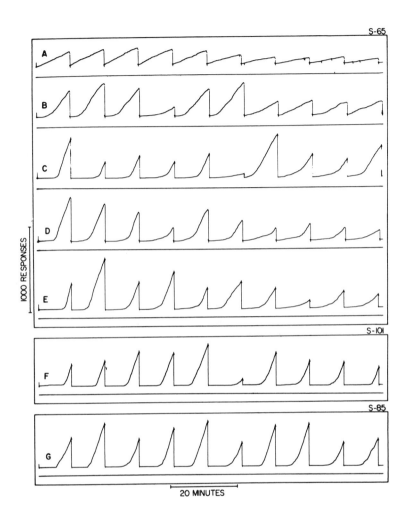

Figure 5 Cumulative records of responding under schedules of shock presentation. Ordinate: cumulative responses. Abscissa: time. The recording pen reset after a FI was completed (B–G). A: concurrent shock avoidance (5.6 mA) and 10-minute FI schedule of shock presentation (ie, the first response after 10 minutes produced a shock). B: FI shock presentation only. C: FI shock presentation with 30-second time-out period after shock. D: FI shock presentation with time-out period eliminated. E: FI shock presentation, time-out period reinstated. Records A–G were collected sequentially, with varying numbers of sessions intervening. F: Monkey S101, FI shock presentation with 30-second time-out. G: Monkey S85, FI shock presentation with 30-second time-out period. Records E, F, and G represent terminal performances of the three monkeys under the 10-minute FI schedule of electric shock termination with the 30-second time-out period. From McKearney (1968), with permission.

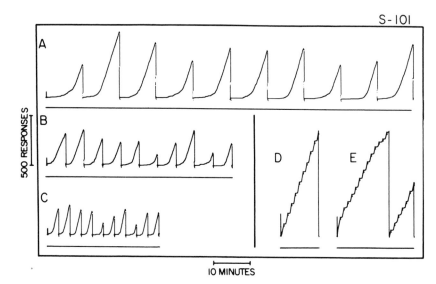

Figure 6   Cumulative records of responding under several parameter values of FI schedules of shock (5.6 mA) presentation (Monkey S101). A: FI 10-minute. B: FI 5 minute. C: FI 3-minute. D: FI 1-minute (10 shocks/session). E: FI 1-minute (20 shocks/session). Except under FI 1-minute, the recording pen reset with each shock presentation. Each record (except A) represents the fifth session under that FI parameter. Note that the pattern of positively accelerated responding persisted despite the tenfold variation in parameter value. From McKearney (1969), with permission.

of electric shock depend on the schedule under which it is presented; responding was maintained under the fixed-interval schedule, but suppressed under the schedule in which each response produced a shock.

Morse, Mead, and Kelleher (1967) have studied the modulation of shock-elicited behaviour under schedules of shock presentation. When electric shocks are delivered to a squirrel monkey's tail, they characteristically elicit pulling of a leash attached to the monkey's collar. These investigators studied this behaviour by attaching the leash to a switch that could record the pulling. When electric shocks were presented every 60 seconds, a high rate of leash-pulling occurred immediately after each shock. Later, the experiment was changed so that the first pull of the leash after 30 seconds produced the shock (30-second fixed-interval); if no response occurred between 30 and 60 seconds the shock was automatically delivered as before. Under this schedule of shock presentation the initially elicited pattern of responding after each shock was altered to a pattern of responding just before each shock; that is, a pattern of re-

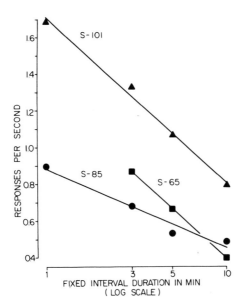

Figure 7 Response rate as a function of FI duration under FI schedules of electric shock presentation. Ordinate: responses per second during the FI. Abscissa: duration of FI (log scale). Each point is the mean of at least five sessions. Lines were fitted by the method of least-squares. From McKearney (1969), with permission.

sponding similar to that seen under fixed-interval schedules. Most shocks that were delivered were produced by reponses. These experiments show that it is possible to change an elicited pattern of responding by presenting response-dependent shocks under a fixed-interval schedule.

Recent experiments in my laboratory have extended the results on schedules of shock presentation. In one set of experiments (McKearney, 1969), in which monkeys responded under fixed-interval schedules of electric shock presentation, elimination of scheduled shocks resulted in a cessation of responding (extinction). When shocks were again presented under the fixed-interval schedule, the previous pattern of positively accelerated responding quickly redeveloped. When electric shock intensity was varied (over a range of from 0.3 to 5.6 milliamperes), response rates were found to be directly related to the intensity of the shock presented. These experiments also investigated the effects of changing the parameter value of the fixed-interval schedule. Figures 6 and 7 summarize the results of these experiments. Over the range of parameter values investigated, rates of responding during the fixed-inter-

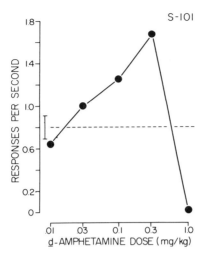

Figure 8   Effects of d-amphetamine on responding under a 10-minute fixed-interval schedule of electric shock presentation. The dashed horizontal line represents the mean rate of responding during three non-drug sessions, and the bracket at left indicates the range of these observations. Each point represents a single administration. d-Amphetamine sulphate was injected intramuscularly immediately before the 100-minute session.

val increased as the duration of the fixed-interval was shortened.

Thus, performances under fixed-interval schedules of electric shock presentation are similar to those engendered under fixed-interval schedules of food or water presentation, not only in the characteristic pattern of positively accelerated responding engendered, but also in the effects of elimination, reinstatement, and variations in intensity of the stimulus maintaining the behaviour, and in the effects of variations in the parameter value of the fixed-interval schedule.

Because the pattern of responding under a fixed-interval schedule of shock presentation is similar to that obtained under fixed-interval schedules of food or water presentation (or of electric shock termination), it was of interest to determine the effects of d-amphetamine. In direct contrast to this drug's further suppression of behaviour suppressed by shock presentation (ie, punishment), the effect was to increase overall fixed-interval responding at low and intermediate doses and decrease responding at higher doses (Figure 8), just as occurs with fixed-interval schedules of food presentation. Figure 9 shows the effects of amphetamine on responding during individual 1-minute segments of the fixed-interval. As with fixed-interval schedules of food presentation (Figure 4), increases

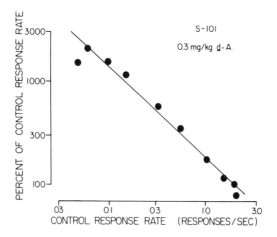

Figure 9   Effects of d-amphetamine on responding during individual 1-minute segments of a 10-minute fixed-interval schedule of shock presentation. Abscissa: control rate during 1-minute segments. Ordinate: rate in 1-minute segments after d-
amphetamine, expressed as percent of control rate. Coordinates are logarithmic.
Each point is the mean of 10 fixed-intervals (single session). Data from same session as the 0.3 mg/kg session in Figure 8. Note that there is an inverse linear relation between control rate and amount of increase after d-amphetamine, just as under fixed-interval schedules of food presentation (Figure 4).

in responding after amphetamine were an inverse linear function of the
control rate of responding.

Recent experiments (McKearney, 1970a) indicate that it is possible to
maintain responding under fixed-ratio and multiple fixed-interval fixed-
ratio schedules of electric shock presentation. Squirrel monkeys, already
responding under a fixed-interval schedule of shock presentation, were
placed under a multiple fixed-interval fixed-ratio schedule; in the presence of one stimulus light, the first response after 10 minutes produced
a 5.6 mA shock (10-minute fixed-interval), and in the presence of another stimulus light, the thirtieth response produced shock (30-response
fixed-ratio). The fixed-interval and fixed-ratio components alternated
throughout the experimental session, and were separated by a 60-second
blackout. Figure 10 shows examples of performance under the multiple
schedule. Performances characteristic of each component schedule developed under this multiple schedule of electric shock presentation. Under the fixed-interval schedule, as in earlier experiments, a pattern of
positively accelerated responding prevailed; under the fixed-ratio schedule, there was a brief pause followed by a high and steady rate until
shock was presented after the thirtieth response. Performance under

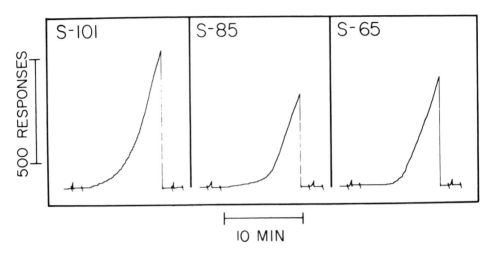

Figure 10   Cumulative records of responding under a multiple 10-minute fixed-interval 30-response fixed-ratio schedule of electric shock presentation. Ordinate: cumulative responses. Abscissa: time. The recording pen reset with each shock presentation. Diagonal strokes indicate the end of the 60-second time-out period. Record segments are from the 18th (S101), 21st (S85), or 22nd (S65) session under the multiple schedule. Characteristic multiple FI FR patterns of responding were maintained under this schedule of shock presentation. From McKearney (1970a), with permission.

both component schedules was similar to that obtained under comparable schedules of food or water presentation or electric shock termination. Characteristic patterns of responding were also maintained when the parameter value of the fixed-ratio component of the multiple schedule was reduced to 3 or 10 responses, and, in the one monkey studied, responding was maintained under a 30-response fixed-ratio schedule of shock presentation alone.

Responding can also be maintained under variable-interval schedules of electric shock presentation. Figure 11 shows performance of Monkey S184. This monkey had been trained to respond under a continuous avoidance schedule, and was then studied for several sessions under a procedure in which the avoidance schedule was suspended and electric shocks were presented independently of responding at 10-minute intervals (Figure 11, Panels A and B, respectively). This monkey was then placed under a 3-minute variable-interval schedule of electric shock presentation. As Figure 11 (Panels C, D, and E) shows, a steady rate of responding, characteristic of variable-interval schedules, developed and was maintained under the VI schedule of shock presentation.

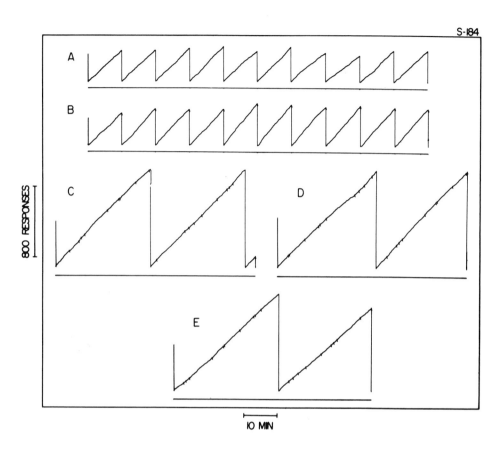

Figure 11   Responding under a 3-minute variable-interval schedule of electric shock presentation (Monkey S184). This monkey had previous training under a continuous avoidance schedule. Ordinate: cumulative responses. Abscissa: time. Diagonal strokes indicate shock (5.0 mA) presentations. A: last session under avoidance schedule. B: last session under procedure in which a shock was presented every 10-minutes independently of responding. In A and B, the recording pen reset every 10 minutes. C, D, and E: first, fifth, and tenth sessions under the VI schedule of shock presentation. Note that a steady rate of responding was maintained under this schedule, in contrast to the pattern of positive acceleration observed under FI schedules of shock presentation (eg, Figure 5).

CONCLUSIONS

What I have tried to show in this paper is that the effects of environmental interventions depend on the precise conditions under which they are presented (the schedule) and on the characteristics of the behaviour upon which they are imposed. In certain cases (eg, the acute administration of a drug) the character of the reference behaviour is a prime determinant; in cases in which the intervention itself is presented under some schedule (eg, responding maintained under schedules of shock presentation), the effects depend jointly on the schedule under which the event is presented and on the characteristics of the already-existing behaviour.

If responding increases when the occurrence of some event is made dependent on a response, that event is identified as a reinforcer, simply as a matter of definition. As Morse and Kelleher (1970) have recently pointed out, however, it is misleading to characterize an event as a reinforcer independently of the subject's ongoing behaviour and of the conditions under which it is presented. Food or water are not reinforcers, but they can serve as reinforcers under appropriate conditions, just as electric shock is not a 'punisher,' even though it can function as such.

Distinctions are often drawn between events that maintain behaviours preceding their postponement or termination (negative reinforcers), and those that maintain behaviours preceding their presentation (positive reinforcers). While such distinctions may be theoretically convenient, they often lack empirical basis or significance. For example, experiments summarized earlier showed that the same electric shock that maintained responding under an avoidance schedule later maintained responding that led to its presentation. Thus, depending on the schedule under which it was presented, the shock met the defining criteria for both 'types' of reinforcer.

The subject's reinforcement history is an important determinant of the effects that new schedule conditions will have. A naive animal exposed to the terminal contingencies of a schedule of shock presentation would be unlikely to press the response key. While we do know that history is important, we do not know exactly what past experiences will favour the development of responding under schedules of shock presentation. It is clear, however, that prior training under schedules of shock postponement or termination is not necessary (Morse, Mead, and Kelleher, 1967; Kelleher and Morse 1968b). Certainly, the general dependence of present and future behaviour on past behaviour is in no way peculiar to experiments involving electric shock.

There are, needless to say, many situations in which response-dependent electric shocks do not maintain behaviour, as the vast literature on the suppressive effects of electric shock will attest. It is important to realize, however, that this inconstancy of effect is not limited to electric shock. There are many situations in which food presentation will not maintain behaviour, or will maintain it poorly (for example, under extended chain schedules), and there are some cases in which it will actually suppress responding (eg, Azrin and Hake, 1969). Similarly, there are many conditions under which electric shock will not suppress behaviour, and some cases in which its presentation will engender and maintain responding. The ubiquity with which food presentation can maintain behaviour, and with which electric shock can suppress behaviour, obscures these important 'exceptions'. Such obscurity, when coupled with theoretically convenient rather than empircally based notions about behaviour, often leads to biases that impede the experimental analysis of behaviour controlled by its consequences.

COMMENT BY R.R. HUTCHINSON.

Following the lead of Kelleher and Morse (1968b), Morse, Mead, and Kelleher (1967), Byrd (1969), McKearney (1969), the author describes the manual manipulative responding observed during schedules of response contingent shock as produced by the contingent application of shock. The occurrence of such schedule-typic performance has then been used to argue for a redefinition of 'positive' and 'negative' reinforcement. Such arguments have been referenced and extended recently (Dews, 1970). In fact, Byrd showed that when two cats were placed on a response-contingent shock following a response-independent shock schedule, response rate decreased, though none of these studies has systematically tested the contingency proposition.

The literature, however, contains several dozen reports of the elevation of behaviours by the non-contingent application of electric shock and other intense noxious stimuli. We have here and elsewhere demonstrated that the response-independent application of electric shock produces identical patterns of performance of the same response with an identical manipulandum and in the same species. It is now even more important than previously that the alleged response generating characteristics of contingent shock application be demonstrated. An extended discussion of these points can be found in Hutchinson, Renfrew, and Young (1971).

REPLY BY J.W. McKEARNEY

Dr Hutchinson argues that response-independent electric shocks can product 'identical patterns' to those that I (McKearney, 1968, 1969, 1970a) and others (Morse, Mead, and Kelleher, 1967; Kelleher and Morse, 1968b; Byrd, 1969) have reported with shocks presented on a response-dependent basis under fixed-interval schedules. A related, though less explicit, argument is that there is some evidence that responding may occur at higher levels under response-independent procedures.

In deciding whether a given event is effectively maintaining behaviour, it is not traditional (and certainly not wise) to rely simply on overall response rate changes as the criterion; instead, we consider the distribution of these responses in time as well. In the cited experiments by Byrd (1969), and in unpublished experiments in my laboratory, the overall rate of responding sometimes does show a transient decrease when the schedule is changed from 'fixed-time' to 'fixed-interval'.[1] However, in these experiments not only the absolute rate but also the temporal pattern of responding was altered by changing the schedule. Under the fixed-time schedule there was a rather uniform rate of responding throughout each fixed-time period, whereas under the fixed-interval schedule, as with fixed-interval schedules in general, there was a pause followed by a gradual increase in responding. In order to develop a characteristic, schedule-specific performance (which is, after all, the only indicator of good schedule control), it is necessary that the animal respond very little during the beginning portions of each fixed interval. This can, of course, result in an overall rate decrease, but it need not; for example, one of Byrd's animals showed a decrease (though, because other things were changed, it is difficult to decide what it was due to), but the other showed an increase in rate when switched from the fixed-time to the fixed-interval schedule. In any case, I do not see how such rate changes alone can warrant any conclusions about the relative efficacy of response-independent and response-dependent events in maintaining behaviour.

Hutchinson, Renfrew, and Young (1971) have shown that patterns of responding that are indeed very similar to those engendered under fixed-interval schedules of shock presentation can be generated in subjects exposed for extended periods to fixed-time (ie, response-independent) schedules of shock presentation. I would like to stress, however, that while the patterns can be similar, they are by no means identical. Morse and Kelleher (1970) have recently published results of experiments, conducted several years ago, that clearly demonstrated the changes in performance that occur when electric shocks are delivered on a response-dependent rather than a response-independent basis. These results are best described by their figure, which is reprinted here.

1 / Under a fixed-time schedule an event is presented at regular times, irrespective of the animal's behaviour, whereas under a fixed-interval schedule the first response after the passage of the time period produces the event.

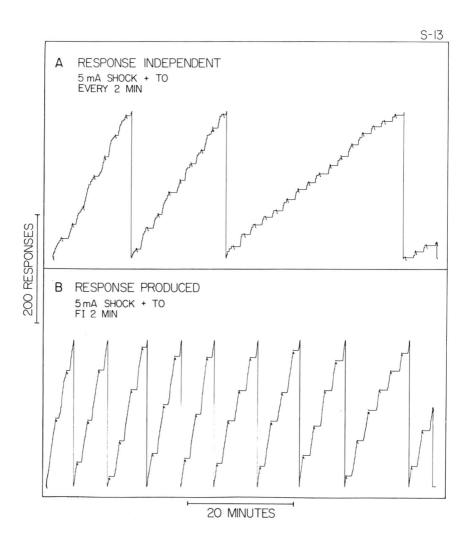

Figure 1 Comparison of performances under schedules of response-independent and response-dependent 5 mA electric shocks (Monkey S13). Short diagonal strokes on the cumulative records indicate presentation of electric shock; a TO period, in which the paper did not move, followed each shock. The recording pen reset to the base line whenever 275 responses had accumulated. A: performance under the schedule of response-independent shock during the seventh session after a single session's exposure to a fixed-ratio four-response schedule of shock termination. B: performance under FI 2-minute schedule of response-produce shock after eight sessions. The rate of responding increased, and the pattern of responding was more clearly positively accelerated with response-produced shocks. From Morse and Kelleher (1970), with permission.

2 Conditioned anxiety and operant behaviour

D. E. BLACKMAN

ANXIETY: THE ESTES-SKINNER PROCEDURE

'Anxiety is almost impossible to define. To list all the phenomena people have subsumed under this term would create a huge inventory that would involve some exceedingly subtle observations' (Sidman, 1964). Perhaps because of this ambiguity of definition, the term 'anxiety' has come to be used widely as an explanatory concept in psychology. To give but one specific example for this claim, it was conventional for some time to explain avoidance behaviour as being maintained by the reduction of anxiety (see review by Herrnstein, 1969), although the direct measurement of this anxiety, and its reduction, has never been satisfactorily achieved. In this paper, attention is concentrated on only one experimental situation from the many noted by Sidman (1964). The original investigation was reported by Estes and Skinner (1941) in a paper entitled 'Some quantitative properties of anxiety.' In their experiment, twenty-four rats were exposed to a schedule of reinforcement that would now be specified as a fixed-interval of 4 minutes, although it was then called 'periodic reconditioning.' The reinforcement programmed by this schedule was food, and the operant response studied was lever-pressing. When the behaviour generated by the schedule had stabilized (ie, become predictable), a tone was introduced. As this tone ended, a shock was delivered to the subjects through the grid floor on which they were standing. This shock was unavoidable and inescapable, its intensity and duration being held constant throughout the experiment (although unfortunately these values are not specified in the report). It may be im-

Parts of the experimental work incorporated in this paper were supported by grants from the Medical Research Council, UK, for which the author is therefore indebted. Thanks are also given to Mrs. Pamela Scruton for her assistance with some of this research, and to Mrs. J.M. Tuck for typing the manuscript.

portant to note that neither the tone nor the shock produced an observable behavioural disturbance in the early stages of this first experiment. Subsequently, however, it was observed that the frequency of lever-pressing decreased during the tone. Estes and Skinner went beyond their observable data and wrote, 'The principle result of [the] experiment was the conditioning of a state of anxiety to the tone, where the primary index was a reduction in the strength of the hunger-motivated lever-pressing behavior.' The implication was clear: the amount of anxiety produced by pairing a neutral stimulus with a noxious stimulus may be measured indirectly in terms of its disruption of operant behaviour.

Throughout this chapter the procedure of superimposing on operant behaviour a stimulus that precedes an unavoidable shock is referred to as the Estes-Skinner procedure. A number of problems arise from the particular experimental procedure used by Estes and Skinner; however, many of these have been investigated subsequently, and it seems churlish to stress them at this point when it is remembered that the experiment was performed all of thirty years ago. However, their interpretation of the data certainly deserves detailed attention. In the first place, it may be noted that the baseline behaviour is described in terms of its motivation ('hunger') rather than its maintaining stimulus ('food'). Secondly, the concept of anxiety is invoked to explain why operant lever-pressing decreased in frequency during the tone. Thus, presumably, anxiety was conditioned by the pairings of tone and shock – this being a respondent (classical) conditioning phenomenon since there was no response contingency programmed in this aspect of the experiment. This process may be described as follows: the respondents elicited by shock (the unconditional stimulus) became elicited by the tone (the conditional stimulus). It may be useful to describe the conditioned respondent behaviour resulting from this procedure as anxiety, but it should be noticed at this point that Estes and Skinner made no attempt to identify or measure these respondents. To put this in another way, Estes and Skinner assumed that such a process was occurring. But they went further than this assumption, for they also assumed (or, at the very least, hypothesized) that this anxiety caused the disruption of operant behaviour that provided the observable data in their experiment. This casual process was not elaborated, but at least two possibilities come readily to mind.

First, it is possible that the conditioned respondents (anxiety) were incompatible with lever-pressing behaviour. Thus, if it is assumed that one aspect of the ill-defined respondent conditioning procedure involved the syndrome of behaviour sometimes known as 'freezing', it is possible that such freezing, being elicited by the conditional stimulus (tone), was physically incompatible with rearing to the lever and pressing it. This will be referred to as the incompatible response hypothesis. It has been made explicit more recently by Kamin (1965). In discussing his work on suppression of behaviour during a pre-shock stimulus, he wrote: '... the most obvious assumption has been that the interference with behavior, which serves as our measure, is largely the result of incompatibility between respondents elicited by S_1 (the pre-shock stimulus) and the ongoing behavior. We believe that we are measuring respondent behavior indirectly, with a surprising quantitative sensitivity.'

A second possible explanation of the decrease in frequency of operant responding might be described as an incompatible motivation hypothesis. Thus the conditioned anxiety resulting from the experimental procedure might be incompatible with, or conflict with, the hunger that Estes and Skinner invoked to explain why the rats pressed the lever. To be more specific, it might be suggested that anxiety in this situation represents some form of negative motivation, which subtracts from the positive motivation 'driving' the operant behaviour, thereby producing a decrease in the frequency or strength of that operant behaviour. In fact, one of the original experimenters has developed such an account quite explicitly. Estes (1969) has argued that 'a stimulus which has preceded a traumatic event e.g. shock ... acquires the capacity of inhibiting the input of amplifier elements from sources associated with hunger, thirst, and the like. If then, while the animal is performing an instrumental response for, say, food reward, this conditioned stimulus is presented, the facilitative drive input will be reduced and so also the probability or rate of the instrumental response. If, on the other hand, the same stimulus is introduced while the animal is performing a response for escape from shock, there will be no similar reciprocal inhibition between drive sources and thus no suppressive effect.'

To return to the Estes and Skinner findings, these may be stated as follows: the frequency of food-maintained behaviour decreased during a stimulus that preceded an unavoidable shock.

These findings have been replicated and extended in many subsequent experiments, and some workers in this field now favour the term 'conditioned suppression of behaviour' as a description of their research interests rather than 'the effects of conditioned anxiety.' In recent years, two comprehensive reviews of the work in this area have been published (Lyon, 1968; Davis, 1968), and it would be superfluous to elaborate the basic findings. For this reason, I have chosen to concentrate on certain theoretical issues and on data obtained by me that seem to be relevant to those issues.

EFFECTS OF DRUGS ON ANXIETY

Much initial interest in this area of research was prompted by the promise of the conditioned suppression procedure for evaluating drug effects on anxiety. The first experimenters to stress the analogy between conditioned suppression and clinical anxiety states were Brady and Hunt, who started their programme of research in 1951. Throughout their reports, on this programme, they explicitly postulated that conditioned suppression was caused by 'an internal state underlying the behavioral reaction ... described in the Skinner Box' (Hunt and Brady, 1951). This internal state was described as a conditioned emotional response (CER): a response, 'because overt reactions are used as indicators of the internal state'; emotional, 'because these overt reactions develop as a consequence of reinforcement with a mildly painful electric shock, and because of the character of the reaction'; and conditioned, 'because the experimental procedure brings these reactions under the control of an ordinary neutral stimulus' (Brady and Hunt, 1952). It is not entirely clear whether Hunt and Brady regarded conditioned suppression in terms of what has here been called the competing motivation hypothesis or in terms of the competing response hypothesis: the terms conditioned emotional response suggests the latter, but references to internal states might be interpreted as favouring the motivational account. The major part of their experimental programme investigated the effects of electro-convulsive shock (ECS) on the conditioned emotional response. The conclusion of this programme was that ECS acts specifically to alleviate the conditioned emotional response, explicitly by means of the convulsions resulting from the treatment. The conclusion is interesting in itself (although perhaps less important than it may have seemed at the time). Of more relevance in the present context, however, is the fact that Hunt and Brady apparently became increasingly interested in the phenomenon of conditioned suppression itself. Some early experiments in their series are marked by a lack of behavioural quantification, the conditioned emotional response procedure being administered in grill boxes and the dependent variables sometimes being no more than freezing and defecation during the pre-shock stimulus. This was complemented to an increasing extent by demonstations of suppression of ongoing behaviour, and eventually the quantification of conditioned suppression provided the primary data. Thus, increased control over the behavioural phenomena developed, and this led to a greater awareness of factors determining the suppression effect.

Goy and Hunt (1953) were the first to observe that the degree of conditioned suppression is determined, at least in part, by variables that control lever-pressing behaviour. They reported that a conditional emotional response was more difficult to establish when behaviour was continuously reinforced or reinforced according to a ratio schedule than when it was reinforced according to an interval schedule. This claim was based on the relative ease of establishing conditioned suppression, not on any direct measurement of respondent behaviour. An attempt to elucidate the crucial variables in this effect was made by Brady (1955), who concluded that the rate at which operant responses were emitted affected the course of extinction of a conditioned 'fear' reaction. This conclusion was based on the following observation. Conditioned suppression was established by means of a uniform procedure, all subjects (rats) being exposed to continuous reinforcement of lever-pressing. Groups of animals were then transferred to different schedules of reinforcement, which generated different rates of lever-pressing. The stimulus that had previously ended with shock was now superimposed on these new patterns of behaviour, but no shocks were delivered in this part of the experiment. The animals pressing the lever most frequently lost the conditioned suppression effect most quickly.

This finding strongly suggests that more attention should have been paid to the interactions between operant behaviour and a conditioned emotional response – to use the terminology of Hunt and Brady. However, no further work has been published by these workers in this context. In spite of this, both Brady and Hunt turned to an analysis of drug effects on the conditioned emotional response (Hunt, 1956, 1957; Brady, 1956). The report by Brady (1956) is of particular interest, and has been widely cited. He established conditioned suppression of intermittently reinforced operant behaviour, using the conventional Estes-Skinner procedure, and then administered amphetamine or reserpine to the experimental subjects. Brady reported that amphetamine increased the strength of the conditioned emotional response. This claim was based on the observation that the drug produced a decrease in the number of responses emitted during the pre-shock stimulus, in spite of an increase in the baseline response rate produced by the drug. Repeated doses of reserpine had the opposite effect, for, although the baseline rate of responding fell, the number of responses emitted during the pre-shock stimulus rose in comparison with control days. It was therefore concluded that reserpine attentuated the conditioned emotional response. Brady claimed that 'the method described does provide an approach to the selective assessment of specific drug-behavior relationships in the affective sphere while providing a control for the general behavioral and motor disturbances that frequently develop as non-specific side effects of such drug administration.'

Unfortunately, subsequent assessment of drug effects on anxiety using the conditioned suppression paradigm has been disappointing. Conflicting or ambiguous results have been the rule rather than the exception. Most workers have established conditioned suppression, arguing that this is caused by a conditioned emotional response or the like. The assumption is that drugs used in clinical practice to alleviate anxiety should attenuate conditioned suppression by alleviating the conditioned emotional response. If the drug has the expected effect, the demonstration is impressive (eg, Brady, 1956). More often, however, the results are equivocal.

Consequently, some have implied that conditioned suppression is not a model of anxiety (eg, Kinnard, Aceto, and Buckley, 1962), or conversely that the drug is ineffective in alleviating anxiety (eg, Ray, 1964). However, it may not be surprising that such a rationale has produced few results of clinical importance. Almost all experiments in this field have uniformly failed to take into account the interactions between anxiety and the behavioural baselines through which it is manifested (to use the concept of an internal state once again). Of particular importance here is an experiment by Appel (1963a). He reported that a dosage of reserpine that reliably reduced conditioned suppression when the shock was of an intensity of 0.8 mA failed to give consistent results when the shock was increased only to 1.0 mA. This suggests that more precise specification of the experimental situation might lead to an increased understanding of drug effects — and in this context the schedule that maintains the operant behaviour should also be included, as will become apparent. One might hope that some generality will be forthcoming from a particular experiment, in order that the other extreme interpretation might be avoided. For example, Davis (1968) has written: 'although it is tempting to discuss the effects of reserpine on "fear" or on "anxiety", it is more productive to discuss the effects of reserpine (i.p.) at 1 mg/kg on conditioned suppression, or more accurately, on conditioned suppression of bar pressing in male Sprague-Dawley rats under a variable interval schedule ($\bar{X}$ = 30 sec, range 5-90 sec) of 45-mg dry food reinforcement, during the presentation of a 1250-Hz tone for 60 sec at 92 db upon which the grid delivery of a 2-sec 0.8-mA electrical shock was contingent.' Davis admits that this might limit the impact of the data, but points out that it allows for replication, extension, and accurate interpretation.

Even some of the apparently less equivocal drug effects on conditioned suppression are not entirely unambiguous. For example, as noted above, Brady showed in 1955 that a conditioned emotional response produced by a standard procedure might result in differing degrees of conditioned suppression, apparently dependent on the rate of operant responding. Yet his argument in 1956 that amphetamine and reserpine specifically affect a conditioned emotional response failed to take this possibility into account. Given that these drugs produce as a side-effect a change in baseline response rate (as was the case), it is possible that changes in conditioned suppression may be contaminated by this rather than reflect a specific drug effect on anxiety alone. This point assumes even greater force if it is also pointed out that Brady's (1955) investigation of the relationships between a conditioned emotional response and conditioned suppression is itself not definitive. While his study did establish that the degree of conditioned suppression is affected by the characteristics of the baseline that is being suppressed, his argument that the crucial variable is response rate is unconvincing. It has been claimed elsewhere (Blackman, 1967) that Brady failed to notice that the animals that responded fastest in his experiment received a greater frequency of reinforcement, and that it therefore remained possible that this was the determining variable of his experimental effeot.

ANXIETY AND POSITIVELY REINFORCED BEHAVIOUR

My initial research in this area attempted to unravel the effects of response rate from the effects of reinforcement frequency in the conditioned suppression situation. At first a yoked-box procedure was used (Blackman, 1966). By these means it was possible to control reinforcement frequency between animals, yet to generate very different rates of responding. In two experiments it was found that animals responding at high rates were more disrupted by the same Estes-Skinner procedure than were animals responding at lower rates. This finding was in complete contrast to expectations, since it was directly opposed to the generalization proposed by Brady (1955). The implication was that Brady's findings may indeed have resulted from uncontrolled differences in reinforcement frequency. However, Brady's demonstration of drug effects (1956) now became equivocal. If high response rates are disrupted by the Estes-Skinner procedure more than low rates, then any procedure that increases baseline response rates might artifactually suggest a more severe conditioned emotional response. Amphetamine had precisely this effect on the behavioural baselines in Brady's experiment.

This suggestion became more plausible with subsequent experimentation. It was found (Blackman, 1967) that response-pacing procedures affected the degree of conditioned suppression produced by an Estes-Skinner procedure. Rats were first exposed to a variable interval (VI) schedule of reinforcement. When their behaviour had stabilized, 1-minute periods of noise were introduced into the chamber every 8 minutes during each experimental session. As these periods ended, an unavoidable shock was delivered (0.5 mA, 0.5 sec). The degree of resulting conditioned suppression was assessed. Then, using a balanced design to minimize sequence effects, response rates were varied by introducing response-pacing procedures (Ferster and Skinner, 1957). Reinforcements were programmed as before, but now only followed a response that satisfied a temporal requirement. This was specified in one of two ways. In order to generate low response rates, the requirement was that a response should be emitted between 5 and 8 seconds after the previous response if it was to be reinforced according to the VI schedule. To generate high response rates, the specification was that a response should be emitted less than 0.3 seconds after the preceding response if it was to be reinforced according to the schedule. These pacing requirements produced large changes in response rate with little accompanying change in reinforcement frequency. Thus the unpaced schedules generated approximately forty responses per minute. The slow pacing requirement decreased these to approximately ten per minute. The fast pacing requirements generated response rates of eighty per minute or more. When each behavioural baseline had stabilized, the 1-minute noise periods were introduced as before. It was found that animals emitted fewer responses during the noise when their baseline response rates were high than they had in the unpaced condition. It was also found that animals showed less conditioned suppression during the noise when paced to low rates than they had in the unpaced condition. In short, the effects on conditioned suppression of changing response rates by pacing requirements bore a striking similarity to the effects attributed to drugs.

It seems, therefore, that the drug effects reported by Brady (1955) might result as much from the indirect effects of the drug on the behavioural baseline as from the supposed effects of the drugs on the underlying conditioned emotional response.

Subsequent experiments (Blackman, 1968b) demonstrated more comprehensively than before that the degree of conditioned suppression resulting from a given Estes-Skinner procedure is related to the rate of operant responding, increasing response rates leading to increasing amounts of suppression. In these experiments, it was also demonstrated that reinforcement frequency had a measurable effect on conditioned suppression when response rates were held constant by response-pacing procedures. The suggestion that conditioned suppression is more severe when reinforcement frequency is low had been made previously by Lyon (1963), but in his experiment he failed to control response rates and therefore confounded two effective variables, as had Brady (1955).

These findings lead one to consider how response rate and reinforcement frequency affect conditioned suppression. Two general positions seem possible. First, one may maintain that suppression always reflects accurately the strength of an underlying conditioned emotional response. In other words, the more severe the behavioural disruption, the greater the underlying conditioned emotional response. If this is true, different degress of anxiety are generated by a standard procedure superimposed on different response rates or different reinforcement frequencies. This implies that anxiety must be measured in terms of behaviour rather than defined operationally by the procedure (intensity of shock, etc.). Such a suggestion appears to be valid both for the competing motivation and the competing response hypotheses. Why the standard procedure can produce different degrees of anxiety remains unexplained. The second position would be that a given conditioned suppression procedure always produces a uniform strength of conditioned emotional response, but that this interacts with the operant baselines in different ways to produce its effect. For the competing response hypothesis, the suggestion might be that the strength of engagement of operant behaviour determines the extent to which a uniform syndrome of conditioned respondents will disrupt that operant behaviour. The concept of strength of engagement is deliberately vague in this context but the difficulties of accommodating the above idea within a framework of frequency of response or probability of response are apparent when it is noted that high response rates are most disrupted. It is possible that 'strength of engagement' of behaviour can be measured independently of the conditioned suppression procedure. The second position (that a given Estes-Skinner procedure produces a uniform CER, which interacts with the behavioural baselines) may be accommodated within the competing motivation hypothesis if one assumes, for example, that animals are highly motivated when reinforcement frequency is high, and poorly motivated when that frequency is low. Anxiety is considered to be a negative motivation that will therefore subtract from these positive motivations. Thus, subtracting a standard conditioned emotional response will result in greater residual motivation when reinforcement frequency is high, producing little suppression; it will result in very little residual motivation when positive motivation is low (ie, reinforcement frequency is low), producing relatively severe suppression. This hypothesis seems fairly plausible when stated as above, but less so when applied to the response-rate data. Here, a similar argument would imply that low response rates (mild suppression) are highly motivated, and that high response rates (severe suppression) are poorly motivated. This certainly does not fit in with many preconceptions about motivation and behaviour.

Many other possibilities may be considered when attempting to 'explain' the effects of response rate and reinforcement frequency on conditioned suppression. It would be too tedious to mention these in detail, although one more observation may be in order. It may be possible to characterize patterns of reinforced behaviour in terms of the negative motivation they generate. It has been established, for example, that animals will work for a time-out from fixed ratio schedules of food reinforcement (Azrin, 1961). This may suggest that such schedules are aversive in some sense. It could be the case that it is the high response rates they generate that are crucial. Thus, by analogy, pacing schedules that generate high rates are relatively aversive and generate high negative motivation. This could summate with the negative motivation of anxiety, and thus produce relatively severe conditioned suppression. The reasoning is *ad hoc*, and implies that pacing schedules that generate very low response rates generate less negative motivation than unpaced schedules. Why this should be so is unclear. The line of argument enjoys little empirical support from situations where animals are allowed to choose between rates of response for a given reinforcement frequency. For example, Fantino (1969) used a concurrent chain situation with pigeons, and found that schedules that specified no particular response frequency were preferred to schedules that required either high or low response rates.

Further theoretical problems are promoted by another experiment, in which it was found that the Estes-Skinner procedure could result in either suppression or enhancement of food-reinforced behaviour, dependent on the schedule by which such reinforcements were delivered (Blackman, 1968a). To be more specific, when a very low rate of responding was differentially reinforced (DRL schedule), acceleration was observed during the pre-shock stimulus. This schedule formed one component of a multiple schedule, the other component generating higher response rates. In all conditions, this second pattern of behaviour was always suppressed during the same pre-shock stimulus. The finding of acceleration of DRL behaviour replicated a previous unpublished report by Finocchio (1963). On the basis of both findings, it seems reasonable to suggest that acceleration of DRL behaviour results from conditions that produce relatively mild suppression of other patterns of behaviour. A tentative suggestion was put forward (Blackman, 1968a) that this acceleration effect is attributable to a disruption of collateral behaviour, which was observed to mediate the lever-pressing behaviour. These stereotyped chains of behaviour were not measured in the experiment, but they characterized the DRL behaviour in control conditions. However, during the pre-shock stimulus the collateral chains were quickly disrupted, and lever-pressing behaviour was then emitted in the absence of these controlling chains. The acceleration effect may therefore represent a partial loss of discriminative control produced by the Estes-Skinner procedure, for it is possible that the completion of a mediating chain set the occasion for a lever-press, and that this completion therefore provided the discriminative stimulus for that lever-press.

This suggestion has been examined in a modified experiment that employed a two-lever situation (Blackman, 1970a). Rats were exposed to a situation in which a response on one lever (B) was reinforced only if a preceding response on the other lever (A) had been made at least 5, 10, or 15 seconds before. It has sometimes been suggested that schedules that differentially reinforce low rates of responding generate behaviour that may be described as 'timing' (eg, Sidman, 1955). This is true to the extent that the animals are required to time a minimum interval between responses on a single lever to obtain reinforcement. Thus any response, operationally at least, both ends the previous timing attempt and begins the next. The present experiment may also be described as generating timing behaviour. However, in this case, separate levers had to be used to initiate (A) and to terminate (B) a given timing attempt. In addition, a white noise stimulus was presented as a discriminative stimulus for timing behaviour. Thus, to summarize the procedure, a response on Lever A switched on the white noise, and started the appropriate delay requirement (if Lever A was pressed when the noise was already present, the delay requirement was reset to the maximum, leaving the noise on). A response on Lever B was reinforced only if the white noise had been present for at least the required time. All responses on Lever B, whether reinforced or not, terminated the noise and switched off the timer that set the minimum A-to-B interval. Any response on Lever B in the absence of the white noise (ie, which followed a previous B response rather than an initiating A response) had no programmed consequence, although these responses were counted.

This two-lever schedule of reinforcement generated efficient behaviour, in that the rats emitted responses on Levers A and B in the correct sequence, and allowed time to elapse between a response on Lever A and the subsequent response on Lever B. When this behaviour had stabilised, an Estes-Skinner procedure was superimposed. One-minute periods of a 1000 Hz tone were presented every 8 minutes. As each period ended, a brief unavoidable electric shock was delivered (0.5 mA, 0.2 sec). After thirty experimental sessions, the tone periods were extended to 2-minutes (presented once every 8 minutes as before). Shock was delivered at the end of each 2-minute period, its intensity and duration being exactly as before.

The results obtained from one of the two rats exposed to a 15-second

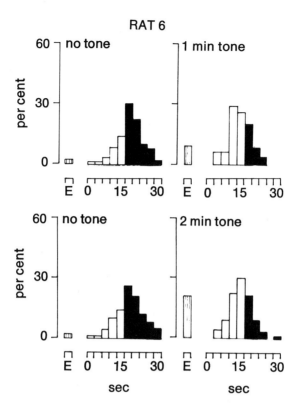

Figure 1 The effects of the Estes-Skinner procedure on two-lever 'timing' behaviour (tone = pre-shock stimulus). Distributions of A-to-B times from one of two rats exposed to a 15-second minimum A-to-B delay. See text. From Blackman (1970a), with permission.

A-to-B delay are shown in Figure 1. This presents data obtained from the last ten experimental sessions with 1-minute periods of pre-shock tone, and from the last ten sessions with the 2-minute periods of tone. In the absence of the tone (left-hand panels), each response on Lever B was classified within one of ten successive 3-second intervals, timed from the preceeding response on Lever A. The number of B responses classified into each time-interval was counted, and these totals were expressed as percentages of the overall number of B responses thus classified. These percentages are displayed in histogram form to the left of Figure 1 (no tone). In addition, a count was made of the number of inappropriate B responses, that is, those emitted without a preceding A response. This number is expressed as a percentage of the total B responses (ie, all B responses, emitted in the presence or the absence of the white noise discriminative stimulus). This percentage is also displayed, to the left of the relevant histogram and labelled E (errors on Lever B). Exactly the same data collection and analysis was performed for the behaviour emitted during the tone pre-shock stimulus for these last ten sessions of each tone duration. In all the histograms, white columns denote the percentages of responses in intervals for which no reinforcement was delivered (ie, appropriate, but premature, B responses): black columns denote percentages in intervals where a B response was followed by reinforcement.

It is clear from Figure 1 that the distribution of A-to-B response times is much changed during the pre-shock stimulus, there being a pronounced shift to the left (shorter delays) in both cases. In addition, the proportion of inappropriate B responses (E on Figure 1) increases markedly during the pre-shock stimulus. This latter finding assumes greater importance when a more gross analysis is made of the effects of the pre-shock tone. It was found that the frequency of A-to-B response sequences was always less during the pre-shock stimulus; that is, there was conditioned suppression of timing attempts taken as units of behaviour. However, it was also found for Rat 6, in the 2-minute tone condition, that the absolute number of B responses increased during the pre-shock stimulus. This discrepancy can be attributed to the increase in the proportion of inappropriate B responses during the tone. Since an inappropriate B response was defined as one emitted with no preceding A responses, and therefore with no discriminative stimulus present, the conclusion is again prompted that acceleration of food-reinforced behaviour during a pre-shock stimulus results from a partial breakdown in the discriminative control of behaviour.

The above discussion is exclusively concerned with the performance of one of the two rats in this experiment that were exposed to a minimum 15-second A-to-B delay. As was mentioned earlier, however, other animals were exposed to 5 or to 10 second delays. It may therefore be appropriate to set the above discussion into the context of the experimental results as a whole. It was found that:

1 During the pre-shock stimulus, the frequency of A-to-B response sequences decreased, whether the delay was 5, 10, or 15 seconds. This confirms and extends the finding of Migler and Brady (1964), who used only 5-second delays and a slightly different experimental situation.

2 With the 5-second A-to-B delay, there was no reliable change in the distribution of A-to-B response times during the pre-shock stimulus. Again, this confirms Migler and Brady (1964). However, with a 15-second A-to-B delay, there was a large change in the distribution, as evidenced in Figure 1. At the intermediate delay requirement (10 seconds), there was a smaller, but nevertheless detectable, change.

3 During the pre-shock stimulus there was an increase in the proportion of inappropriate B responses. It was more marked with longer A-to-B delay requirements. This breakdown in discriminative control of the animals' behaviour may be in accord with Hearst's (1965) report that aversive stimuli produce a deterioration in discriminative performance. Hearst established a pattern of behaviour in which periods of responding for occasional reinforcement were mixed with periods of little responding when no reinforcements were available. Non-contingent shocks produced an increase in the latter behaviour, especially when these shocks were preceded by a warning signal (as in the present experiment). The increase in responses in the absence of a discriminative stimulus associated with food availability is similar to the increase in inappropriate B responses in the present experiment. One difference, however, is that the discriminative breakdown in Hearst's experiment was not confined only to a pre-shock stimulus.

The increase in inappropriate B responses may contribute to an increase in the absolute frequency of response on Lever B during a pre-shock stimulus (Rat 6, 2-minute tone). The effect is analogous to the acceleration of DRL responding with a single lever previously reported by Finocchio (1963) and by Blackman (1968a).

The results obtained from this experiment may be interpreted in many ways. Here, no particular emphasis will be placed on the changes in A-to-to-B response times, although these may be significant. A point that deserves attention in the present context, however, is that the Estes-Skinner procedure may in certain circumstances produce an increase in response rate rather than the more normal decrease. This apparently depends on the schedule of reinforcement which maintains the operant behaviour, and may be explicable in terms of a breakdown in the discriminative control of behaviour. Because the acceleration effect has thus far been limited to fairly rigorous 'timing' schedules, an attempt is now being made to extend the generality of the effect. It is hoped to produce acceleration in situations that demand a less rigorous time delay by manipulating the degree to which the baseline behaviour is under explicit discriminative control.

It is interesting to consider how the acceleration effect can be accommodated by the competing response and competing motivation hypotheses. It would seem necessary for both to concentrate on the role of collateral behaviours. Thus, for example, the conditioned respondents elicited during the pre-shock stimulus may be incompatible with these collaterals, because these occupy a large proportion of the experimental time. However, these respondents are apparently not incompatible with other patterns of operant behaviour, namely the responses on Lever B in the above experiment. To the extent that these hypotheses focus attention on the collateral behaviour, it would seem that they would also need to invoke some concept of discriminative control for lever pressing behaviour.

ANXIETY AND AVERSIVELY MAINTAINED BEHAVIOUR

The finding of acceleration of behaviour during a pre-shock stimulus has been reported in other experimental situations. When operant behaviour is maintained by schedules of shock avoidance, it is found that such behaviour increases in frequency during a stimulus that precedes an unavoidable shock (Sidman, Herrnstein, and Conrad, 1957). Experiments on this effect have also been summarized and reviewed by Davis (1968) and again, therefore, it is unnecessary to provide a detailed account here.

It is not clear how this finding of acceleration in avoidance responding may be explained in terms of the competing response hypothesis; however, it offers no difficulties for the competing motivation hypothesis. Thus, avoidance behaviour may be described as negatively motivated; the Estes-Skinner procedure produces its own negative motivation: these two motivational forces summate to produce a greater total negative motivation; avoidance behaviour therefore increases in frequency. However, it is less clear how the competing motivation hypothesis can account for the findings that food-reinforced behaviour will increase in frequency during a pre-shock stimulus if the experimental subject has an unextinguished history of avoidance conditioning (Herrnstein and Sidman, 1958). It seems more appropriate to consider an alternative account suggested by Sidman (1960). He argued that the increase in responding in both these conditions may result from an adventitious contingency that is produced by the occasional unavoidable shocks; these may act as false discriminative cues, and thereby evoke behaviour appropriate to a shock avoidance schedule. If this is true, the concept of the discriminative control of operant behaviour noted earlier again becomes relevant to an understanding of the effects of the Estes-Skinner procedure. For this reason, an experiment was performed in which the discriminative control of avoidance behaviour was manipulated (Blackman, 1970b). Three rats were exposed to schedules of free operant avoidance (Sidman, 1953). With these schedules, behaviour is not brought under the explicit control of an identifiable stimulus, except in so far as any session stimulus provides the occasion for operant responding in general. Three other rats were exposed to similar avoidance schedules that included an additional stimulus (Ulrich, Holz, and Azrin, 1964); with such schedules it has been reported that avoidance responding is brought un-

der the explicit control of an exteroceptive stimulus. The effects of signalled unavoidable shock (the Estes-Skinner procedure) were studied
with these six animals. The reasoning behind the experiment was that
the strong stimulus control exerted by the second type of schedule
might not be susceptible to the adventitious contingencies discussed by
Sidman (1960), and therefore that the behaviour generated by these schedules would not show the acceleration effect.

The six rats were tested daily for 6 hours. Shocks (intensity 2.0 mA,
duration 0.3 seconds) were programmed every 5 seconds if the animal
made no lever-press (shock-shock interval 5 seconds). For Rats 1 and 4,
a response delayed the next shock by 20 seconds (the response-shock
interval). For Rats 2 and 5, the response-shock interval was 15 seconds,
and for Rats 3 and 6 it was 10 seconds. Each response reset the response-shock interval, thus allowing the subject to avoid shock indefinitely. For all six animals, auditory or visual stimuli were present for the
entire 6-hour session. After the twelfth session, the stimulus conditions
were changed for Rats 4-6, their appropriate auditory or visual stimuli
now being presented only when a shock was due within 5 seconds: any
lever-press during the stimuli therefore had the effect of switching them
off. A further twenty experimental sessions were given (Sessions 13-32,
Phase 1).

Following this phase of the experiment, a 2-minute stimulus was superimposed on the avoidance schedules once every 10 minutes. For Rats 1
and 4 it was a 1000 Hz tone, and for Rats 2, 3, 5, and 6 it was white
noise. The stimulus had no consequence in this phase of the experiment,
which lasted for five successive sessions (Session 33-37, Phase 2).

During Sessions 38-47, one unavoidable shock was delivered as each
2-minute stimulus ended. The shock had the same intensity and duration as the avoidable shocks (Phase 3).

During Session 48, the avoidance schedules were not implemented.
The animals were placed in the chambers as usual, but neither the stimuli associated with the schedules, nor the avoidable shocks were presented. However, the appropriate 2-minute stimuli continued to be presented once every 10 minutes, and were terminated with one unavoidable
shock as before (Phase 4).

During the final two sessions of the experiment (49 and 50, Phase 5),
the avoidance stimuli were once more programmed, as in Sessions 13-47.
However, no avoidable shocks were delivered, and the animals were
therefore in a conventional extinction condition for avoidance behaviour. The 2-minute stimuli, with their associated unavoidable shocks,
were still programmed exactly as before.

The main results of the experiment are shown in Figure 2. This com-

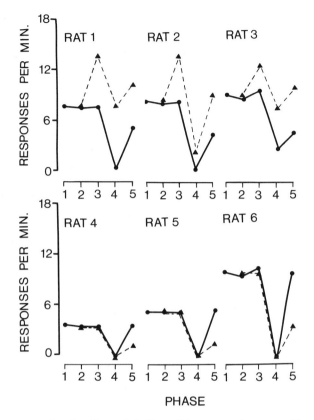

Figure 2   The effects of the Estes-Skinner procedure on avoidance behaviour. Rats 1-3 were exposed to various schedules of shock-avoidance with a continuous session stimulus. Rats 4-6 were exposed to similar schedules with intermittent schedule stimuli. Solid lines denote response rate in absence of 2-minute stimuli. Dotted lines denote response rates during 2-minute stimuli which ended with an unavoidable shock. See text for phases of experiment. From Blackman (1970b), with permission.

pares, for each animal, the rate of operant responding in the presence and absence of the 2-minute stimulus that preceded the unavoidable shock. The data for Phase 1 describe the avoidance behaviour generated by the various schedules, and are the means of the last five sessions of this phase of the experiment. In addition, it should be noted that Rats 4, 5, and 6 emitted almost all their responses in the presence of the intermittent schedule stimuli. The data shown for Phase 2 are the means of the last three sessions of this phase. They show that the 2-minute stimulus alone had no measurable effect on the response rate of the animals. The data shown for Phase 3 are the means of the last five sessions of this experimental phase. It is clear that Rats 1-3 show the acceleration effect previously reported, for their response rates were higher during the 2-minute stimulus than in its absence. However, Rats 4-6 (whose behaviour was under strong exteroceptive control) showed no such acceleration of responding. An essentially similar result is shown by the data from Phase 4 (no avoidance schedules). Rats 1-3 responded faster during the stimulus which ended with an unavoidable shock than they did in its absence. In contrast, Rats 4-6 made no operant responses at any time during this phase of the experiment, and therefore failed to show any evidence for the acceleration effect. Finally, in Phase 5 (extinction of avoidance), an even clearer difference may be observed between Rats 1-3 and 4-6. The former continued to show the acceleration effect, but the latter now showed a clear suppression of their behaviour during the signal that ended with an unavoidable shock.

Figure 3 displays representative cumulative records obtained from Rats 3 and 6. The differential effects discussed above may be seen in Phases 3, 4, and 5.

These findings suggest that the acceleration effect cannot be attributed simply to the interactions between a conditioned emotional response and avoidance behaviour (or its supposed motivation). To this extent, the competing motivation hypothesis now becomes less tenable. Instead, it is more useful to consider the degree to which the baseline operant behaviour is under the explicit discriminative control of the experimental environment. Since it has been noted previously that the effects of the Estes-Skinner procedure on food-reinforced behaviour may also be usefully interpreted in this way, it is possible that the concept of discriminative control may provide a means of synthesis. The results of the Estes-Skinner procedure may depend on the degree of discriminative control exerted by a schedule, rather than on the nature of the motivation maintaining the baseline performance. Acceleration of some types of avoidance responding may depend on poor discriminative control of that behaviour, as does acceleration of food-reinforced behaviour. However, caution should be exercised at this point, because it is important to note that the acceleration of food-reinforced behaviour demonstrated thus far has been specific to one type of schedule, and then only when the unavoidable shock is relatively mild (though nevertheless strong enough to suppress other patterns of behaviour).

This discussion implies that any behaviour that is under strong discriminative control should be suppressed during a pre-shock stimulus. This is in direct contrast to the motivational account of behaviour recently developed by Estes (1969) and noted earlier in this chapter. In the sec-

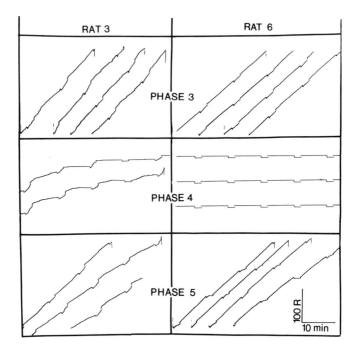

Figure 3   Effects of the Estes-Skinner procedure: acceleration or suppression of avoidance behaviour. Representative cumulative records of responses from Rats 3 and 6, Phase 3, 4, and 5. Shocks are not shown; the pen was deflected downwards during each 2-minute stimulus (R's = responses). From Blackman (1970b), with permission.

tion quoted then, Estes specifically precluded the possibility that shock escape behaviour might be suppressed by the Estes-Skinner procedure. The present formulations, on the contrary, would predict suppression of escape behaviour if that behaviour was under strong discriminative control. A preliminary experiment has been carried out, but the results throw little light on the phenomenon in question, and will therefore be discussed only briefly. Three rats were trained to press a lever to escape shock (intensity 0.2 mA). These shocks were presented once every 30 seconds, and terminated when the lever was pressed, or after 1.5 seconds, whichever was the sooner. The experimental chamber was in darkness except when an escapable shock was being delivered, when stimulus lights were illuminated. Records were compiled of the latencies from shock onset to the escape response. The animals were under strong stimulus control, emitting their escape responses promptly, and

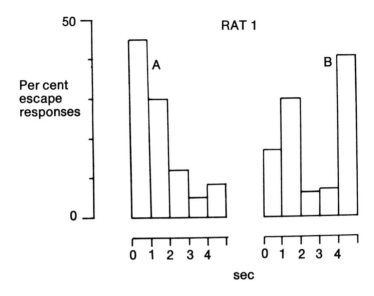

Figure 4 Effects of the Estes-Skinner procedure on escape behaviour. Frequency histograms of escape latencies in control conditions (A) and during the pre-shock stimulus of the Estes-Skinner procedure (B). Each escape response was classified within successive 1-second time bins from shock onset to 4 seconds, or in a final bin if the latency was greater than 4 seconds. The histograms show the totals within each bin expressed as percentages of total escape responses. These data summarize six consecutive daily sessions for one animal, but do not reflect the terminal performance (see text).

responding only rarely in the absence of shock. An Estes-Skinner procedure was then incorporated into the experimental session, the pre-shock stimulus (white noise) lasting for 2 minutes and being presented once every 8 minutes, and the unavoidable, inescapable shock (1.0 sec, 2.0 mA) being presented without an accompanying light. Preliminary evidence suggested that escape latencies were longer during the pre-shock stimulus than in its absence — in other words, there was conditioned suppression of escape behaviour. Figure 4 shows the distributions of escape latencies obtained from one animal at this stage of the experiment and the suppression effect may be clearly seen. However, continued testing in this situation led to some deterioration in the behavioural baseline with one animal and to a loss of the suppression effect with the other two. Perhaps the most remarkable feature of the terminal stage of the experiment, however, was that the distribution of latencies with two animals showed not the slightest evidence for either a lengthening or a shortening of response latencies during the noise periods. These results can therefore best be described as equivocal (although a zealot might notice that the prediction of acceleration lacks confirmation more thoroughly than the prediction of suppression). A number of reasons have suggested themselves for these disappointing results, and it is clear that further experiments are required on this issue.

DISCUSSION

To summarize, then, it appears that the effects of the Estes-Skinner procedure can be adequately understood only by reference to the discriminative control of operant behaviour. In other words, the schedule of reinforcement that maintains the baseline behaviour may be more important than the nature of that reinforcement in determining the effects of a pre-shock stimulus. Thus anxiety is a schedule-dependent effect. To this extent, the original experimental demonstration by Estes and Skinner (1941) is fundamental, because these workers were the first to measure anxiety in terms of its effects on an experimentally controlled baseline of behaviour.

As with most motivational theories of behaviour, the competing motivation hypothesis of conditioned suppression is not easy to refute. Data that are difficult to incorporate in a given account may be relatively easily incorporated if further assumptions are made. At the very least, the data reviewed in this paper demand that extra assumptions be made; whether these will prove useful remains to be seen. In particular, it is not adequate to predict that the effects of the Estes-Skinner procedure will be suppression of positively-motivated behaviour and acceleration of negatively-motivated behaviour; some reference to discriminative control may also be needed. Since the data reported in this paper on suppression or acceleration of avoidance behaviour were obtained, some further reports have appeared of suppression of avoidance behaviour *without* an added stimulus (Hurwitz and Roberts, 1970; Pomerleau, 1970; Scobie, 1969). However, such a finding is not necessarily contrary to the generalization concerning the role of discriminative control; indeed, these reports further emphasize the inadequacy of a traditional motivational hypothesis for the effects of the Estes-Skinner procedure.

The competing response hypothesis suffers one notable failing, namely the difficulty in specifying the patterns of respondent behaviour that are said to be incompatible with operant behaviour. No direct measurements are usually made of the autonomic or visceral responses generated by the Estes-Skinner procedure. Even in those experiments in which such measurements have been attempted, the relationships between conditioned autonomic behaviour and suppression of operant behaviour have often been equivocal. This is the case in a recent report by Brady, Kelly, and Plumlee (1969). Using rhesus monkeys as subjects, these investigators measured changes in heart rate and in diastolic and systolic blood pressure during the conditioned suppression of operant behaviour produced by a conventional Estes-Skinner procedure. The procedure undoubtedly resulted in changes in autonomic behaviour, but it is clear from the reported data that the operant suppression is not adequately described as being causally dependent on these. The striking conclusion of Brady and his associates deserves verbatim quotation: '... it would appear that the cardio-vascular and skeletal changes are more accurately represented as independently conditioned effects of the same environmental contingencies. This characterization of the emotional conditioning process, if correct, reflects unfavorably upon theoretical formulations that emphasize either the causal interdependence of behavioral and physiological events or the primacy of either one.' (1969, p. 973). It would certainly be of the utmost interest to measure such autonomic responses in some of the experimental situations whose data are discussed in detail in this chapter.

It should also, perhaps, be noted that a slight shock, which may cause little or no disruption of operant behaviour when delivered before the conditioning process has developed its effect (see Estes and Skinner, 1941, for example), can produce suppression over fairly long periods of time during a stimulus which signals it. This seems to imply that, if suppression is to be explained solely in terms of respondent conditioning, the conditioned respondents are more pronounced than the unconditioned respondents in this situation – an unusual possibility. Weiskrantz (1968) has discussed a number of difficulties with the competing response hypothesis; in particular, he notes that one cannot be certain that response contingencies are absent. Thus, for example, not-responding, crouching, and other patterns of behaviour may occur during the pre-shock stimulus because they reduce the noxiousness of the shock when it is delivered. If this is true, then the competing response hypothesis might incorporate competing operant behaviour as well as competing respondent behaviour. Despite this possible complication, many people still favour a version of the competing respondent hypothesis. Thus Kamin is confident that the measurement of conditioned suppression of operant behaviour offers 'a sensitive technique for the analysis of Pavlovian conditioning' (1965). Rescorla and Solomon (1967) go further than this; they suggest that '... it might very well turn out that instrumental responding is as sensitive, perhaps even more sensitive, a measure of Pavlovian conditioning procedures than are traditionally measured conditioned visceral or motor reflexes themselves.'

Some of the data reviewed in this paper suggest that the relationship between Pavlovian conditioning and conditioned suppression may not be simple. However, a competing response hypothesis remains viable, whether the competing responses are respondents or operants. In particular, acceleration of food-reinforced behaviour can be explained in these terms if it is assumed that the mediating chains of behaviour are most liable to disruption. Once again, however, the concept of discriminative control seems necessary for a full explanation.

It could be profitable to place less emphasis on the conventional causal, but essentially hypothetical, explanations of conditioned suppression. The assumed internal state does not have a uniform effect on different patterns of behaviour; the competing responses are difficult to specify. Anxiety is only manifested in these experiments through operant behaviour.

It might therefore be better to talk of anxiety as these disruptions of emitted behaviour, rather than as a cause of them. Anxiety would then become a description of observable interactions between certain specified operations and various patterns of emitted behaviour. Such a suggestion has been partly anticipated by Schoenfeld (1950), who pointed out that a full specification of anxiety should involve a) specification of the stimulus operations involved; b) description of the respondent effects of these operations; and c) description of the effects of the procedure on operant behaviour. In the absence of definitive accounts of the respondent effects, it may be wise to concentrate more on the first and third components of Schoenfeld's specification.

The conceptual advantages and disadvantages of this suggestion remain to be explored. However, it may be useful to consider it in a specific context. This may be provided by the earlier discussion of Brady's (1956) assertion that amphetamine and reserpine act directly on anxiety, in spite of their effects on baseline response rates. It has been argued that this demonstration is equivocal, for the changes in conditioned suppression observed by Brady may have been at least partially attributable to the drugs' side effects on behaviour. It may therefore be tempting to assume that the drugs have not been demonstrated as effective in changing emotional states by acting on them directly. But this in no sense suggests that these drugs have no effect on conditioned suppression, for it is clear that they do. If conditioned suppression is regarded as anxious behaviour, then the drugs may be said to affect anxious behaviour. The side effects of the drugs are a contamination only if it is insisted that anxiety should be reified in preference to the description of the drugs' effects on anxious behaviour.

In concluding, two suggestions are made:

1 The effects of a pre-shock stimulus on behaviour are schedule-dependent.

2 Anxiety as an abstract causal concept may be less useful than the description of behavioural disruptions as anxious if they result from certain operations.

SUMMARY

The effects on operant behaviour of a stimulus that precedes an unavoidable shock have often been attributed to anxiety. A selective review suggests that no clear explanation emerges for these behavioural effects; that is to say, the precise nature of the assumed anixety remains to be specified. Data are considered that present some difficulties for the competing response and the competing motivation hypotheses of anxiety. It is suggested that the effects of the procedure should be considered as schedule-dependent, for these effects are determined to a certain extent by the patterns of operant lever-pressing that provide the behavioural baseline, and these patterns are the result of schedules of reinforcement. It is further suggested that the motivational nature of the stimulus that maintains the baseline operant behaviour (eg, food or shock) may be less important in determining anxiety effects than these schedule-dependencies.

3 Drugs as reinforcers: schedule considerations

T. THOMPSON and R. PICKENS

That presentation of drug solutions contingent on operant responses can maintain and increase behaviour leading to their presentation has been the subject of growing research interest (Pickens and Thompson, 1971; Schuster and Thompson, 1969). The focus of much of this research has been the type of drug reinforcer as a critical variable determining the pattern and rate of responding (Thompson and Pickens, 1969, 1970). However, the significance of schedule variables in drug self-administration and interactions of drug self-administration with other schedule-maintained behaviours has not gone unnoticed (Thompson and Schuster, 1968; Thompson and Pickens, 1969). The importance of schedule variables in understanding drug-maintained responding comes as no surprise to those who have been involved in the analysis of operant behaviour during the past thirteen years (Ferster and Skinner, 1957). Indeed, one would be surprised if drug administration as a maintaining consequence functioned very differently from other reinforcers, most of which appear to be subject to similar schedule influences. Nonetheless, different classes of drugs appear to maintain different patterns of responding, and drug reinforcement can engender behavioural baselines differing from those of other types of reinforcers, neither of which could have been predicted from our prior knowledge (Thompson, Bigelow, and Pickens, 1969; Pickens, Thompson, and Yokel, 1970; Thompson and Pickens, 1970, 1971). This chapter explores some of the ways in which drug self-administration is influenced by schedule phenomena, and the interaction of drug self-administration with other schedule-maintained behaviours.

This research was supported in part by research grants MH 15349, MH 14112, and MH 08565 from NIMH to the University of Minnesota. The authors are indebted to G. Bigelow, R. Meisch, R. Yokel, and W. Anderson for allowing us to reproduce portions of their research in this paper.

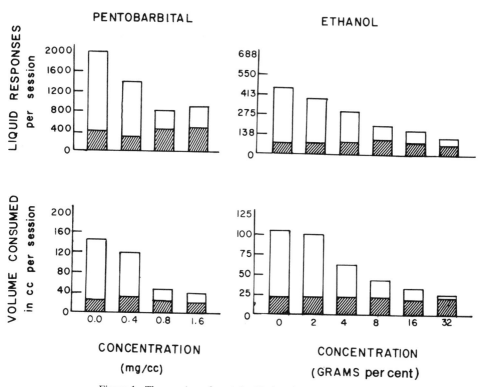

Figure 1   The number of pentobarbital and ethanol responses per 5-hour session and volume of drug solutions orally consumed by rats, as a function of concentration of drug solutions. The hatched portion indicates responses during the first hour. In both cases, there is an inverse relation between concentration and responses and volume consumed. From Meisch and Pickens (1968).

SCHEDULE-INDUCED DRUG SELF-ADMINISTRATION

Rats working under intermittent schedules of food-reinforcement develop concurrent patterns of excessive fluid intake (Falk, 1961a). This phenomenon, called schedule-induced polydipsia, has been used as a procedure for inducing oral self-administration of drugs by substituting a drug solution for tap-water during concurrent food reinforcement. Lester (1961) first reported oral self-administration of ethanol via schedule-induced polydipsia, a finding replicated and extended by Meisch and Pickens (1968), Senter and Sinclair (1967), and Hawkins, Schrot, Githens, and Everett (Chapter 5). Schedule-induced oral drug self-administration has been demonstrated with morphine (Thompson and Pickens, 1970) and pentobarbital (Meisch, 1969) as well.

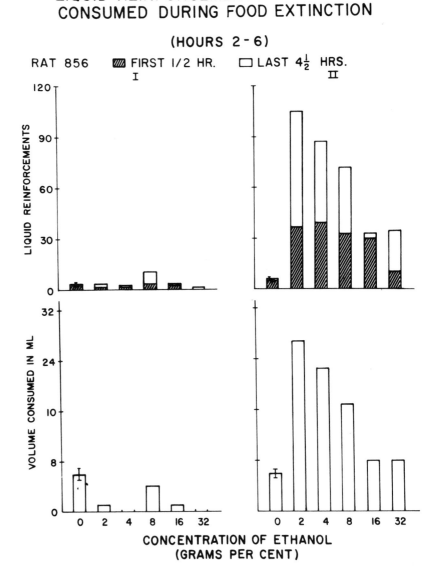

LIQUID REINFORCEMENTS AND VOLUME CONSUMED DURING FOOD EXTINCTION

(HOURS 2 - 6)

Figure 2   The effect of ethanol experience on subsequent disposition to orally selfadminister ethanol by rats. The graphs on the left show liquid reinforcements and volume consumed over a 5-hour period prior to exposure to each concentration in a schedule-induced polydipsia situation, and the graphs on the right show the changes following exposure to each concentration, after the polydipsia contingencies were discontinued. The hatched portion refers to the first half hour. From Meisch and Pickens (1968).

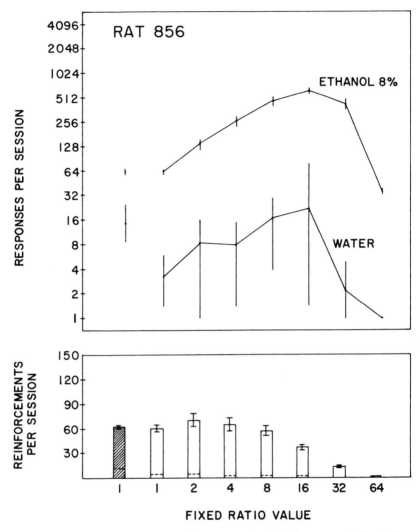

Figure 3   Fixed-ratio schedules of 8 per cent ethanol reinforcement in the rat. Responses and reinforcements per session vary in an inverted U-shaped fashion with the value of the fixed-ratio schedule. Note that the responses per session on water-control days were well below responses for ethanol (there was no overlap in distributions of scores). From Meisch, Anderson, and Thompson (1970).

Meisch and Pickens (1968) trained rats on a VI-1 minute schedule of food reinforcement (45-mg Noyes pellets) and made water concurrently available contingent on a single lever press. After a stable pattern of responding for water had emerged, ethanol or pentobarbital of varying

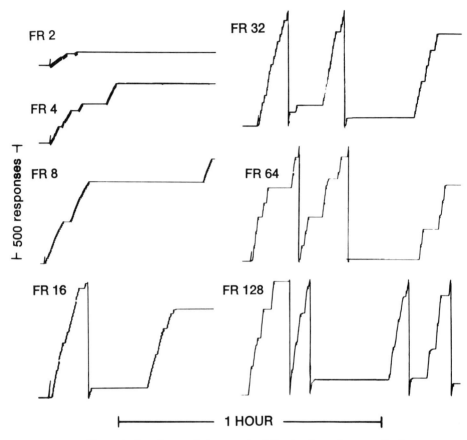

Figure 4   Sample cumulative records of fixed-ratio performance for 8 per cent ethanol reinforcement in the rat, at ratios ranging from FR 2 to FR 128. From Meisch, Anderson, and Thompson (1970).

concentrations were periodically substituted for water. Figure 1 shows the number of liquid responses and volume consumed for tap water, pentobarbital (0.4-1.6 mg/cc), and ethanol (1-32 per cent) under poly-dipsia conditions, indicating that the fluid responses and volume con-sumed for these two depressants follow a similar pattern.

Though little ethanol was consumed prior to polydipsia training, much more was consumed once animals were experienced with a range of concentrations, even though the food reinforcement contingency was discontinued (Figure 2). The left half of this figure shows ethanol re-sponses and intake prior to polydipsia training while the right half shows the same measures after a history of oral ethanol self-administration

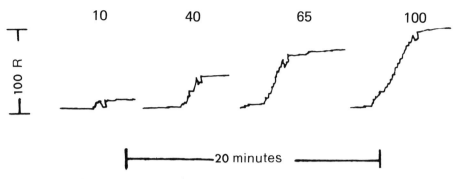

Figure 5   Fixed-ratio schedules of intravenous morphine reinforcement (1.25 mg/kg) in Rhesus monkeys. At low ratio values (FR 10) performance is irregular; however, as ratio value increases, the pause-and-run performance characteristic of ratio schedules emerges.

when the VI-1 food reinforcement contingencies were no longer in effect. There is clearly a very marked increase in ethanol responding, apparently indicating that the drug is serving as an effective reinforcer.

SCHEDULES OF DRUG SELF-ADMINISTRATION

Fixed Ratio Schedules

Much of the research on drug self-administration has employed ratio schedules. In the limiting case, all studies begin with FR-1 schedules (ie, continuous reinforcement). Higher ratios have been explored with morphine (Weeks, 1962; Thompson, Bigelow, and Pickens, 1969), cocaine (Pickens and Thompson, 1968), d-amphetamine (Pickens and Harris, 1968), and methamphetamine (Pickens, Meisch, and McGuire, 1968). Recently FR schedules of ethanol reinforcement have been reported as well (Meisch, Anderson, and Thompson, 1970) (Figure 3). In the latter case, rats with ethanol experience via polydipsia were placed on varying fixed-ratio schedules of 8 per cent (W/V) ethanol reinforcement, and the concurrent food schedule was discontinued. There is a curvilinear relation between the number of responses for ethanol and FR size, with responding increasing to about FR 16 and decreasing at FR 32. Nearly all of the FR responding occurs at the beginning of the session, with periodic pausing varying with increasing ratio size (Figure 4). The foregoing pattern is unlike that seen with stimulant drugs, which produce pauses of extremely predictable duration and many hours of continuous responding prior to an abstinence period (Thompson and Pickens, 1970).

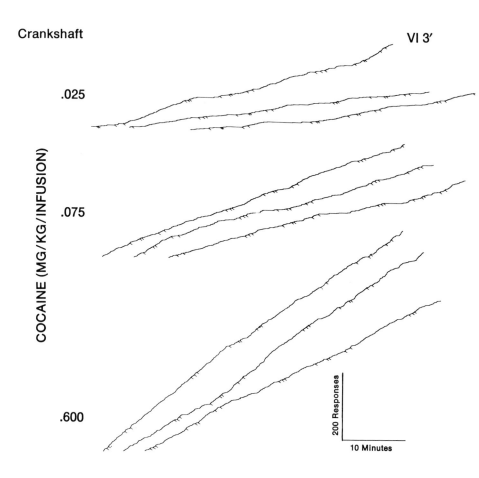

Figure 6   Variable-interval schedules of intravenous cocaine reinforcement in the rat. (Variable interval 3 minutes schedule at 0.025, 0.075, and 0.60 mg/kg.) The characteristic low regular rate of responding emerges at 0.075 mg/kg with rate varying directly with cocaine dose. From Pickens and Thompson (1971), with permission.

The pattern of FR responding with morphine differs somewhat, with irregular pausing, but reliable ratio runs (Thompson, Bigelow, and Pickens, 1969) (Figure 5).

Interval Schedules

Fixed and variable-interval schedules of drug reinforcement have received

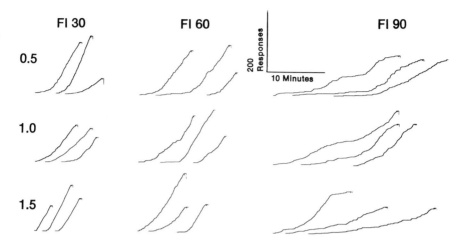

Figure 7   Fixed-interval 30, 60, and 90 minute schedules of intravenous cocaine reinforcement in Rhesus monkeys, at 0.5, 1.0, and 1.5 mg/kg. At FI 30 and 60 minute values, scalloping is well maintained; however, at FI 90 minutes, scalloping degenerates. There is a direct relation between response rate and dose at FI 60 and FI 90 values. From Pickens and Thompson (1971), with permission.

less attention. Woods and Schuster (1971) conditioned monkeys to self-administer morphine intravenously (0.01 to 10.00 mg/kg per infusion), and generated stable response rates. Pickens and Thompson (1971) reproted reliable VI performance of cocaine reinforcement in monkeys (Figure 6), and characteristic FI performance at interval values of 30-90 minutes (Figure 7). At shorter intervals, performance was erratic and characteristic scallops did not occur. Meisch, Anderson, and Thompson (1970) explored fixed-interval schedules of ethanol reinforcement, and, as with FR schedules, found a curvilinear relation between schedule value and ethanol responses per session (Figure 8). The pattern of FI responding is similar to that with other reinforcers (Figure 9) on FI schedules, but occurs in erratic bursts over a five hour session.

Complex Schedules

Several studies have used more complex schedules. Thompson and Schuster (1964) studied an FI-FR chained schedule of intravenous morphine reinforcement (1 mg/kg). Though self-administration was well maintained for many months, cumulative records of the FI-FR chain did not reveal good schedule control.

In another study, Thompson, Bigelow, and Pickens (1969) investigated a very complex heterogeneous chain, the terminal member of which was an FR-75 leading to intravenous infusion of morphine. The

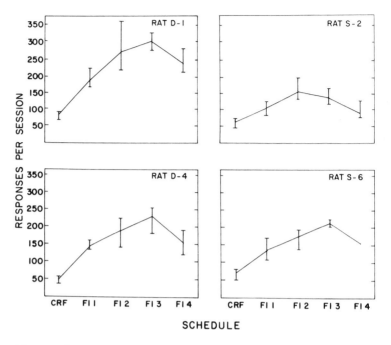

Figure 8   Fixed-interval schedules of oral ethanol reinforcement in four rats. Responses per session vary in an inverse U-shaped fashion with FI value. Ranges are shown by vertical lines. From Meisch, Anderson, and Thompson (1970).

experimental situation consisted of a multi-compartment space in which monkeys earned all food, water, and fruit, and intravenously self-administered morphine via a radio-controlled infusion pump. The experimental space was divided into three compartments. A large compartment was connected to each of the two smaller compartments by individual, solenoid-locked doors. The larger compartment was an exercise and social chamber, and the smaller chambers were used to provide individual access to morphine or to food, water, and fruit.

Two subjects were conditioned, one to work for food, water, and fruit under visual stimulus control in one compartment of the chamber, and the other to self-administer morphine under visual stimulus control in another compartment.

The terminal behaviour sequence leading to food, water, and fruit reinforcement consisted of: 1) Standing on a platform scale immediately outside the food, water, and fruit compartment in the presence of an appropriate stimulus light. When the correct animal stood on the scale (as

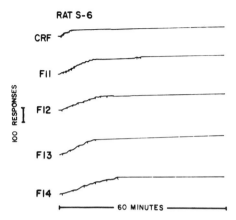

Figure 9 Representative cumulative records of fixed-interval performance for oral ethanol reinforcement by rats. In each case most of the responding and ethanol consumption took place during the first 20-60 minutes of the session, with the duration of responding varying directly with schedule value. There were subsequent pauses from 1 to 4 hours followed by erratic resumption of responding. From Meisch, Anderson, and Thompson (1970).

determined by his weight), the solenoid lock would release and the animal could open the door and enter the work compartment. 2) When the door was opened and closed, a stimulus light was illuminated on the screen panel that separated this compartment from the adjacent morphine compartment. 3) If the monkeys in the two adjacent compartments concurrently held their respective toggle switches closed for a specified interval, the stimulus lights over the food, water, and fruit levers would be illuminated. 4) The monkey could then proceed to work for these substances by operating each lever a fixed number of times. This work session lasted for a fixed time period, after which the lights were extinguished. 5) Operation of a pushbutton alongside the compartment door allowed the animal to re-enter the large-cage social area at the end of the work session. The programme then recycled.

The terminal behaviour sequence leading to morphine reinforcement was comparable. Entrance to and exit from the morphine compartment were controlled in the same manner as for the food compartment. The consequence of both animals satisfying the simultaneous response requirement was illumination of the stimulus light for the drug self-administration lever. A fixed number of responses on this lever produced a morphine infusion, during which the stimulus light flashed. Only one drug infusion was permitted during each work session.

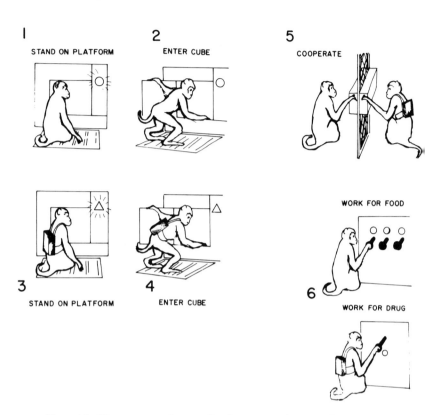

Figure 10   The sequence of responding for two monkeys, one leading to a three member non-reversible option reinforced by food, water, and fruit, and the other an FR 75 reinforced by intravenous self-administration of morphine. Diagrams 1, 2, 5, and 6 show responses for the food-water-fruit monkey, while Diagrams 3, 4, 5, and 6 show responses for the morphine animal. See text for further description. From Thompson and Pickens (1971), with permission.

During some portions of the experiment, these two behavioural sequences were combined as shown in Figure 10. In this sequence, once the food monkey had entered his compartment, the stimulus light on the door to the morphine compartment was illuminated to allow the drug monkey to enter his compartment. Once both compartments were occupied, the two animals could operate their switches simultaneously and then work for their respective reinforcers. This combined behaviour sequence was designed for eventual expansion to a three-monkey situation in which each animal would have the opportunity to self-administer morphine, and every animal would work for his food, water, and fruit. Pairing arrangements could be established such that for each monkey each class of reinforcers was uniquely paired with a different animal.

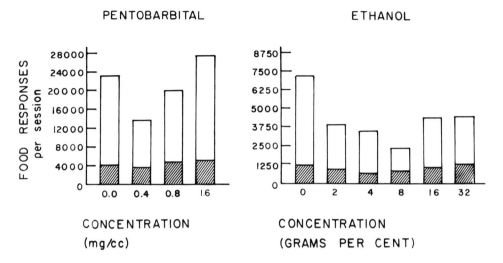

Figure 11   Effects of oral ethanol (right) and pentobarbital (left) concentrations
on number of food responses per 5-hour session in a schedule-induced polydipsia
situation. The hatched portion indicates food responses during the first hour.
From Meisch and Pickens (1968).

It was possible to maintain unrestrained monkeys chronically self-ad-
ministering morphine for periods of nearly one year, with only brief in-
terruptions. Social inter-dependencies have also been successfully maintained for long periods, with pairs of animals.

EFFECT OF DRUG SELF-ADMINISTRATION ON OTHER SCHEDULE-CON-
TROLLED PHENOMENA

In the area of human drug self-administration a major practical concern
is the effects of drug use on other behaviours. Few animal experimental
procedures address themselves to this problem. Concurrent or sequentially scheduled opportunities to engage in behaviours maintained by
other reinforcers as well as drugs provides for such an analysis.

In schedule-induced drug self-administration, the effects of the drug
self-administered are reflected on the concurrently ongoing VI-1 food
baseline. The effects of ethanol and pentobarbital on the number of
food reinforcements earned per session are shown in Figure 11. Although there is an inverse relation between ethanol concentration and
food responses, pentobarbital appears to exert a more complex effect,
with reduction of food responding at low concentrations and increase
in food responding at higher concentrations. This may reflect the fact

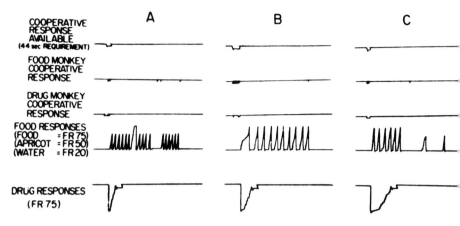

Figure 12   Representative performance on several of the operants in the complex multi-operant situation in which one monkey self-administered morphine intravenously, while a paired monkey worked for food, water, and fruit. The top event's record shows periods during which the cooperative response was made available, the two events' records below show each attempted cooperative response by both monkeys. Responding by the monkey in the three member non-reversible option for food, apricots, and water are shown in the cumulative record second from the bottom, and the FR 75 performance for morphine is shown on the bottom cumulative record. The samples A, B, and C were selected from different periods during a single 24-hour session. See text for further details. From Thompson and Pickens (1971), with permission.

that relatively less drug is consumed at higher concentrations (eg, 32 per cent (W/V) ethanol and 1.6 mg/kg pentobarbital).

Alternatively, the effects of self-administered drugs can be assessed using a multiple schedule, with distinctive stimulus conditions under which the organism can work for food, avoid aversive events, and self-administer drugs. Thompson and Schuster (1964) employed a multiple schedule to study interactions between food-reinforced, shock-avoidance, and morphine-reinforced components, using rhesus monkeys as subjects. Behaviour was well maintained on this schedule for many months, with little day-to-day change. Because food and shock periods were programmed to occur shortly before and shortly after each morphine self-administration period, it was possible to assess the effects of the drug on these behaviours. No discriminable effects could be detected using a 1.0 mg/kg dose of morphine in tolerant animals. However, if the opportunity to self-administer morphine were discontinued, both shock avoidance and FR-food reinforced behaviours deteriorated. Hence for the physically dependent animal, drug presence was a necessary condition to support normal schedule-maintained performance.

Using the more complex situation discussed earlier, Thompson, Bigelow, and Pickens (1969) explored interactions between FR-75 morphine-reinforced responding and a series of complex operants. Figure 12 shows performance on five of the eight operants involved in this situation (see Figure 10). In general, all components were well maintained, except during periods of prolonged morphine deprivation. Morphine self-administration, per se, seemed to have little effect on performance during other components of this complex multi-operant schedule.

DISCUSSION

Schedule influences on drug self-administration appear no less important than schedule influences on behaviour maintained by other reinforcers. Failure to develop stable response patterns leading to drug presentation appears to reflect inappropriate dose (reinforcement magnitude) or inadequate deprivation. For example, monkeys working for morphine on an FR-1 schedule will sometimes respond erratically; however, if the schedule is changed to a multiple FR-Ext schedule with a low or moderate value FR, stable patterns of drug responding emerge quickly, with characteristic ratio performance. Similarly, if the dose of cocaine is too low, responding will be highly erratic and ratio control may never be established, whereas intermediate dosage ranges will maintain highly characteristic ratio runs and pausing (Pickens and Thompson, 1968).

Drugs often have immediate effects that preclude or markedly alter further responding, a complication in drug self-administration research. Hence, to obtain reliable schedule performance, it is often necessary to schedule drug self-administration opportunities on a multiple schedule with extinction periods separating drug-intake opportunities. The length of the extinction period should vary with drug dose.

A further difficulty in interpreting deterioration of schedule control arises in any attempt to differentiate the direct suppressing effects of a drug from satiation. One solution is to use multiple schedules with at least one additional reinforcer (eg, food). A generalized depressant effect would presumably suppress food-reinforced responding as well as drug-reinforced responding. Failure to obtain such an effect would argue in favour of a more specific satiation action on the drug-reinforced behaviour.

A final problem in engendering good schedule control with drugs arises when the onset of a drug is very gradual. It has generally been difficult, if not impossible, to obtain reliable self-administration of hallucinogen drugs. Part of the difficulty relates to the long delay between time of the self-administration response and onset of discriminable drug effect. The development of appropriate potent conditioned reinforcers would facilitate establishing schedule control with such compounds.

It was suggested in the introduction that drug reinforcement has unique properties — namely, drugs have direct stimulating or depressing effects that alter subsequent responding, and drugs of physical dependence must continue to be administered to avoid disruption of all responding (Pickens and Thompson, 1971). Over and above these effects, most other properties of drug reinforcement that have been investigated seem to be consistent with our knowledge of other reinforcers. Drug reinforcement generates patterns and rates of responding under various reinforcement contingencies that closely resemble those obtained with other reinforcers.

4 Schedule-dependence, schedule-induction, and the Law of Effect

J. D. KEEHN

OPERANT BEHAVIOUR AND THE LAW OF EFFECT

Although the definition and analysis of operant behaviour is recent (Skinner, 1938), the province of behaviour so called has existed in the name of voluntary actions for ages. It was Thorndike who released this class of behaviour from the whim of a capricious will and placed it in bondage on the authority of the Law of Effect. The Law of Effect thereby mechanized behaviour once thought to be free, although it is clearer now that it is not mechanization but orderliness in behaviour that the law has brought to light. It is worth examining the current status of the Law of Effect, some limits to its powers in bringing behaviour to order, and some signs of order in voluntary behaviour that seem to be outside the province of the law.

The role of the Law of Effect in sustaining a paradigm shift in psychological science in the sense explained by Kuhn (1962) for physical science has been described elsewhere (Keehn, 1969a). Because of the law, the guiding paradigm of psychological investigation and explanation has been redirected from one that was labelled S-O-R (stimulus-organism-response) to one that can be summarized S-R-S^R (stimulus-response-reinforcement). The sense of change is apparent in an early formulation of the law (Thorndike, 1911), which begins in an approximation to the language of S-R-S^R psychology:

The Law of Effect is that: of several responses made to the same situation, those which are accompanied or closely followed by satisfaction to the animal will, other things being equal, be more firmly connected with the situation, so that, when it recurs, they will be more likely to recur; those which are accompanied ... by discomfort ... will be less likely to recur ...

and ends in the purview of S-O-R:

The greater the satisfaction or discomfort, the greater the strengthening or weakening of the bond.

We might now look beyond the Law of Effect, first by placing the law in a context of change from intrapsychic to interpersonal analyses of the behaviour of man, and second by describing some experiments on the behaviour of animals that have generated data that may go beyond the original pronouncement of the Law, or even a recognizable revision.

THE ANALYSIS OF BEHAVIOUR

'Psychic' dependence: the Intrapsychic Law of Effect

The Law of Effect was used in the S-O-R sense by Thorndike as soon as he began talking of bonds between stimuli and responses. Hull (1943) employed the law similarly when he postulated increments in habit strength ($_SH_R$) to account for behaviour changes following a reinforcing state of affairs. Behaviourism as developed by Hull, therefore, continued the tradition of attributing behaviour to intra-organismic events, and did so in classical structural fashion. Thorndike and Hull were followers of Freud in this respect, insofar as they attributed the causes of behaviour to factors outside a conscious mind but still inside an organism whose consciousness they merely did not need to examine.

On this account the classical Law of Effect may be qualified as the Intrapsychic Law of Effect ('psychic' may be objectionable, but it is acceptable on the same conditions as 'psychology'); it was an incremental datum in mental philosophy dominated by structuralism (the unconscious, habits, bonds), atomism (stimuli, sensations), and associationism (learning, perception), all of which acknowledged that the analysis of behaviour pre-required the analysis of mind or one of its substitutes (conceptual nervous system).

Schedule-dependence: the Interpersonal Law of Effect

The Law of Effect was used entirely in the S-R-S^R sense when Skinner discarded the notion of reflex reserve (Skinner, 1950). His rhetorical query: Are theories of learning necessary? was not a rejection of theory but a rejection of S-O-R psychology, because theories of learning are about the population politics of O, not about the acquisition and maintenance of behaviour. That the experimental analysis of behaviour according to the scheduling of reinforcers (Ferster and Skinner, 1957; Skinner, 1938) entails the analysis of a mutually reinforcing relationship between one organism and another was introduced in a symposium on the operational status of psychology (Skinner, 1945), and depicted humourously in a cartoon in the *Columbia Jester* some years ago. Seen this way the classical Law of Effect can be qualified as the Interpersonal Law of Effect.

Such a qualification of the law imputes control of an organism's behaviour to events beyond the limits of its skin, just as the Intrapsychic Law of Effect located the agents of behaviour behind the surface of the skin. With its interpersonal qualification the Law of Effect represents not an incremental but a revolutionary datum for psychology (Kuhn, 1962); according to this version of the law, behaviour is not psychic-dependent but schedule-dependent, and the analysis of behaviour proceeds not by psycho-analysis but by analysis of the interpersonal transactions in which the subject is continually engaged (Keehn, 1969b). Qualified as interpersonal rather than as intrapsychic, the Law of Effect demands that schedule-dependence precedes psychic-dependence, which parallels the Sartrerian plea that existence precedes essence, and gives scientific respectability to Sartre's aphorism.

Freedom and the Law of Effect

Like the unconscious described by Freud, Thorndike's Law of Effect served to release voluntary behaviour from control by a mental faculty of will. Yet, whereas the Freudian revelation may seem to add a dimension to the pyschological freedom of man, stimulus-response connectionism is said to reduce man to a stimulus-response slot machine (Burt, 1962).

Actually, Freud's trauma-structured 'unconscious' and Thorndike's effect-strengthened 'connection' threaten freedom alike by transforming acute environmental happenings into chronic properties of organisms. It is this transformation that raises threats to personal freedom, for if chronic intrapsychic implants result from punctate historical events, then it is possible for an organism to be permanently controlled by a limited set of managed incidents in early life.

The loss of freedom demanded by the Interpersonal Law of Effect is not loss of personal freedom but loss of lawlessness of behaviour in the scientific sense. According to the interpersonal law, voluntary behaviour is lawful (operant); but the control of behaviour is vested in the total spatial and temporal reinforcing environment of a behaving organism, so that any limitation of freedom imposed by an environment on an organism is reciprocal and temporary: schedule-dependence requires a schedule to be in effect.

The Law of Effect, then, pertains to relationships between the behaviour of an environment and the emitted behaviour of an organism. In the first instance the law (intrapsychic) replaced the concept of will by static complex of stimulus-response bonds in the neural organization of an organism; in the second instance the law (interpersonal) replaces the concept of will by a dynamic matrix of organism-environment transactions. Orderliness in behaviour specified by reinforcement schedules indicates the province of the law. Recently, data have gone beyond the original boundaries of the Law of Effect both in regard to disorderlines in schedule-specified behaviours and in regard to orderliness exhibited by behaviours not specified by certain reinforcement schedules.

BEYOND THE LAW OF EFFECT?

Schedule-specified behaviour

Behavioural drift with negative reinforcement

Most laboratory work on the control of behaviour through schedules of reinforcement has been conducted with animal subjects and mechanical reinforcement dispensers. In this work a particular response has been specified, for example, a bar-press by a rat or a key-peck by a pigeon, and the rate and temporal pattern of emission of the schedule-specified response has been examined as a function of the pre-determined reinforcement schedule (Ferster and Skinner, 1957). Normally, work of this kind generates behaviour that is stable over long periods of time, or predictable as to direction of change when instability occurs. Sometimes, however, there is a shift from schedule-specified to other behaviour in the course of training (Breland and Breland, 1961, 1966), or a drift in the pattern of emission of a response (Sidman, 1960). An example of the latter phenomenon is the declining success that some animals exhibit after reaching a high level of proficiency in so-called avoidance learning experiments.

Insofar as learning refers to a relatively permanent intra-organismic condition (eg, as S-R bonds strengthened according to the Intrapsychic Law of Effect), it may be surprising to find that shock-avoidance performance sometimes declines from a high to a low level with no apparent change in experimental conditions. Yet the phenomenon is not

TABLE 1

Signal onsets and per cent signalled shocks avoided by three
guinea pigs in successive 30-minute periods

	1	2	3	4	5	6	7	8
Animal S1								
Sess. 1 Signals	41	33	15	12	42	11	13	22
Per cent avoidance	0.0	6.1	53.3	83.3	57.1	81.9	61.5	63.6
Sess. 2 Signals	21	23	45	29	32	40	32	51
Per cent avoidance	90.5	91.3	86.7	93.1	78.8	95.0	65.6	76.5
Animal S2								
Sess. 1 Signals	30	23	30	32	36	48	38	65
Per cent avoidance	6.7	4.3	33.3	56.3	58.3	58.3	55.3	55.4
Sess. 2 Signals	45	47	36	32	49	41	36	36
Per cent avoidance	88.9	76.7	33.3	34.4	20.4	34.4	30.6	22.2
Animal S16								
Sess. 1 Signals	20	7	14	17	10	17	11	35
Per cent avoidance	0.0	14.3	42.9	58.8	60.0	88.2	81.8	94.3
Sess. 2 signals	58	80	80	77	85	84	71	92
Per cent avoidance	97.3	96.3	97.5	85.7	89.4	85.7	73.4	80.4

From Keehn and Webster (1967), with permission.

TABLE 2

Signal onsets and per cent signalled shocks avoided by a guinea
pig in successive 30-minute periods of a single 15-hour session

	1	2	3	4	5	6	7	8
Sess. 1*								
Signals	15	21	55	55	67	64	60	61
Per cent avoidance	0	4.8	80.0	76.4	79.1	71.9	66.7	50.8
Sess. 2								
Signals	60	50	54	58	62	55	63	57
Per cent avoidance	65.0	38.0	37.0	39.7	21.0	30.9	28.6	19.3
Sess. 3								
Signals	57	63	64	61	67	70	73	67
Per cent avoidance	14.0	28.6	14.1	6.6	6.0	4.3	11.0	0.0
Sess. 4								
Signals	72	65	71	65	67	67		
Per cent avoidance	13.9	1.5	5.6	3.1	7.5	4.5		

*'Session' refers to 4-hour periods of a single session that lasted 15 hours.

From Keehn and Webster (1967), with permission.

unusual in rats (Keehn and Sabbagh, 1958; Coons, Anderson, and Myers 1960; Reynierse, Zerbolio, and Denny, 1964), guinea pigs (Keehn and Webster, 1967; Sansone and Bovet, 1969), or pigeons (Rachlin, 1969).

Some detailed data are contained in Table 1, which summarizes the behaviour of three guinea pigs with respect to discriminative stimulus control and shock avoidance in two successive 4-hour sessions. In these sessions signalled brief (0.3 second) shocks recurred every 5 seconds (SS interval) unless a bar was pressed. A bar-press terminated the signal and postponed the next onset of the signal for 15 seconds from the time the bar was released (RL interval), and the next onset of the shock for 5 seconds after that (LS interval). Thus, whenever the bar was released there was a signal-free RL interval in which shocks were never delivered, a signalled LS interval that was terminated by a bar-press or a shock, and an SS interval in which shocks were delivered in the presence of a signal until the bar was pressed. A bar-press re-established the beginning of the RL interval, although this interval did not begin to time-out until the bar was released.

Table 1 shows the number of times each animal allowed the signal to appear in successive half-hour periods during the sessions, and the percentages of shocks avoided by responses made in LS intervals. None of the subjects avoided many shocks in the first hour of Session 1, but thereafter all three guinea pigs showed a substantial rise in the percentage of shocks avoided. However, this percentage fell for every animal from the beginning to the end of Session 2.

Exactly the same sequence of events was observed in another guinea pig trained in the same way as the others, but in a single 15-hour session. The results are summarized in Table 2. The table shows a dramatic decline in the animal's avoidance of shocks from about 80 per cent in the second hour to about 6 per cent in the fifteenth hour, but its rate of bar-pressing hardly changed at all. This can be observed in Figure 1, which contains conventional cumulative records of bar-presses made by the animal during the hours marked on the figure. These data are typical of those of several guinea pigs we have studied with this procedure.

The procedure was such that shock density could be reduced by responses in the RL, RS, or SS intervals, and either bar-pressing or bar-holding could serve to prolong the signal- and shock-free RL interval. In spite of this, responding in the RL interval ceased almost entirely, and most reponses occurred for a while in the LS interval, indicating good stimulus control of the response. However, within sessions every animal responded less in the LS interval and more in the SS interval as a session progressed. There was, though, no decrement in response output as the slopes of the cumulative records show, only a drift in the stimulu

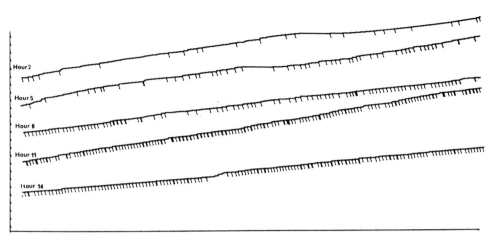

Figure 1 Cumulative bar-press records at the designated portions of a 15-hour session in which a guinea pig was trained on a Sidman discriminated avoidance procedure with SS-5 seconds, RL-15 seconds, LS-5 seconds, and bar-holding functional. Lateral spurs indicate shocks. From Keehn and Webster (1967), with permission.

controlling the response – from the signal alone to the signal plus shock.

The avoidance-decrement without performance-decrement could mean that the performance (response output) was determined solely by the motivating properties of shock once the avoidance-decrement appeared. That this was not so is suggested by data produced by a guinea pig trained with a discriminated Sidman procedure in a double-compartment box (Mowrer and Miller, 1942). In this case a tone preceded brief (0.3 seconds) shocks by 5 seconds (LS interval) after which time shocks recurred every 5 seconds (SS interval) until the animal crossed compartments, whereupon the tone was terminated for 15 seconds (RL interval). Each response (compartment-crossing) in the RL interval postponed the next tone onset for 15 seconds, but relatively little signal-postponing behaviour occurred, and most compartment-crosses were made in LS intervals. Even so, avoidance-decrement occurred, although not so dramatically as in the bar-pressing situation, and it occurred sooner and more profoundly from the first session to the last. The cumulative crossing response records are reproduced in Figure 2. They indicate almost no change in response output that corresponded to the fall in the number of shocks avoided in succeeding hours in each of the first two sessions.

Two conditions were changed in the third session. For part of the time the tone was terminated by the experimenter instead of by the subject, and for another part the tone was turned off entirely. Both changes

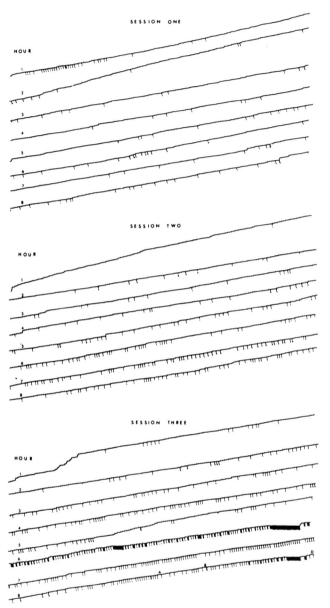

Figure 2   Sample cumulative compartment-crossing records from the designated portions of three 8-hour sessions of a guinea pig trained in a double-compartment box with a Sidman discriminated avoidance procedure with SS=5 seconds, RL=15 seconds and LS=5 seconds. During the fifth hour and between the points marked A and B of Session 3 the signal terminated 1 second or 2 seconds prior to shock. During the sixth hour and between the points marked B and D of Session 3 the signal was omitted.

sharply altered the animal's behaviour. The first change was made four hours after the session began, and lasted for one hour. During this hour the tone was terminated by the experimenter one or two seconds before shock was due. This served to eliminate the contiguity between tone, response, and shock that had previously existed, and had the effect of temporarily increasing the response rate and the number of responses emitted in the LS interval. Secondly, throughout the sixth hour of the session the tone was turned off. The result was that the animal no longer crossed compartments after every shock, and by the end of the hour it hardly responded at all. The effects of both of these changes were reversible, and they were replicated in the eighth hour of the session.

Differential probability of positive reinforcement

A schedule of reinforcement is defined according to the programme by which reinforcers are dispensed after a response. Schedules do not normally provide reinforcement for every specified response, but it is usual to insist that reinforcement of a response be immediate (Holland and Skinner, 1961; Reynolds, 1968; Skinner, 1938). A recent experiment by Herrnstein and Hineline (1966), however, suggests that a response can be established and maintained when immediate reinforcement is not a programmed consequence of that response.

Herrnstein and Hineline (1966) arranged a two-level schedule of shock delivery in which a specified response (bar-press) temporarily changed the probability of shock from a higher to a lower level, but did not affect the delivery of shocks programmed at the lower level whenever it was in effect. Such a programme corresponds, in the case of positive reinforcement, to a two-tier schedule of free food delivery in which a specified response produces a temporary change from a less to a more frequent delivery of food pellets to a hungry animal, but not necessarily by immediate reinforcement. Figure 3 depicts such a differential probability of reinforcement schedule: in the absence of responses (R) reinforcers (S^R) are delivered on the average every 120 seconds (FVI 120), but after a response the next reinforcement occurs at the rate of one per 15 seconds (FVI 15). Responses marked R change the frequency of pellet delivery from the lower to the higher level; all other responses are ineffective. Reinforcers marked H are delivered from the FVI 15-second schedule, and return the rate of pellet delivery back to the lower level.

More than thirty rats were trained to bar-press under a schedule of this kind by Grant Coulson at York University (Coulson, 1970). A particularly elegant result obtained with one animal is shown in Figure 4. As indicated in the figure, food pellets were delivered on the average every

Figure 3   A differential probability of reinforcement (dpr) schedule. The top line indicates the frequency level of free pellet delivery: high, every 15 seconds on the average (FVI 15), or low, every 120 seconds on the average (FVI 120). The middle line indicates responses; the bottom line indicates food pellet deliveries. Responses that initiate the high frequency schedule are marked R; all other responses are ineffective. Food pellets delivered from the high frequency schedule are marked H. With these pellets the low frequency schedule is reinstated.

120 seconds (FVI 120) for twenty-seven sessions, every 15 seconds (FVI 15) for eighteen sessions, every 30 seconds (FVI 30) for forty-two sessions, and every 120 seconds for fifteen sessions. In all cases the effect of a bar-press was to instate an FVI 15-second schedule of free food delivery. The result was that when the density of pellet delivery was increased by a bar-press, a rise in the rate of bar-pressing occurred, but when the rate of pellet delivery remained the same whether the bar was pressed or not, the rate of bar-pressing declined to zero. This result goes beyond the Intrapsychic Law of Effect (even taking account of delay of reinforcement), for it demonstrates that the pattern of response emission can be manipulated when the consequences of not-responding (the 'background' schedules: FVI 120, etc.) are varied.

Not all animals exhibited such an orderly relationship between rate of bar-pressing and 'background' rate of free food delivery. A different kind of relationship, in the data of another animal, is shown in Figure 5. This animal responded at a higher rate than the previous example, and its bar-pressing rate was less sensitive to changes in the rate of free food delivery. Bar-pressing did, however, extinguish when the rate of food delivery after a bar-press (FVI 15) was lower than that in the absence of bar-presses (FVI 10), and it increased in rate when the probability of reinforcement was higher following a bar-press than following other behaviour.

The fact that rate of bar-pressing varies according to the relative frequencies of food delivery before and after a bar-press justifies designation of the food pellets as reinforcers and the schedule as differential probability of reinforcement. The fact that such a designation corresponds to the method of programming the dispensation of reinforcers, however, does not preclude the possibility that the bar-press perfor-

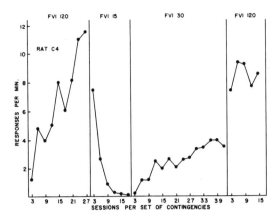

Figure 4   Response rate as a function of background schedule when bar-presses changed the frequency of pellet delivery from the indicated values to FVI 15 seconds. Rat C4. From Coulson (1970), with permission.

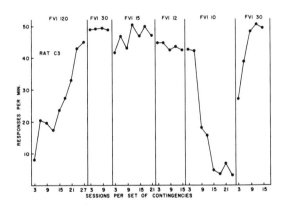

Figure 5   Response rate as a function of background schedule when bar-presses changed the frequency of pellet delivery from the indicated values to FVI 15 seconds. Rat C3. From Coulson (1970), with permission.

mance is acquired and maintained on the basis of occasional immediate reinforcement. That is, although the programmed effect of a bar-press is only to make a free reinforcement available on an average of 15 seconds later, the emission of further bar-presses after the one that increased the probability of reinforcement could result in a fortuitous coincidence of a response and reinforcement delivery. In this event bar-pressing would be maintained on a coventional schedule of VI 15 seconds. That this is

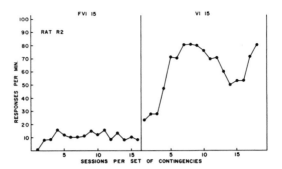

Figure 6   Response rate when bar-presses were reinforced on schedule FVI 15 seconds or VI 15 seconds, both against a background schedule of FVI 120 seconds. Rat R2. From Coulson (1970), with permission.

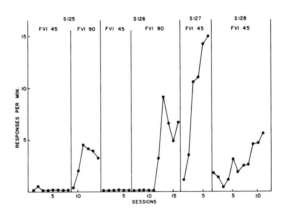

Figure 7   Response rate as a function of background schedule when bar-presses changed the frequency of pellet delivery from the indicated values to FVI 15 seconds, with the restriction that no pellet could be delivered within 3 seconds of a bar-press. Rats S125, S126, S127, S128. From Coulson (1970), with permission.

not the case is apparent from Figure 6, which shows the rates of bar-pressing by a rat when bar-pressing was reinforced on a FVI 15-second schedule against a background schedule of FVI 120 seconds, and when bar-pressing was reinforced on a conventional VI 15-second schedule against the same background.

In order to eliminate the possibility that a food pellet immediately followed a bar-press, in one experiment a 3-second delay was introduced between a bar-press and a free reinforcement from the FVI 15-second schedule. In the absence of bar-presses reinforcers were delivered on schedule FVI 45 seconds, in the presence of bar-pressing they were delivered on schedule *tandem* FVI 12 seconds, DRO 3 seconds; that is, reinforcements were delivered on the average every 15 seconds after a bar-press, but if a bar-press occurred in the final 3 seconds of an interval, the interval was extended by 3 seconds every time a bar-press occurred.

Figure 7 shows the results of this experiment, which utilized four Sprague-Dawley ninety-day-old naive male rats. Two of the animals acquired the response of bar-pressing with the original background schedule of a free food pellet every 45 seconds on the average; the others acquired the response only after the free pellet delivery rate was reduced to an average of one in 90 seconds. In all cases, though, bar-pressing was acquired and maintained on the basis of a differential probability of reinforcement schedule even when the possibility of immediate reinforcement of a bar-press was precluded; and acquisition varied according to the schedule of background reinforcement while the consequences of bar-pressing remained unaltered.

Schedule-induced behaviour

Schedule-induced 'freezing' with negative reinforcement

When a response terminates or avoids an aversive event, the Law of Effect specifies that the escape or avoidance behaviour will increase in strength. Apart from the restriction 'other things being equal,' it says nothing about the increase in strength reaching such proportions that the strengthened response precludes reinforcement consumption (Skinner, 1966) or occasions as much discomfort as it serves to counteract. Examples of the latter appear in the phenomenon of 'freezing' (Bolles,. 1970; Hoffman, 1966) or bar-holding (Dinsmoor and Hughes, 1956; Migler, 1963a, b) during avoidance and escape training.

An amusing example of the phenomenon is shown in Figure 8, which is a cumulative bar-pressing record of a rat trained with a free-operant (Sidman, 1953) avoidance procedure with R-S = S-S = 10 seconds, and shock durations as marked on the figure. What is peculiar is that the animal was trained in a two-bar apparatus in which the other bar was operative, not the one that the animal was pressing. We thought at first that the animal's responses to the irrelevant bar were superstitious escape responses (Keehn and Chaudrey, 1964), but it now seems more probable that the animal was normally holding the bar depressed, and released it only when it was jolted off the bar by a shock.

Several investigations of schedule-induced bar-holding were undertaken, first, to find ways of eliminating it (cf Feldman and Bremner,

D-13   JUNE 11

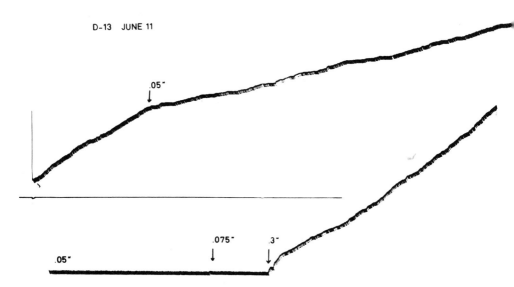

Figure 8   Cumulative record of a rat's responses on a non-functional bar during its nineteenth 3-hour session of training with an avoidance schedule with S-S = R-S = 10 seconds. Arrows indicate changes in shock durations, which were normally 0.3 seconds. The response rate of about 13 rpm is typical of the animal's rate in earlier sessions at 0.3-second shock duration. Shocks displaced the recorder pen downwards, which is the reason for the thickness of the record. From Keehn and Chaudrey (1964), with permission.

1963), and second, to examine its parameters. It was found that when S-S = R-S = 15 seconds, and bar-holding prolonged the R-S interval, bar-holding continued indefinitely. This is shown in Figure 9, which contains a cumulative bar-holding record produced on a cumulative recorder that stepped once for every .2 seconds that the bar was held depressed. Such behaviour was characteristic of rats but not of guinea pigs (Keehn and Webster, 1967). But it was possible to curtail bar-holding by rats by response differentiation through differential reinforcement of shorter and shorter bar-hold durations (Keehn, 1967c); by a double-discrimination avoidance procedure in which bar-presses and bar-releases were signalled by different stimuli (Keehn, 1967a); or by a double-discrimination avoidance procedure in which bar-presses and bar-releases were signalled by the onset and offset of a single stimulus (Keehn, 1968).

As experimentation progressed the emphasis changed from consideration of bar-holding as a duration attribute of a single response, a bar-press, to consideration of a sequential pair of responses, a bar-press and a bar-release (Millenson and Hurwitz, 1961). In the first instance, bar-holding was explained either as a preparatory response for a forthcom-

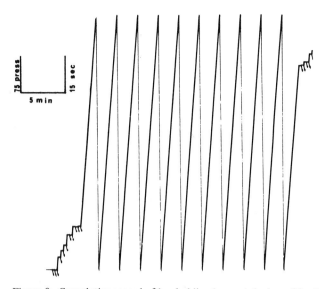

Figure 9   Cumulative record of bar-holding by a rat during a 30-minute period of a session in which S-S = R-S = 15 seconds, and in which the R-S interval began when the bar was released. Each bar-press stepped the record and extra steps were produced by each 0.2-second holding time. Lateral spurs indicate shocks. From Keehn (1967c), with permission.

ing bar-press (Dinsmoor, 1968) or as perseverance of an emitted bar-press (Keehn, 1967b). Neither of these accounts examined the consequence of a bar-release. Such an examination was undertaken in two experiments (Walsh and Keehn, 1969; Keehn and Walsh, 1970) in which it was shown that bar-holding is a function of release-shock intervals: that is, the release response is under the control of the interval from the emission of the release response to the next programmed shock. Figures 10 and 11 contain data on this relationship: when release-shock intervals are short, for example, 20 seconds, bar-releasing is unlikely to occur, so that bar-hold durations are long; when release-shock intervals are long, for example, 125 seconds, bar-releasing occurs almost immediately after bar-pressing, so that bar-hold durations are short. The problem still remains as to why bar-holding from shock to shock occurs with short release-shock intervals when shock density is unaffected whether the bar is held or released (Figure 11). The behaviour may be a species-specific defence reaction (Bolles, 1970) or it may be that there is a differential reinforcing effect of one kind of behaviour (totally on the bar) over another (totally off the bar), as suggested by Keehn and Walsh (1970). In either event it is necessary to go beyond the Law of Effect either by making the law discriminatory according to response topo-

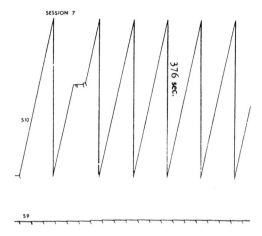

Figure 10   Cumulative bar-holding time records of two rats over a 40-minute period of conventional avoidance training. A light-tone combination (S_1) preceded potential shocks by 5 seconds, and unavoided shocks were terminated by a bar-press. S_1 onset occurred 120 seconds and 15 seconds after bar-release for S9 and S10 respectively. From Walsh and Keehn (1969), with permission.

graphies (Breland and Breland, 1961, 1966) or by examining more closely the components of what is commonly called a response. Such an examination is not normally required in the case of continuous positive reinforcement, for a bar-press produces a stimulus for some other behaviour (approaching a magazine) that necessitates a bar-release.

Schedule-induced drinking and polydipsia

When a food-deprived organism is fed immediately after emitting a response, the Law of Effect predicts that the food-producing behaviour will increase in strength. It says nothing about 'other behaviour' beyond the obvious inference that direct competitors of the reinforced response will weaken. Falk (1961a), however, noticed that when the bar-pressing of hungry rats was reinforced with food on a variable-interval schedule of reinforcement, 'Shortly after a pellet is earned a burst of licking ensues, followed by a return to bar-pressing until the next pellet is delivered.' Subsequently he paid more interest to the quantities of fluid his animals consumed than to the characteristic pattern of behaviour he was among the first to report, and gave the phenomenon its original name of schedule-induced polydipsia (Falk, 1964, 1969).

Our first investigation of the phenomenon were also oriented to quantity, inasmuch as we capitalized on Falk's discovery to produce exces-

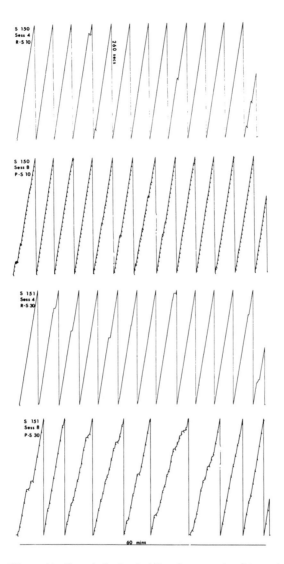

Figure 11   Cumulative bar-holding time records of two rats trained with two procedures in which unsignalled response-terminable shocks were scheduled either 10 seconds (S150) or 30 seconds (S151) after a bar-press (P-S interval) or bar-release (R-S interval). Where P-S intervals are specified, bar-holding was not functional and and a bar-press could only terminate shocks. Where R-S intervals are specified, bar-holding postponed shocks. Lateral spurs indicate shocks.

sive fluid consumption as a means of examining the possibility of limiting over-drinking with anticholinergic drugs (Keehn and Nagai, 1969).

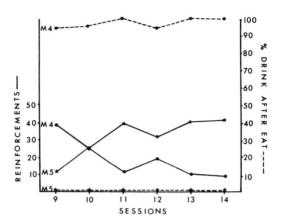

Figure 12   Number of reinforcers consumed, and per cent of occasions that drinking immediately followed eating, by the experimental (M4) and control (M5) animals. Reinforcers were scheduled on VI 1 minute for bar-presses by M4 but either animal could consume them. From Keehn (1970), with permission.

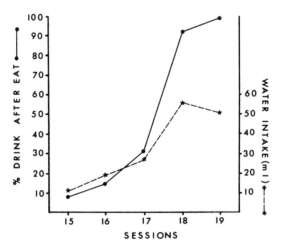

Figure 13   Water intake during a 3-hour session and per cent of drinks following 100 reinforcers by rat M5 from the first session in which this animal earned its own reinforcers (on schedule VI-1 minute). From Keehn (1970), with permission.

When we found easier ways of inducing animals to ingest enormous quantities of fluid (Gilbert and Sherman, 1970; Matsunaga and Keehn, 1969), we became less enthralled with schedule-induced polydipsia, with its attendant emphasis on 'normal' physiologically-controlled levels of fluid intake, than with the schedule-induced eat-drink pattern of behaviour that Falk originally observed.

Two experiments were begun for the purpose of investigating the stability of the eat-drink sequence of behaviour. In one, wheel-running was made available as an additional response to compete with drinking (cf Levitsky and Collier, 1968; Segal, 1969a); in the other, a companion animal was introduced as an alternative stimulus to water. Although the results were not fully analysed, the first experiment confirmed that schedule-induced running could displace schedule-induced drinking. The second experiment produced an unexpected result: undeprived companion (control) animals often stole food pellets that experimental subjects produced. One pair of animals was studied in detail (Keehn, 1970).

Figure 12 shows the number of pellets consumed by the experimental animal, M4, and its companion, M5, and the percentage of occasions when drinking followed eating, during observation periods in which the experimental subject produced 50 food pellets on a VI 1-minute schedule of reinforcement, each reinforcer comprising one pellet. Up to and including the ninth 3-hour session, animal M5 was neither food nor water-deprived; thereafter it was not fed for 20 hours before each session, and its weight was reduced to 87 per cent of its free-feeding level by Session 14. This animal did not once drink after eating although the experimental animal drank after every pellet it obtained.

Late in Session 14 M5 began to bar-press, and from Sessions 15 to 19 it was run alone at 87 per cent of its free-feeding weight with bar-pressing reinforced once every minute on the average (VI 1 minute). Figure 13 shows the concurrent development of schedule-induced polydipsia and schedule-induced post-pellet drinking. It is not likely that the schedule-induced polydipsia occurred because 'rats have a strong tendency to drink after they have finished a meal' (Stein, 1964), for this rat showed no such tendency at all until it was exposed to the VI-1-minute schedule of reinforcement under which the elevated water intake developed.

Changes in the animal's drinking behaviour as its water intake rose are shown in Figure 14. The cumulative records contain both bar-presses and licks, but the two kinds of responses are easily distinguishable on the basis of rate and consistency (Davis and Keehn, 1959): the steep smooth portions are licks; the shallower grainier parts are bar-presses. The curves reset to the baseline on reinforcement delivery, so it is easy to discern the reliability of post-pellet drinking in the record of Session 19. This record also shows many occasions on which post-pellet drinking continued up to the point where it was immediately followed by a reinforced bar-press. These are the occasions on which an adventitious drink-press chain of responding could be strengthened (Clark, 1962);

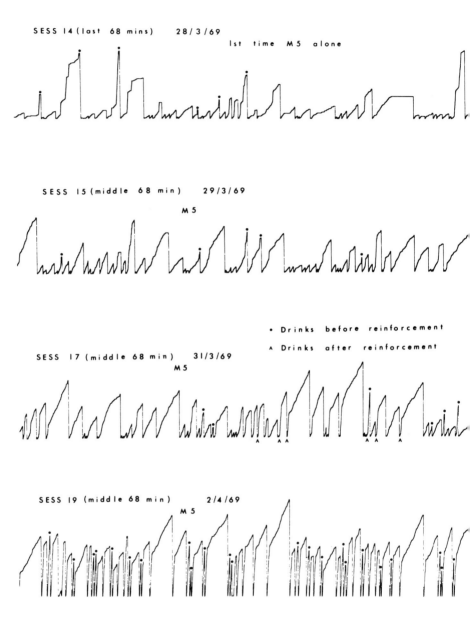

Figure 14 Combined cumulative licking and bar-pressing records of rat M5 from
the first time it was reinforced for bar-pressing. High rate responses are licks; low
rate responses are bar-presses. The recorder reset on reinforcement delivery. The
dots mark occasions when a reinforced bar-press shortly followed licking. Occasions when licking immediately followed eating are marked (∧) in Session 17;
licking followed almost every reinforcer in Session 19. From Keehn (1970), with
permission.

they occur more often in the records prior to Session 19 than do examples of post-pellet drinking. Similar data have been published by Falk (1966a, Figure 3).

The most obvious change in the animal's behaviour between Sessions 14 and 19 is in the relationships between eating, drinking, and bar-pressing. At first these behaviours occurred in no discernable sequence: they appear at the beginning of the record for Session 14 in the order press, *eat*, press, drink, *eat,* press, *eat,* press, *eat*, press, drink, press, drink, press, drink, press, drink, press, *eat*. By Session 19 there were only two deviations from the sequence drink, press, *eat*, drink ... in the whole 3-hour session. Less obvious is an apparent decrease in the variability of drink durations as the regularity of post-pellet drinking is established. This terminal regularity is clearer in Figure 15, which shows cumulative records of licking and bar-pressing by other animals well-trained with fixed-and variable-interval reinforcement schedules of 1 and 2 minutes (Keehn and Colotla, 1970a). The regularity of the durations of post-pellet bursts of licks is particularly noticeable in the FI 2-minute record.

Figure 16 is an alternative representation of post-pellet bursts of drinking. The animals are the same as those that produced the data in Figure 15, but the records are accumulated bursts of drinking only, constructed by accumulating successive bursts of licks between reinforcers. If drinks were all of equal duration, the curves would be straight lines with slopes proportional to drinking times. Both the variable-interval curves are remarkably close approximations to straight lines for the whole of their lengths. The fixed-interval curves are a little more ragged and exhibit longer durations of drinking at the beginning of the sessions (cf Falk, 1966b), but still permit reasonable predictions of drink durations most of the time.

Attempts at controlling drink durations were undertaken in experiments in which fluid palatability, meal size, and meal distribution were varied. In the first of these experiments the duration and pattern of schedule-induced water-drinking was compared with that of schedule-induced saccharin (0.4 per cent w/v) - drinking. Sessions were normally 2 hours long, and 45-mg Noyes pellet reinforcers were scheduled on VI 1 minute. As expected, saccharin intakes consistently exceeded water intakes, but anticipated differences in durations of post-pellet drinks of the two liquids were found in only one of the three animals used in the experiment. That animal was atypical in that it did not develop polydipsia with water, exhibiting instead a number of stereotyped behaviours between reinforcements, such as rearing and running to the corners of the experimental chamber. The other animals drank for about as long after eating pellets (post-pellet drinking) when the available fluid was saccharin as they did when the fluid was water. The difference was that

FI 1'

FI 2'

VI 2'

VI 1'

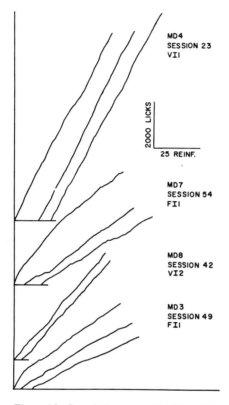

Figure 16   Cumulative post-pellet licks of four hungry rats reinforced on the designated schedules. From Keehn and Colotla (1970a), with permission.

they would frequently return to the drinking tube after having left it (inter-pellet drinking) when the tube contained saccharin. They did not do this when the tube contained water. Illustrations of post- and inter-pellet drinking of water and of saccharin are shown in Figure 17.

Examples of accumulated post-pellet and inter-pellet drink times of all three animals are shown in Figures 18 and 19 respectively. Except in the case of the non-polydipsic animal, S486, post-pellet drink durations exhibit the same consistency and regularity described above. Inter-pellet

Figure 15 (facing page)   Typical cumulative records of drinking and bar-pressing responses of hungry rats reinforced with 45-mg Noyes pellets on reinforcement schedules FI 1 minute (top, Rat MD4, Session 57), FI 2 minutes (next, Rat MD8, Session 63), VI 2 minute (next, Rat MD8, Session 23), VI 1 minute (bottom, Rat MD4, Session 53). Records reset with reinforcement. Smooth steep segments after reinforcement depict drinking; other segments, bar-pressing.

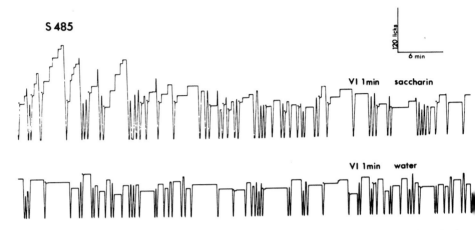

Figure 17   Typical cumulative records of schedule-induced drinking of saccharin and water. The pen reset to the baseline with reinforcement. Water-drinking was almost entirely post-pellet; saccharin-drinking was both post-and inter-pellet. The end of post-pellet drinks when inter-pellet drinking followed are marked by dots on the records. Bar-presses normally occurred between post and inter-pellet drinks, but they are not shown in the figure. From Keehn, Colotla, and Beaton (1970), with permission.

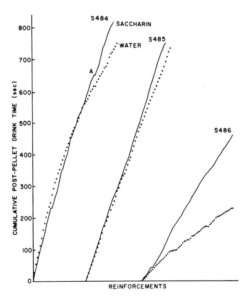

Figure 18   Cumulative durations of drinks that immediately followed reinforcers (post-pellet drinks) scheduled on VI 1 minute when the available fluid was water or 0.4 per cent (w/v) saccharin. That part of the record of Rat S484 marked A shows an occasion when licking did not follow reinforcement. From Keehn, Colotla, and Beaton (1970), with permission.

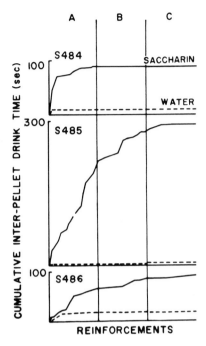

Figure 19 Cumulative durations of drinks other than those immediately following reinforcement (inter-pellet drinks) when the available fluid was water or 0.4 per cent (w/v) saccharin. Segments A, B, and C are from the first, middle, and final 20-minute periods respectively of a 2-hour session. From Keehn, Colotla, and Beaton (1970), with permission.

drinks of saccharin, however, were erratic in length and unpredictable as to occasion, except that they were more frequent early than late in a session. More illustrations of the difference between post- and inter-pellet drinking are contained in Figure 20. The data in this figure were collected during 1-hour sessions (in which bar-presses were reinforced with pellets on VI 1 minute, and saccharin was the available fluid) that immediately followed 2-hour extinction periods in which either saccharin or water was available. When water was available during extinction (Session 83) the animals consumed hardly any fluid prior to the normal session (S484, 4 ml; S485, 0 ml); when saccharin was available during extinction (Sessions 75 or 76), S484 drank 43 ml and S485 drank 45 ml before the normal session. This pre-session drinking can be seen to have depressed the inter-pellet drinking of both animals during the normal session, but to have left their post-pellet drinking unaffected.

These data indicate that palatability-induced drinking is different from

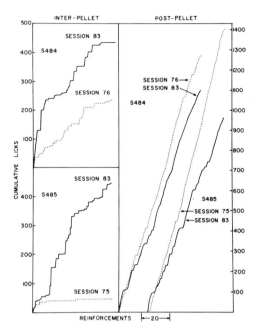

Figure 20   Cumulative records of post- and inter-pellet licks at a tube from a bottle containing saccharin following high (Sessions 75 and 76) and low (Session 83)
pre-session fluid intake. In the 2-hours immediately before Sessions 76 and 83, rat
S484 had drunk 43 ml saccharin and 4 ml water respectively. In the 2-hours immediately before Sessions 75 and 83 S485 had drunk 45 ml saccharin and 0 ml water
respectively. From Keehn, Colotla, and Beaton (1970), with permission.

schedule-induced drinking. The former is erratic in duration, unpredictable as to occurrence, and subject to satiation, whereas the latter is reliably emitted, relatively constant in duration, and apparently immune
to satiation.

The taste of the fluid does not seem to prolong the duration of schedule-induced post-pellet drinking although it may well curtail it (Falk,
1966c). What about the characteristics of the schedule-delivered food?
Falk (1967) has reported some effects of type, size, and spacing of
meals on the quantity of fluid ingested. Our approach to similar relatior
ships has been different: we have searched for stimuli that set the occasion for drinking to begin, and stimuli that signal the time for drinking
to stop. We have done this by controlling the availability of food pellets
by means of mixed and multiple schedules of reinforcement.

The basic reinforcement schedule employed through a sequence of experiments was mix FI t min crf (n). That is, after a fixed interval of t
minutes the next n responses were continuously reinforced, after which

the fixed-interval requirement again came into effect, and so on. Manipulated variables were values of n, values of t, and presence and absence of stimuli indicating the beginning and end of t. These stimuli signalled respectively the end of the continuous availability of food (and hence the occasion when drinking would not interfere with feeding) and the time when food was again available after a bar-press (and hence the occasion when continued drinking would interfere with feeding).

The first experiment was concerned only with the effect of varying n. The fixed interval value was set at 1 minute, and continuous reinforcement was given for 1, 3, 6, or 9 bar-presses at the end of this interval. The experiment can be thought of as varying meal-size with a FI 1-minute schedule of reinforcement, although the whole meal was not delivered by a single bar-press at the end of the interval. Six experienced male albino rats were used. They were maintained at 80 per cent of their free-feeding weights while they were run on alternate days for 2-hour sessions. In general, the animals consumed more water per session the smaller the size of the meal — because there were fewer larger than smaller meals in a session, not because they drank more after smaller than after larger meals (Keehn and Colotla, 1970b).

The animals did not drink after every pellet they consumed. Modal behaviour was for an animal to continue bar-pressing and eating until a bar-press went unreinforced, whereupon it would drink before resuming bar-pressing. The stimulus for drinking was not the presence of a pellet in the mouth, but the absence of a pellet following a bar-press (Keehn and Colotla, 1970b).

Three more naive white rats were trained on the same schedule as described above, except that the fixed interval was 30 seconds instead of 1 minute and the crf segment of the mixed schedule was continued up to 21 pellets. These animals were trained first with mix FI 30 seconds crf 1 (which is also FI 30 seconds) and then with crf segments of 3, 6, 9, and 21 pellets in that order. Once again drinking became confined to the period immediately after the last pellet in the crf segment, and occurred after this pellet about 80-100 per cent of the time following stabilization. Typical cumulative records of licking behaviour with different meal sizes are shown in Figure 21. The data amply confirm that the stimulus for the onset of schedule-induced drinking is an event that signals the nonavailability of food: as long as a bar-press produced a food pellet, the animals continued to bar-press and eat; as soon as a bar-press or two did not produce a food pellet, the animals went to the drinking spout and drank. Thus, although drinking was invariably a post-pellet phenomenon, it was not the stimulus of food in the mouth that occasioned a burst of drinking. It is therefore more accurate to describe schedule-induced drinking as a pre-interval phenomenon than as a post-pellet pheno-

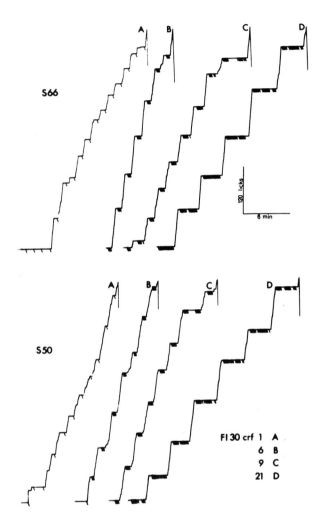

Figure 21   Cumulative licking records of two hungry rats reinforced for bar-pressing on the designated schedules. Reinforcers are indicated by lateral spurs on the records. Record A (FI 30 crf 1) of each animal appears to indicate drinking after reinforcement. The other records show that drinking actually occurs when food is not available. From Keehn and Colotla (1971), with permission.

menon even though the latter account is more compelling in the uncom plicated fixed- or variable-interval schedule of reinforcement cases. The initiation of drinking may not depend on the meal just eaten, but the during or amount of drinking may. There are indications in Figure 21

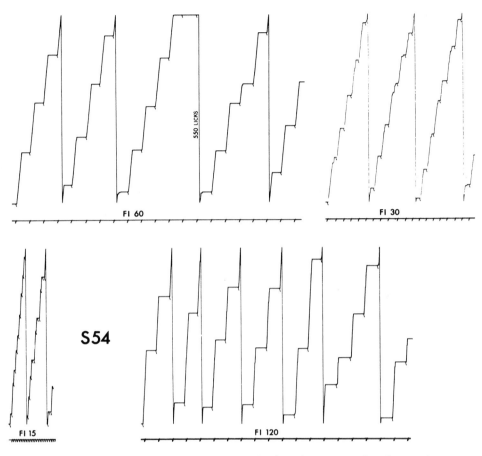

Figure 22   Cumulative licking records of two hungry rats whose bar-pressing was reinforced on the designated schedules. Licking ceased more quickly the shorter the interval between food reinforcers. From Colotla, Keehn, and Gardner (1970), with permission.

TABLE 3

Mean water intake (ml) per meal according to meal size
(n pellets) and inter-meal time (t sec)

No pellets (n)	1	3	6	9	21
S50	.52	.57	.42	.38	.59
S53	.36	.53	.47	.46	.66
S66	.32	.46	.40	.37	.58

Interval (t)	15"	30"	60"	120"
S54	.24	.38	.54	.66
S65	.35	.45	.60	.64

that larger meals induce longer drinks. More data are contained in Table 3. The upper half of the table shows mean intakes of water per meal by three rats over ten sessions with the designated meal sizes when the interval between meals was held constant at 30 seconds; the lower half of the table shows mean water intakes per meal by two other rats over ten, fifteen, or twenty sessions with the designated inter-meal intervals when the meal size was held constant at 1 pellet. Once again, the relation between meal size and drink size is weak with meal sizes up to 9 pellets. The relation between inter-meal interval and drink size seems to be stronger (cf Falk, 1969); it suggests that at shorter inter-meal intervals the duration of drinking after eating is controlled by the probability of the availability of food at the end of a passage of time. A graphic expression of this relationship appears in Figure 22.

These data may help to bring schedule-induced drinking under the rubric of the Law of Effect, for they show drinking to begin when food stops being available and to stop sooner, the sooner it becomes available again. But there is much more to the phenomenon than this as other data from our own and other laboratories attest.

CONCLUSION

The Law of Effect has lived in common lore for ages, particularly in its punitive aspect. Because Thorndike did not disturb the lore of effect in solemnizing the Law of Effect it has been necessary to go beyond his static law and exchange it for a dynamic Law of Effect that is both transactional and relative (Herrnstein, 1970; Keehn, 1969b).

Most of the experimental psychology of the Law of Effect has been confined to the study of animals in mechanically reinforcing environments, so the nature of experimentation operated against the discovery of a transactional Interpersonal Law of Effect (except in jest), though not against the generation of apparently unlawful data. Schedule-induced behaviours and drifts in schedule-specified behaviours appear to go beyond the Law of Effect in this respect. These phenomena transcend the static Intrapsychic Law of Effect but they may not go beyond the relativistic amendment that Herrnstein (1970) has proposed: 'the absolute rate of any response is proportional to its associated relative reinforcement.' The differential probability of reinforcement schedule studied by Coulson (1970) is one of the simplest qualitative exemplifications of a relative law. Schedule-induced and drifting schedule-specified behaviours may be more complex examples of the operation of a dynamic relative law, or they may exemplify properties of behaviour beyond the province of the law.

5 Schedule-induced polydipsia: an analysis of water and alcohol ingestion

T. D. HAWKINS, J. F. SCHROT,
S. H. GITHENS, and P. B. EVERETT

J.L. Falk (1961a) introduced the phenomenon of schedule-induced polydipsia to the general scientific community. He found that each of his food-restricted rats consumed prodigious quantities of water concurrent with their performance on a simple variable-interval bar-press schedule. The mean water intake during the daily 3.17-hour sessions was 92 ml, more than three times the normal 24-hour fluid intake.

Falk's observation that such excessive quantities of fluid are consumed in so brief a time has remained a puzzle to this day. The drinking would appear to serve no water regulatory function, as indicated by Stricker and Adair's (1966) finding that the polydipsic rat becomes severly overhydrated as a consequence of inordinately high ingestion rates. There also exists no satisfactory behavioural account. Stein (1964) attributed polydipsia to the dryness of the food employed. Clark (1962) assumed that polydipsia was an example of superstitious conditioning. However, Falk (1969) has voiced reservations to both of these simplistic positions, maintaining that neither one provides an adequate account of the polydipsia phenomenon. Unfortunately, there has been little interest in reevaluating either the induced-thirst or the superstition positions or in attempting a more comprehensive theoretical formulation that might account for the bulk of the polydipsia data and provide guidelines for future investigations.

An examination of the relevant polydipsia literature led us to conclude that much of the rhetoric surrounding the theoretical arguments was superfluous and incomplete, being based primarily on anecdotes and unsound predictions, with the primary cause of confusion being the lack of general information about the phenomenon. In this light, we proceeded to explore more completely those variables previously suggested to be of importance in the elaboration of the phenomenon. Armed with several years of experience with schedule-induced polydipsia, our attention also turned toward determining the effectiveness of spaced-pellet techniques in maintaining high rates of alcohol ingestion.

GENERAL PROCEDURE

The subjects were adult, male Wistar rats from the Walter Reed colony. Each was naive at the beginning of its experiment or series of experiments. With only a few exceptions, each rat was maintained at a 250 g body weight by limiting food access. Without the food restriction procedure the projected normal weights would have been 400 g or more at the time of testing. The rats were housed individually under conditions of constant illumination and an ambient temperature of 80° F. In each study, the rats received most of their daily food ration during the experimental sessions. Whenever necessary, a small additional supplement was given after the individual sessions to maintain the desired body-weight levels.

The experimental boxes were small, commercial rat chambers, equipped with a variety of standard devices (feeders, lickometers, etc.). Each experimental box was individually placed in a larger plywood box containing a house light and air blower. Several of these isolation boxes were placed in each experimental room. Continuous masking noise was provided. Programming was automated with a variety of electro-mechanical and solid-state devices maintained separately outside the experimental rooms.

All experiments were conducted seven days a week with experimental sessions for each rat starting at about the same time every day.

WATER INGESTION

Interval studies

Polydipsia has been observed with a variety of procedures in which food pellet delivery is spaced over time. Since the appearance of Falk's (1961a) initial report, large amounts of drinking under variable-interval schedules have also been observed by other investigators (Clark, 1962; Stricker and Adair, 1966). Stein (1964) and Falk (1966b) made similar observations with fixed-interval schedules. Likewise, Segal and Holloway (1963) found large amounts of drinking during DRL schedules in which low rates of bar-pressing are reinforced. With each of the above reinforcement schedules, a response is followed by pellet delivery if the response is emitted after some programmed time has elapsed since the delivery of the last pellet. Thus, in each case, there is some minimal spacing between successive pellet deliveries.

Considering the results from a number of other studies, it would seem that the pellet spacing or interval duration is a critical determiner of the drinking, but the explicit dependency between the selected operant response and the pellet delivery is not. For example, Segal and co-workers (1965), Falk (1961a), and Reynierse (1966) have all reported that large quantities of water are ingested if pellets are delivered independently of the rat's performance.

In spite of the large number of studies implicating the importance of pellet spacing or interval duration, there was only one early study (Falk, 1966b) in which the interval duration was systematically manipulated over a wide range to determine its relation to the amount of water ingested. In Falk's study, the fixed-interval duration was gradually increased from two seconds to 300 seconds. Initially, as the fixed-interval duration was increased, the amount of water ingested gradually increased, with a maximum intake of about 90 ml being observed at 3-minute intervals. Water intake declined precipitously when the interval duration was further increased to 5 minutes.

Falk's (1966b) examination of fixed-interval duration was a parametric study, and it seemed to be an appropriate starting point for our analysis of polydipsia. The first experiments reported below are several we have performed to determine the most general formulation that describes the functional relation between the interval duration and the degree of polydipsia. In each study the interval between pellet deliveries was systematically varied, but the exact experimental details were altered from one experiment to the next to determine if other variables were also influencing the measures of water intake.

Variable-feeding schedules

Falk's (1966b) fixed-interval study suggested that water intake is an inverted U-shaped function of the fixed-interval duration. Our first study was conducted to determine if a similar function obtains when pellets are presented automatically on an aperiodic basis, with no bar-press requirement being in effect.[1]

During the initial variable-feeding schedule, the intervals between pellet deliveries averaged 1 minute overall, but the individual interval

1/ This procedure has been designated variable-feeding schedule to avoid confusion with variable-interval schedules where a dependency exists between responding and the reinforcement delivery.

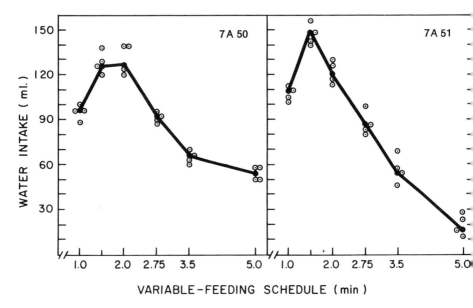

Figure 1   Total session water intake by Subjects 7A50 and 7A51 as a function of the variable-feeding schedule duration. The data points represent the amounts drunk during the last five sessions of each condition.

durations varied from 5 seconds to 120 seconds. After thirty-five sessions on this 1-minute condition the mean interval duration was gradually increased to a maximum of 5 minutes. During each session a total of 200, 45-mg rat pellets was delivered.

Figure 1 illustrates the changes in water intake obtained by increasing the average interval duration. For both rats, as the interval duration was progressively increased, the water intakes first increased and then decreased sharply with the longest intervals. Generally, the data of this first study corroborated Falk's (1966b) fixed-interval data. In order to facilitate a direct comparison, the results of both studies have been converted into a standard form by calculating the amount drunk per interval, since the total number of intervals varied between the studies. This comparison is depicted in Figure 2. The data selected from Falk's (1966b) study are estimates for Rat 110, which was exposed to the widest range of fixed-interval values. Both curves show an inversion as the interval increases. At about 3 minutes and 5 minutes on the abscissa the two curves fall quite close to one another, especially considering they represent data from two different experiments.

Although the curves shown in Figure 2 show some similar features,

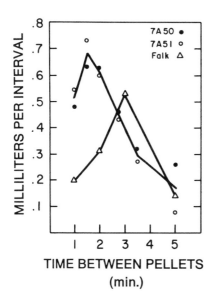

Figure 2   The amount of water ingested per interval related to the interval duration: a comparison of data from the subjects in the variable-feeding experiment (7A50 and 7A51) with the fixed-interval data reported by Falk (1966).

suggesting a common effect of the interval duration, their divergence from one another at the shorter interval durations is pronounced. This divergence indicated to us that the interval duration was not the only important variable determining the water ingestion in these two experiments. At this point we had no way of knowing which of the curves, if either, most adequately reflected the influence of the interval duration. To suggest only a few possibly relevant differences in procedure, either the absence of the bar-press requirement or the aperiodicity of the pellet deliveries may have accounted for our water intake curves deviating at the shorter intervals from those reported by Falk (1966b).

Fixed-feeding schedules

In the second experiment, pellets were delivered at regular (equal) intervals, by contrast with our initial study. This could also be viewed as a step closer to a direct replication of Falk's (1966b) fixed-interval procedure in which pellets were delivered approximately on a fixed periodic basis. As an additional variation, only 100 pellets per session were delivered. Again, as with our first study, there was no bar-press requirement.

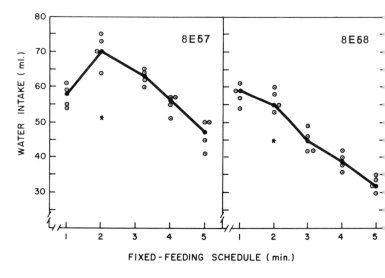

Figure 3   Total session water intake as a function of the fixed-feeding schedule duration for Subjects 8E57 and 8E58.

During the initial 1-minute condition, fluid intakes for both rats increased gradually from day to day reaching an asymptotic level in abou fourteen days. For the last five days of the 1-minute condition the intakes for the two rats were quite close, averaging 58 ml for Rat 8E57 and 59 ml for Rat 8E58. With the change to the 2-minute intervals, the water intakes for the two subjects separated and remained different across the subsequent schedule conditions. The results for the various interval values are shown in Figure 3. The curve for 8E57 is inverted. The curve for 8E58 decreases monotonically. This latter curve has proved to be the exception. The relative amounts drunk per interval during the 1-minute condition (.58 ml and .59 ml by 8E57 and 8E58, respectively) were almost identical to the relative intakes shown by the rats in the variable-feeding experiment (see Figure 2). However, the intakes of the present subjects did not decline as much during the longer intervals.

Judged as an attempt to replicate more closely Falk's (1966b) fixed-interval study, the second experiment was not very successful. The relative intakes (ml per interval) that obtained for both the shortest and the longest intervals deviated substantially from those reported by Falk. At this point, we considered that perhaps there was something different about drinking during fixed-interval schedules that warranted examination.

Fixed-interval schedules

The initial portion of our third experiment entailed a comparison of drinking during twenty-eight daily sessions on a 1-minute free-pellet schedule and twenty-eight sessions on a 1-minute fixed-interval schedule, with ten sessions of continuous reinforcement intervening between the two interval conditions. Drinking during both of these interval conditions was quite similar for the two rats, with the medians for the two conditions ranging from .50 to .56 ml/pellet, indicating that there really was no difference in drinking that we could attribute to the fixed-interval procedure. In contrast, drinking during the continuous reinforcement sessions was negligible, as expected from earlier reports (Falk, 1967), never exceeding 5 ml per session.

For the remainder of the fixed-interval experiment, unlike our earlier experiments and Falk's (1966b) study, we subsequently decreased the number of pellets per session in direct proportion to the increases in the interval duration. For fixed-interval 1, 2, 3, 4, and 5 minutes, the pellets allotted per session were 100, 50, 33, 25, and 20, respectively. This provision resulted in session lengths that were approximately 100 minutes each across all fixed-interval values. Consequently, as the fixed-interval duration was increased, the total amount of water ingested per session decreased for both rats. Examination of the relative amounts drunk per pellet (or per interval) revealed drinking levels that first increased, then decreased, as the interval duration was gradually lengthened. Figure 4 depicts these relationships, with an inverted curve being evident for each rat. With the longer intervals, the declines in relative intake were not very sharp. This minor difference from our earlier interval studies in which more abrupt declines were noted was probably the result of holding constant the session duration across each interval condition.

General effect of interval duration

Throughout the data of the experiments in which the interval duration has been systematically varied, a trend appears that probably represents the general influence of the interval-duration variable. Considering the results from our three interval studies and Falk's (1966b) study, the typically occurring function relating the amount consumed per interval (or per pellet) and the interval duration is an inverted U-shaped curve. This inverted curve was obtained when free pellets were delivered aperiodically or on a regular basis. Similar functions were also obtained in the present fixed-interval study and in Falk's (1966b) study although the

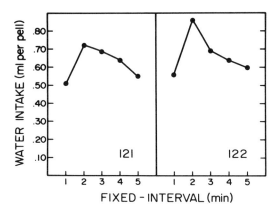

Figure 4   Relative water intakes for Rats 121 and 122 as a function of the fixed-interval duration. The interconnected points represent the median values for the last five days of each condition.

two studies differed on some important procedural grounds.

In his recent review, Falk (1969) suggested that an inverted U-shaped curve is the general function relating the amount of drinking (total fluid consumed) to the rate of consummatory behaviour, or interval duration for the purposes of this discussion. However, it would seem that this formulation is an example of the more general case. If one holds constant the total number of pellets delivered per session, and systematically increases the interval duration, the resultant changes in total fluid intake are represented by an inverted curve. If the session duration is held constant as the interval duration is increased, total fluid consumption decreases monotonically. That there is a common effect of the interval durations obtained with these two types of procedures is revealed only when a measure of relative intake (ml per pellet or ml per interval) is employed; the common, most general result is not revealed in the absolute amount drunk (ml). Although the use of a relative measure of drinking is necessary in establishing the general influence of the interval duration, it is not, of course, sufficient. The generality of this variable can only be established by counterbalancing the experimental procedures to cancel the possible influence of other co-variables (eg, session duration); a simple mathematical manipulation is not adequate. This requirement has been satisfied, at least, by the experiments examining fixed-interval duration.

In Falk's (1966b) experiment the number of pellets was held constant allowing session duration to vary. In the fixed-interval study presented here, the session duration was held constant allowing the number of pelets to vary. These two procedures are necessary complements of one another. Neither of these procedures alone strongly establishes the effect of interval duration, but both procedures in concert greatly enhance the general formulation, which states that the amount drunk per interval is an inverted U-shaped function of the interval duration.

It is noteworthy that the interval between the delivery of food portions is of general importance in determining the level of polydipsia, especially so since the spacing of food reinforcements has proved to be of ubiquitous influence on the levels of operant performance (eg, Catania and Reynolds, 1968). At first glance, it would seem that the influence of interval duration on drinking is quite different from the influence of interval duration on operants, for in the present studies we have obtained inverted drinking curves as opposed to the frequently cited monotonic curves for operants. However, this difference lies primarily in the measures employed rather than in fundamental differences in the behavioural dynamics.

The marked similarity between polydipsic drinking and typical operant performance is immediately apparent if the data from the present experiments are converted into rate form. For this illustration, the water intakes for each of the highest drinkers from the first three experiments are presented in Figure 5. The functions relating rate of ingestion to interval duration are decreasingly monotonic for each rat. Moreover, the ingestion rates of the rats not selected for illustration would have served just as well. This similarity between the rate of drinking and the rate of operants on a functional level strongly suggests that the underlying processes responsible for the strength of these different behaviours are quite similar. Rephrased, one can reasonably interpret the functional relationships revealed in our interval data as indicating that the process of reinforcement accounts for the very high levels of drinking exhibited by a hungry rat exposed to spaced pellet procedures.

We are not suggesting that the determinants of schedule-induced polydipsia and typical operant performance are identical. An obvious and often cited difference is the temporal patterning of the respective behaviours. Usually, polydipsic drinking closely follows the pellet delivery. The expected scalloping effect occurring shortly before reinforcement delivery is rarely, if ever, seen. The scalloping tendency is extremely weak even when there are explicitly programmed dependencies between drinking and food delivery (Segal and Deadwyler, 1965). This difference between drinking and more typical operants (bar-press or key-peck) suggests that there are additional, perhaps topographic, variables influencing the temporal pattern of one and not the other.

The possibility that a complex constellation of variables may be com-

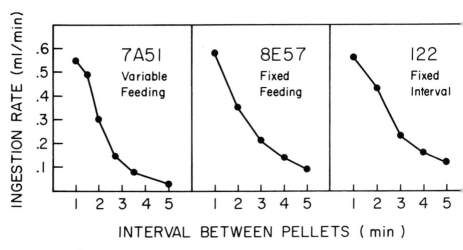

Figure 5 A comparison of the water ingestion rate of three rats selected from three different interval experiments.

ing into play with respect to the temporal patterning of drinking in no way negates the suggestion that conditioning or reinforcement variable also have considerable influence on schedule-induced drinking. We still must account for the striking observation that with respect to the mani pulation of interval duration, or inferentially, frequency of reinforcement, schedule-induced drinking and operants exhibit a fundamental functional similarity. This similarity gives exceptionally strong support to Clark's (1962) earlier position that schedule-induced polydipsia is a product of the process of adventitious reinforcement.

Size of food portion

A study reported by Falk (1967) suggested that, in addition to interval duration, the size of the food portion was an important variable in determining the extent of polydipsic drinking. Using both a 1-minute and a 2-minute variable-interval baseline, Falk reported reduced intakes for those sessions during which two pellets were delivered per interval instead of the usual one. This purported effect of the larger portion sizes was of great interest to us since the direction of change was opposite to that often produced in operant studies when the magnitude of reinforc ment is increased. In the study presented below, we attempted to repli cate systematically Falk's (1967) findings using fixed-feeding schedule with the pellets being automatically delivered on a periodic basis.

As in Falk's (1967) study, the experimental procedure consisted of inserting probe sessions to determine the influence of increases in portion size. Initially the rats were exposed to a 1-minute fixed-feeding schedule for 25 days to permit drinking to become very stable. A total of 150 pellets per session was delivered at the rate of one pellet per interval. This baseline condition will be designated one minute: one pellet (1m1p). After drinking stabilized, a probe session was inserted every three to five days. On probe days, two pellets were delivered per interval (1m2p). During these probe sessions the total number of pellets delivered was held constant at 150 per session, necessitating a reduction by one-half in the total number of intervals and the session durations. As our measure, the fluid level in the reservoir was recorded at the end of each 25 intervals on each probe day and on each baseline day immediately preceding the probe days. After collecting data for a total of three probe sessions on the 1-minute schedule, the interval duration of the baseline schedule was increased to 2-minutes (2m1p). For the 2-minute condition, the total number of pellets was held constant at 100 per session. After ten days on the baseline schedule, probe sessions were again initiated (2m2p) every three to five days. Thus, we collected data for four different conditions, two each with the 1-minute schedule (1m1p and 2m2p) and two each with the 2-minute schedule (2m1p and 2m2p).

The average cumulative water intake curves for each of the four experimental conditions are presented in Figure 6. For both subjects, during the two-pellet probe conditions, the ingestion rates increased above the respective baseline rates. In addition, the 1-minute baseline rates were consistently higher than the 2-minute baseline rates.

From the data shown in Figure 6, it would seem that the general effect of increasing the food portion size was to enhance the level of drinking rather than to reduce it, as was reported by Falk (1967). Procedurally, this study and Falk's were almost identical. Then how do we resolve this apparent discordance? Close examination of the data from the two studies reveals that the difference lies not so much in the empirical results as in the type of measure used to depict the results. Falk's (1967) statement that a larger portion size reduces the amount of drinking was based on his observation that the total ml consumed per session was lower during the two-pellet probes. This difference is also evident in our data. For example, compare the total cumulative intakes for the 1m1p condition and the 1m2p condition shown in Figure 6. A considerable difference is evident for both rats. However, it is also evident that this difference is due primarily to the session length and not to the food portion size and can be evaluated only if the different session durations are taken into account in the measure depicting the drinking behaviour. This

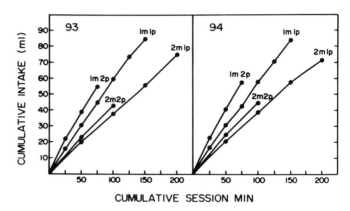

Figure 6   Cumulative ingestion rates for Subjects 93 and 94 during four different schedule conditions: 1-minute, 1-pellet (1m1p); 1-minute, 2-pellet (1m2p); 2-minute, 1-pellet (2m1p); 2-minute, 2-pellet (2m2p).

can be accomplished by evaluating differences in drinking rate rather than focusing on the total intake per session.

That the enhanced rate of ingestion due to increasing portion size is a general effect is also revealed in Falk's (1967) data. If one estimates the ingestion rates during Falk's one-pellet versus two-pellet conditions one finds that, for a total of six comparisons, rates for the two-pellet conditions were higher in four cases, approximately equal for one, and lower for only one. Thus, the present data are consistent with Falk's observations even when ingestion rates are considered. Similar changes in drinking rate have also been reported quite recently by Rosenblith (1970), employing second-order fixed-interval schedules. Data from these three studies, in which the influence of portion size was examined, show that increasing the portion size enhances the rate of water ingestion. This change of rate is in the same direction as observed when the magnitude of reinforcement influences operant performance. These observations give added support to our earlier contention that the process of reinforcement accounts for the strength of polydipsic drinking.

Lick-dependent delays

Several investigators have noted that lick-dependent delays of pellet delivery have little or no effect on schedule-induced polydipsia (Falk, 1961b; Hitzig, 1968). This type of observation has been used as evidence in criticisms leveled against the notion that polydipsia is an example of superstitious conditioning (eg, Falk, 1969). These criticisms may be untenable for they imply that if the drinking were conditioned, then one should be able to eliminate it with a lick-dependent delay procedure. However, even if the drinking behaviour were attenuated by delays, this would not serve as a sufficient indication that the drinking was conditioned in the first place. The delay effects would simply indicate that the drinking was conditionable. Also, it does not necessarily follow that all conditioned behaviours will be influenced by delays of reinforcement, in the same way if at all.

In our experience with lick-dependent delays we have found also that polydipsia is quite resistant to change. Well-established drinking is not altered even with delays as long as 4 or 5 minutes. This is not so surprising in view of the efficacy with which high levels of drinking are maintained by pellets delivered at relatively long intervals.

Taking a slightly different tack in some recent studies, we have been examining the possibility that long lick-dependent delays might interfere with or prohibit the development of polydipsia even though these same delay durations have little influence on firmly established polydipsia. In the first of these studies, the background schedule consisted of delivering pellets once per minute if no licks on the water tube occurred. This procedure, of course, readily produces polydipsia. In addition, if a drink (defined as five licks) occurred, the 1-minute clock stopped and a 4-minute clock determined the next pellet delivery. After the delayed pellet was presented the 1-minute clock resumed operation. (Note that this is a variant of the differential probability of reinforcement procedure described by Keehn in Chapter 4.)

Figure 7 shows the results for five naive, food-deprived rats subjected to the 4-minute delay procedure for fifteen consecutive sessions. The drink probability remained quite low for three of the five rats (220, 293, and 232).[2] Rat 226 showed a gradually increasing tendency to drink followed by a sharp decline to a low level, which, incidentally, was maintained for an additional ten sessions not shown here. In contrast to most of the rats, Subject 294 showed an extremely strong tendency to drink, as indicated by the rapid rise in the drink probability and its continued maintenance at a high level for the remaining sessions. In fact, the drinking shown by Rat 294 developed in a fashion almost indentical to that shown by Subject 298, which was exposed to only 1-minute delays.

These preliminary delay data suggest that the presence of very long lick-dependent delays can prohibit the development of polydipsia in most rats. Since the above study was conducted, we have resubstantiated the suggested effects of 4-minute delays with additional rats and

2 / Drink probability was computed for each 50-minute session by dividing the number of intervals in which a drink occurred by the total number of intervals.

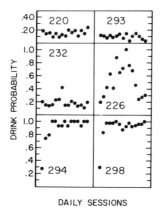

DAILY SESSIONS

Figure 7   Drink probability scores for six rats during fifteen consecutive sessions.
Pellets were delivered at 1-minute intervals if no drinking occurred. Five licks occurring within any interval delayed the delivery of the next pellet for a specified
time.

are currently attempting to determine the minimal duration which will
reliably attenuate the development of polydipsia. In addition, the fact
that low drinking levels were maintained in four subjects even though
the empirically determined rate of pellet delivery ranged from about 1.:
per minute to 2.0 per minute indicates that these frequencies of food d
livery are not sufficient for producing polydipsia, although it has been
our experience that polydipsia is readily developed by every rat at these
frequencies in the absence of lick-dependent delays.

Even with the limited nature of our current delay data, some support
can be marshalled for the conditioning view of polydipsia. In line with
our earlier argument, the suggestion that delays do have some effect on
polydipsia may not be particularly relevant to the conditioning hypothesis. Documenting the delay effect is important in elaborating the
phenomenon of polydipsia, but this demonstrates only that drinking is
conditionable, that is, that it can be modified (reduced) by the delay
procedure. Support for the conditioning explanation of polydipsia com
potentially from another source, that is, from observation that the deve
lopment of polydipsia can be attenuated by delays even though well-
established drinking is quite resistant to delay effects. In other words,
there is an indication that the stronger the drinking behaviour, the less
influence lick-dependent delays will have. In explaining this, we could
quite reasonably presume that the process of reinforcement produces
the strength that results in this resistance to the delay effects (eg, see
Herrnstein, 1966).

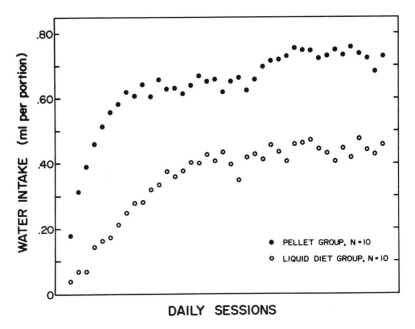

Figure 8   The gradual development of polydipsia for two groups of rats during 40 consecutive sessions. One group received 45-mg food pellets. The other group received 90-mg portions of liquid diet. Both types of food were delivered at 1-minute intervals.

Type of food[3]

Shortly after Falk (1961a) documented schedule-induced polydipsia, the controversy arose as to whether or not polydipsia is produced by the thirst-eliciting properties of the food. The data presented to date give some, but by no means unequivocal, support to this notion. Stein (1964) reported almost complete attentuation of drinking when 0.15-ml portions of milk were substituted for 45-mg food pellets. Similarly, Stricker and Adair (1966) compared drinking attendant with the delivery of food pellets to 0.06 ml portions of Wesson oil, finding much lower levels of drinking with the oil. In contrast, Falk (1967) reported that high levels of drinking resulted with 22-mg portions of liquid monkey diet. As Falk has concluded, his data indicate that dry food pellets are not a necessary condition for producing polydipsia. However, this limited conclusion does not negate the possibility that thirst or, more specifically, oral factors are important in the development and maintenance of

3 / These studies were conducted by J.F. Schrot as a senior investigator.

polydipsia, for the data of Stein (1964) and Stricker and Adair (1966) must somehow be taken into account.

Preliminary work in the lab also revealed that liquid monkey diet can sustain fairly high levels of drinking. However, the polydipsia seemed to develop more slowly than we had observed earlier with food pellets. There also appeared to be a difference in the terminal levels of drinking depending on whether pellets or liquid diet were used. Subsequently, we attempted to document carefully these suggested differences with a fairly large number of subjects.

The daily means for two groups of rats (ten each on 45-mg pellets and ten each on 90-mg liquid diet) are presented in Figure 8. Two differences between the groups are immediately apparent. First, the pellets produced a consistently higher average level of drinking. Second, the drinking of the pellet group developed at a considerably faster rate, reaching an initial asymptotic level in about ten days.

The nature of the differences between subjects of the two groups is revealed in more detail by the data from some of the individual rats. In Figure 9 representative individual curves are presented for one-half of the subjects. Generally, the drinking for each of the pellet subjects developed faster across sessions and was maintained at higher levels. Four of the ten liquid-diet rats drank at levels comparable to or slightly above the pellet group average (eg, 199 and 196). Two of the liquid-diet subjects showed quite slow, gradual increases (eg, 204). Four of the liquid-diet subjects showed almost no drinking at all (eg, 195 and 202), quite in contrast to the average of 0.40 ml per portion drunk by the lowest pellet rat, Subject 263. The liquid-diet rats as a group showed a much wider range in drinking level than the pellet group.

The present data indicate that the type of food has a considerable influence on the development of polydipsic drinking. We obtained consistently lower levels of drinking with the liquid-diet subjects, although there were a few notably high drinkers in this group. The emergence of these high drinkers with 90-mg portions is somewhat in conflict with Falk's (1967) report that only liquid diet portions as small as 22 mg will sustain drinking. This discrepancy is perhaps due to the different session lengths employed in the two studies. Our sessions were quite short, 50 free-food deliveries at 1-minute intervals, compared to Falk's 3-hour sessions. With long sessions, progressive satiation probably has a considerable influence, yielding the low drinking levels reported by Falk for 62-mg and 353-mg portions.

With ten of the liquid-diet rats from our initial study we continued with a comparison between drinking sustained by pellets and drinking

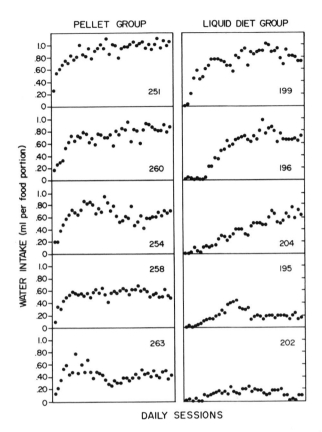

Figure 9 Relative water intake scores for individual rats selected from the pellet and liquid diet food groups.

sustained by liquid diet by delivering food pellets for 28 sessions or more and then reverting again to liquid diet. These manipulations revealed within-subject differences comparable to those obtained when the different groups were intially compared. The mean intakes for the individual subjects during the respective experimental conditions are presented in Figure 10. In general, drinking was higher during the pellet condition whenever there was a difference between the levels of drinking in the two conditions. These data from the second phase of the liquid-diet studies help to clarify the crucial role of the type of food in the elaboration of polydipsia, showing that the type of food determines not only the rate at which polydipsia develops, but that it also contributes to the day to day maintenance of a sustained drinking level.

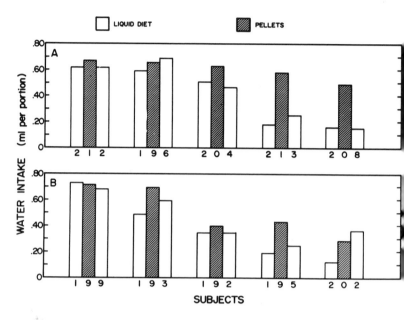

Figure 10 A comparison of the water intakes of individual rats, each subjected to two different feeding conditions, periodic delivery of 45-mg food pellets (hatched areas) or periodic delivery of 90-mg portions of liquid diet.

Current working position

On the surface, the liquid-diet data presented above and the reports by Stein (1964) and Stricker and Adair (1966) suggest that induced thirst is an important determinant of polydipsia because, in each of the studies, the liquid-food portions resulted in consistently lower drinking. This notion of induced thirst is not necessarily incompatible with our earlier evidence that reinforcement variables contribute to the level of polydipsia. As we had obtained support for the induced thirst explanation and also for the superstition or conditioning explanation of polydipsia, we considered that perhaps both explanations were correct, that is, that schedule-induced polydipsia is determined by the combined effects of both thirst-producing and reinforcement variables.

In order to establish firmly the feasibility of such a dualistic explanatory scheme, it is important to obtain estimates of the relative reinforcing efficacy of the foods that produce different levels of drinking. For example, if liquid diet proved to be equal to or more effective than food pellets in maintaining general operant performance, then induced thirst is indirectly supported as a concept accounting for the reduced levels of drinking. This would be a reasonable position, because we would need some explanation other than relative reinforcement value to account for this reduced drinking. However, if liquid diet proved to be the weaker reinforcing agent, one could parsimoniously maintain that the attenu-ated drinking levels are the result of this property only, mitigating any need for the concept of induced thirst.

In our attempt to determine the relative reinforcing efficacy of 90-mg portions of liquid diet versus 45-mg pellets we employed a progressive-ratio schedule, previously shown to be an effective discriminator of re-inforcement value (Hodos and Kalman, 1963). This schedule requires that the subject emit an increasing number of responses (bar-presses in this case) for each successive reinforcement, with the size of the highest ratio attained serving as the index of reinforcement strength.

The results from four rats tested on a progressive-ratio of ten are shown in Figure 11. The height of the bars represents the mean perfor-mance for the last ten days of the respective conditions. Three of the rats consistently completed longer ratio runs for liquid diet than for pel-lets. Subject 199 was a clear-cut exception to this general trend. The dif-ferences in bar-press performance maintained by the two reinforcers were most extreme for the initial comparisons; as the conditions were re-peatedly reversed, the differences tended to diminish. This is perhaps a reflection of the diminishing importance of reinforcement strength in maintaining differential levels of responding, which is generally assumed to occur as operant training progresses.

Minimally, the progressive-ratio data indicate that 90-mg portions of liquid diet are at least as effective as 45-mg pellets in sustaining operant performance, rendering improbable the hypothesis that the different levels of polydipsic drinking that the two types of food sustain are due to differences in general reinforcement value. Rather, it would seem that the different levels of drinking that obtain with liquid diet as opposed to food pellets should be attributed to the relative dryness of the respec-tive foods. Therefore, in contrast to those investigators who have reject-ed both the induced thirst explanation and the superstition explanation, we have tentatively concluded that schedule-induced polydipsia is a complex phenomenon that is produced by the combined effects of thirst variables and reinforcement variables.

ALCOHOL INGESTION

In the same year that Falk (1961a) documented extremely high amounts

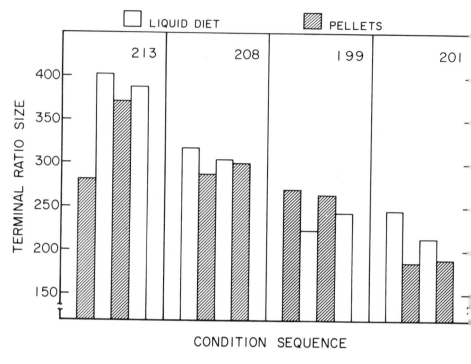

Figure 11   Bar-press performance for four rats on a progressive-ratio schedule that increased in increments of 10. Two different reinforcers were tested, 90-mg portions of liquid diet and 45-mg pellets (hatched areas). The abscissa represents the average size of the last ratio completed within the 1.5-hour sessions during the final ten days of each condition.

of water consumption during variable-interval pellet schedules, Lester (1961) reported a similar finding, but the fluid to which Lester's rats had access was a 5.6 per cent (w/v) solution of ethanol. Lester found that his nine food-deprived rats were drinking themselves into a high state of inebriation. No similar observations of self-intoxication in rats antedated this report and, until recently, no additional reports have followed.

From his preliminary analysis of the alcohol ingestion, Lester suggested that there was an order of importance to the variables which he had examined. A bar-press requirement appeared to be of primary importance, aperiodicity in the pellet delivery was next, and the presence of fluid during training was cited as least important. Recent studies have not substantiated these earlier suggestions, however. For example, ingestion of ethanol solutions during fixed-interval schedules has been obtained by Holman and Myers (1968) and also by Freed and Lester (1970), indicating that aperiodicity in the operant schedule is not a necessary condition. Everett and King's (1970) demonstration of high rates of alcohol ingestion during the aperiodic delivery of free pellets challenges Lester's suggestion that an explicitly programmed response requirement is essential to the alcohol ingestion phenomenon.

In the following series of studies selected from our current alcohol work we have found that free pellets delivered on a periodic basis, the least likely case in terms of Lester's analysis, maintain substantial levels of alcohol ingestion. In these studies we employed the spaced-pellet technique, alone and in combination with other variables, to determine the extent to which we could raise the total alcohol intakes and the rates of alcohol ingestion in three food-deprived rats. Since our primary concern was in producing the most alcohol ingestion, this work is best considered as a technological exercise rather than as an intensive functional analysis.

Preliminary observations

Initially the three food-restricted rats (220 g) were allowed fifty 45-mg pellets per session delivered at exactly 1-minute intervals. Before the exposure to 5 per cent alcohol (v/v), each rat had access to water for at least fifteen sessions. After five days exposure to the alcohol solution the number of pellets per session was increased in an attempt to raise the session intakes.

Figure 12 shows the median fluid intakes for the last five water sessions compared to alcohol intakes for each subsequent five-day period. With the fifty-pellet sessions, intakes dropped to consistently lower levels when 5 per cent alcohol was substituted for water. When the number of pellets per session was increased to 100, all three rats showed higher median intakes, but the increases were somewhat less than twice the levels seen during the fifty-pellet sessions. Although intake increases occurred, they were not proportional to the increases in the pellet number. This was probably due to the marked deceleration in drinking during these longer sessions noted from the cumulative lick records. Likewise, increasing the pellet number to 150 for Subject 191 produced no additional increases in alcohol consumption.

These preliminary observations made it clear that hungry rats would consume large quantities of alcohol during periodic, free pellet procedures. Recognition that the consumed alcohol was having a pronounced effect on the rats did not require a trained eye, for each rat was grossly ataxic and flaccid, particularly at the ends of the longest sessions.

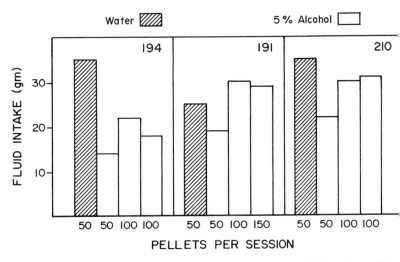

Figure 12   Median fluid intakes (water and 5 per cent alcohol) for Subjects 194, 191, and 210 during four consecutive periods of five sessions each. The hatched areas represent water.

Split versus continuous sessions

Because the declining ingestion rates within the preliminary alcohol ses-sions were probably due to progressive intoxication, we thought that we might be able to increase the intake per 100 pellets if we employed a fifty-pellet morning session and a fifty-pellet afternoon session. These two sessions were separated by 2.5 hours, allowing some time for the al-cohol ingested in the morning session to be metabolized before the after-noon session began.

For this experiment, the 1-minute pellet schedule was retained for Subjects 194 and 191. Subject 210 was shifted to 1.5 minute intervals. The experimental sequence and median 5 per cent alcohol intakes for each consecutive five-day period are illustrated in Figure 13. Rats 191 and 210 both showed substantial increases in total alcohol intake during the split sessions as compared to the intakes during the continuous ses-sions. That the increases were due specifically to the procedural change is even more firmly established by the complete reversibility of the ef-fect when the continuous sessions were reinstated. Results from Subject 194 showed similar trends. However, large day-to-day fluctuations in his intakes made it difficult to evaluate the influence of the split session condition. The differences in total alcohol intake between 191 and 210 were quite noticeable, particularly since their intakes had previously

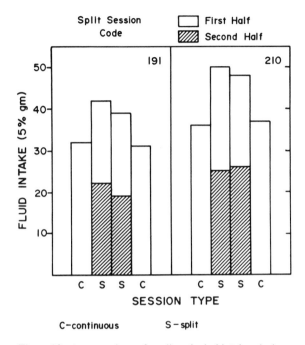

Figure 13 A comparison of median alcohol intakes during continuous (c) and split-session (s) conditions for subjects 191 and 210. The continuous sessions consisted of 100 consecutive intervals. A fifty-interval morning session followed 2.5 hours later by a fifty-interval afternoon session (hatched areas) comprised the split-session condition.

been similar. As we will show later, these differences were probably due to the different interval durations employed for each rat.

Continuous access to 5 per cent alcohol

Concomitant with the experiments reported here, we were conducting several others to determine the amounts of different alcohol concentrations that food-deprived rats would consume in the home cage during each 24-hour period. An average intake of 50 g per day (5 per cent solution) proved to be typical for a rat maintained at a 220 g body weight. These data raised the possibility that consumption of a 5 per cent solution would occur both in the home cage and during the spaced-pellet sessions, if the rats had continuous access to the alcohol solution.

During the present experiment all three rats were shifted to the baseline condition of 100 pellets per session delivered at 1.5-minute inter-

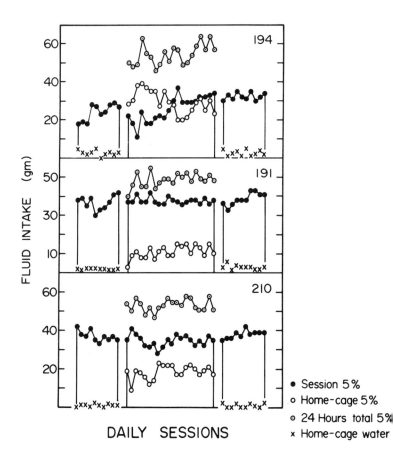

DAILY   SESSIONS

- • Session 5%
- ○ Home-cage 5%
- ◎ 24 Hours total 5%
- × Home-cage water

Figure 14   Fluid intakes in the home cage and in the spaced-pellet test chamber for Subjects 194, 191, and 210. On the first and the last ten days, 5 per cent alcohol was available during sessions only and water was available in the home cage. During the middle twenty days, 5 per cent alcohol was available in both places.

vals. Initially, a 5 per cent alcohol solution was available during the sessions, with only water available in the home cage. In the second phase, the 5 per cent solution was available also in the home cage. The final step consisted of reverting back to water in the home cage. Thus, the experimental changes were made only with respect to the fluid available in the home cage; the session conditions remained constant throughout.

A complete documentation of the fluid intakes for the rats during the third experiment can be found in Figure 14. During the first condition, all three rats drank substantial amounts of alcohol during the sessions, but they drank almost no water in the home cage. When the 5 per cent

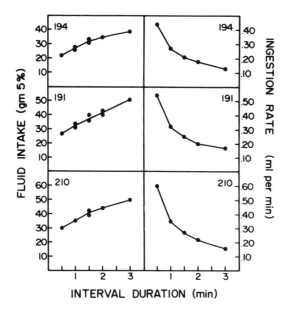

Figure 15   Total alcohol intake and rate of alcohol ingestion as a function of the interval duration.

solution was continuously available, all three rats showed some additional consumption in the home cage. The session intakes remained at the same high levels as before. Only with Rat 194 was there any suggestion that continuous access to 5 per cent alcohol detracted from the session drinking. This proved to be only a temporary disruption, however. As exhibited by the 24-hour totals, the net result of allowing continuous access to the 5 per cent solution was a reliable increase in the total alcohol consumed, with the high-rate session drinking remaining essentially intact.

Manipulating interval durations

During our earlier analysis of water intake we learned that the total water consumed is an inverted U-shaped function of the interval duration, if the number of pellets delivered per session is held constant across all interval values. The next experiment was performed to determine if a similar functional relation exists between 5 per cent alcohol intake and the interval duration. Different interval durations were tested within the range of .5 minutes to 3.0 minutes. The sequence was different for each rat, with each new condition remaining in effect for five sessions. Throughout, the pellet number remained at 100 per session.

Without exception, the 5 per cent alcohol intakes for each rat proved to be an increasing function of the interval duration. However, the intake increases were somewhat less than proportional to the increases in interval duration, resulting in overall ingestion rates that were a decreasing monotonic function of the interval duration. These relationships are depicted in Figure 15.

Apparently, the functions relating the amount ingested to the interval duration differ, depending on whether the fluid available is water or a 5 per cent alcohol solution. In contrast to the inverted curves typically obtained with water, there was no inversion in the curves obtained here. Each curve was close to a linearly increasing function of the interval duration. It is possible that the differences were related to the intoxicating properties of the alcohol. For example, with the 1-minute intervals, the alcohol intakes were quite low (about .30 g per pellet) compared to those expected with water (about .60 g per pellet). As the interval duration was increased, the session durations also increased, perhaps allowing time for the consumed alcohol to be metabolized, and thus permitting the alcohol intakes at the longer intervals to approach those typically obtained with water. By contrast, the functions that relate rate of ingestion to interval duration are quite similar for water and 5 per cent alcohol in that both are represented by decreasing monotonic curves.

Alcohol intake during limited access periods

In evaluating the effectiveness of spaced-pellet procedures in enhancing the rate of alcohol ingestion, it is important to know how much alcohol is consumed during comparable periods of time if the food is given all at once. Observations with other 220 g, food-restricted rats indicated that only about 17 g of 5 per cent solution is consumed during a 5-hour period following a feeding of 4.5 g of rat chow. This is considerably less than the amounts consumed by the spaced-pellet rats during the 3-minute intervals in the preceding experiment, although the total amount fed and the duration of the testing period were identical. These differences give a strong indication that the spaced-pellet procedure *per se* is quite effective in enhancing the alcohol ingestion. As an additional check, we wanted to insure that these same relationships would obtain for a single food-restricted rat, depending on whether or not it was subjected to the spaced-pellet conditions. For this demonstration we selected Rat 194, which drank the least per session, and was then least likely to show a difference.

Having already collected the spaced-pellet data in the previous experi

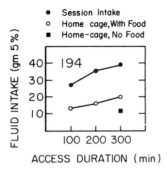

Figure 16 A comparison of the alcohol intakes of Subject 194 during the spaced-pellet sessions and during home cage conditions.

ment, comparative data were collected in the home cage. On each day, 5 per cent alcohol was made available to the rat for a duration of 100, 200, or 300 minutes. These access durations were each in effect on two different occasions for five days. The sequence of presentation was counter-balanced against order effects. At the beginning of each access period a 5-g supplement of rat chow was given. This approximated the amount of food that was given to the rat during the earlier spaced-pellet sessions.

A comparison of the alcohol intakes during the various conditions is depicted in Figure 16. Although the intakes were higher during the longer access periods, these totals were only about one-half of those obtained earlier during spaced-pellet sessions of comparable length, again illustrating the importance of the pellet spacing in producing high alcohol intakes. Even though the drinking was lower without the pellet spacing, the availability of the 5-g supplement did promote some of the drinking. This was evident during an additional ten-day condition when the alcohol was available 300 minutes per day, but the solid food supplement was not given until the alcohol bottle was replaced by a water bottle at the end of the access period. During this final condition, the intake dropped even further to about 10 g per period. This reduced intake in the absence of solid food has proved to be quite reliable, in that we have obtained similar reductions in each of six additional food-restricted rats under comparable conditions.

Manipulating interval durations with continuous access to 5 per cent alcohol

In the fifth experiment we combined two procedures found in the earlier experiments to enhance alcohol intakes, for the purpose of determining their joint effects. Substantially more alcohol per day was consumed by the three spaced-pellet rats when they had continuous access to alcohol, since the high rate session drinking remained essentially inta In the experiment that followed, employing intervals longer than 1.5 minutes yielded the highest session intakes. The present experiment evaluates the combined effects of these two procedures.

Only two rats (191 and 210) were used in this and the remaining experiments. A 5 per cent alcohol solution was available as the rat's sole source of fluid in both the home cage and the experimental box. Three interval durations (1, 2, and 3 minutes) were presented each for two di ferent five-day periods in a mixed sequence, yielding a total of ten experimental days for each interval condition.

As we had observed earlier, the session intakes increased regularly as the interval durations increased (Figure 17). In fact, the median scores were just slightly lower than those we had observed when alcohol was available only during the sessions (see hatched line for earlier data). Although there was a slight tendency for the home cage intakes to be inversely related to the session intakes, the cumulative 24-hour totals ave aged about 10 g higher on the days in which the 3-minute intervals wer employed than on the days when only 1-minute intervals were in effec An absolute (100 per cent) alcohol scale is included with Figure 17. Us ing this scale, it can be seen that the maximum intakes approached 2.5 and 2.75 g for Rats 191 and 210, respectively. These Absolute alcohol intakes were higher than any we had observed previously with food-deprived rats under any experimental conditions.

Manipulating interval durations with 10 per cent alcohol in the home cage.

In auxiliary experiments we were finding that food-restricted 200-g rat consistently drank more Absolute alcohol from a 10 per cent solution than from a 5 per cent solution during a 24-hour period, with typical averages being 1.8 and 2.3 g for 5 and 10 per cent solutions, respective ly. This suggested that we could combine the spaced pellet procedures and home-cage access to 10 per cent solutions, thereby obtaining even higher daily alcohol intakes.

The subsequent experiment was very similar to the preceding one in that alcohol was always available to the rats. A 5 per cent solution was available during the sessions and 10 per cent alcohol was available in th home cage. For the fifteen experimental sessions, each interval duratio (1, 2, or 3 minutes) was in effect for five days.

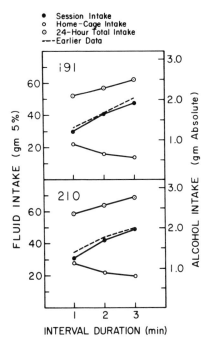

Figure 17   Several measures of 5 per cent alcohol intake in relation to the interval duration.

Figure 18 depicts the overall medians of the various alcohol measures taken. The intakes of 5 per cent solution were higher for both rats during the 2-minute condition compared to the 1-minute condition. Further increases in intake obtained only during the 3-minute condition for Rat 210. However, both rats ingested about twice as much Absolute alcohol from the home cage 10 per cent solution as they had consumed from the 5 per cent solution in the preceding experiment. The session totals and the home-cage totals, when combined, resulted in a grand total of 3.1 and 3.5 g of Absolute alcohol for 191 and 210, respectively. The primary reason for these increased totals, of course, was the increased amount of alcohol consumed in the home cage.

The high amounts of alcohol consumed in the home cage were probably also responsible for the reductions in session consumption observed. The rats appeared to be much more intoxicated than we had ever seen them, particularly at the ends of the 300-minute sessions. It became commonplace to find the rats completely stretched out and lying on their sides when we went to remove them from the experimental box. In this state, the rats showed no hesitation in crawling over the edge of

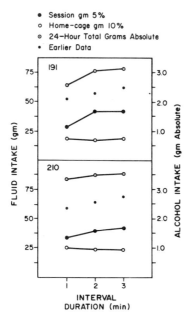

- Session gm 5%
- Home-cage gm 10%
- 24-Hour Total Grams Absolute
- Earlier Data

Figure 18   Fluid intakes for Subjects 191 and 210 when 5 per cent alcohol was available in the home cage. The Absolute alcohol scale applies only to the 24-hour totals and the earlier data.

a cliff, taking into consideration that they couldn't hold on to anything anyway.

Manipulating home-cage alcohol concentration

In the two preceding experiments we found that the total alcohol consumption increased when a 5 per cent solution was made available in the home cage and that total consumption of Absolute alcohol increased even more when a 10 per cent solution was available. From here, we might have tried additional combinations of variables and obtained even higher alcohol intakes. However, at this point, there were two questions which concerned us more. First, was it possible to maintain the high alcohol levels for substantial periods of time, or were these fleeting, spurious values? Second, how much of the increasing totals was due to gradual changes over time rather than to the changes in the home cage alcohol concentration? The next experiment was performed to answer these two questions.

The session conditions remained constant throughout the experiment. A total of 100 pellets was delivered at 2-minute intervals and 5 per cent

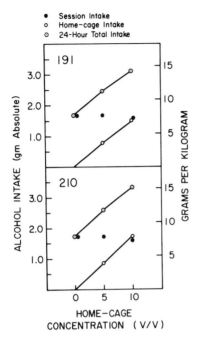

Figure 19   Session and home cage alcohol intakes by Subjects 191 and 210 as a function of the home cage alcohol concentration.

alcohol was always available in the experimental box. For the first twenty days, 10 per cent alcohol was available continuously in the home cage. During the next twenty days, a 5 per cent solution was available. As the final condition, the home cage fluid was changed to water.

That we were able to maintain the extremely high alcohol intakes for extended periods of time is revealed in Figure 19. The highest points on the 24-hour Absolute alcohol intake curves represent the medians for the additional twenty days of the 10 per cent condition. For both rats the day-to-day determinations of session intake and home cage intake deviated very little from the overall medians. A similar degree of stability was exhibited during the twenty days of the 5 per cent condition. The median amount of Absolute alcohol consumed in the home cage was about one-half that consumed when the solution was 10 per cent, replicating our earlier findings. The session drinking was remarkably stable, remaining unchanged during the entire course of the experiment. Nevertheless, the session intakes contributed substantially to the total amount of alcohol consumed during each 24-hour period. It should be noted that the medians for the zero concentration days represent only three sessions for Rat 191 and two sessions for Rat 210, due to unexpected termination of the experiment. This small number of days should be of little concern however, because these last session averages were virtually identical to each of the other session averages we obtained.

The overall trends exhibited in the present data answered the questions that reflected our major concern. As for the reliability of the extremely high intakes obtained earlier, we were able to maintain comparable levels in the present experiment for another twenty days. In addition, the differences in total 24-hour Absolute alcohol intake, presumed to be due to manipulation of the home cage alcohol concentration, were also found again.

In Figure 19 we have included a scale that shows the amount of Absolute alcohol consumed in relation to the body weights of the rats. Reference to this gram-per-kilogram scale reveals that each rat consumed approximately 15 g/kg of alcohol per day during the peak intake conditions. Considering those studies in which the capability of rats to metabolize alcohol has been documented, intake values of 15 g/kg/ day would appear to be inordinately high. For example, Aull, Roberts, and Kinard (1956) reported that rats metabolize alcohol at the rate of approximately 300 mg/kg/hour; converted, this would be only 7.2 g/kg/ day. Does this mean that our rats consumed twice as much alcohol as they could metabolize? We suggest that they did not. One explanation for the apparent disparity may be that the metabolic activity of these rats increased during the prolonged exposure to alcohol. On the other hand, the difference may lie in the metabolic index. Is it not plausible that the adult food-restricted rat can metabolize the same total amount of alcohol per day as the non-deprived adult rat that weighs considerably more? If it is true that these two hypothetical rats can metabolize exactly the same total amount of alcohol, then converting this absolute measure into a relative measure based on body weight would yield an artificial difference between the values for the deprived and nondeprived rat. This artificial difference would increase as a regular function of the differences in body weight.

Whatever the validity of the above discussion, it serves to emphasize the extremely high amounts of alcohol the two rats were consuming in the last experiment. Of course, as there were only two rats, additional confirmation is needed. However, the data do hold out the promise that we have a powerful tool for studying the biological effects of intoxication attendant with high rates of alcohol ingestion. And perhaps more ...

Withdrawal

The final study in the above alcohol series was terminated unexpectedly by the death of Subject 210. On the third day of the last experimental condition, this rat consumed no food or alcohol. After being removed from the test situation and placed back in the home cage, the rat showed a progressively declining physical condition and expired that evening.

Autopsy of Subject 210 revealed that the immediate cause of death was probably a volvulus. However, we suspect that this acute condition was not the sole cause of his expiration. A more complete account is, perhaps, that the additive stress of the intestinal twisting and the attendant effects of alcohol deprivation were responsible for his rapid departure. In fact, removing the alcohol from the home cage, prohibiting continuous ingestion, may have precipitated the intestinal disruption.

Attributing some of the 'ultimate' effect to alcohol deprivation is even more reasonable when our observations of the second rat are considered. When its running mate died, Subject 191 was removed from the immediate experiment for the purpose of collecting comparative home cage alcohol intake data. On subsequent days, the rat was subjected to a procedure under which a 5 per cent alcohol solution was available for only 5 hours each day. At the beginning of this limited access period the rat was fed a solid food supplement, estimated to be sufficient to maintain its 220-g weight.

On the first day with the above procedure, Subject 191 drank only a small amount of the 5 per cent solution (.8 g Absolute alcohol), considerably less than that consumed during each of the immediately preceding three days (median, 1.7 g Absolute alcohol). This was well within the intake range established by our other rats with a similar procedure. At the beginning of the access period on the second day, we noticed that the food supplement was not consumed immediately, extremely unusual behaviour for a food-deprived rat, although the entire supplement was consumed by the end of the 5-hour period. On the third day, a similar pattern was evident, with the supplement being consumed quite slowly. Also, during this day, the rat showed signs of diarrhoea and appeared to be in generally poor physical condition, remaining huddled in the far corner of the cage for most of the day. In fact, the technical assistant expressed concern that this rat too would die. On the fourth day, a portion of the supplement was consumed immediately. By the fifth day the rat was back to a normal appearance, consuming his food voraciously and showing a typical level of general activity. No further problems with its general state of health were observed over the next several weeks.

We suspect that the symptoms of both rats described above were the result of rapid reductions in the daily alcohol intake coincident with the procedural changes. There was some similarity of symptoms. Both subjects showed evidence of gastrointestinal distress, Subject 210 to the point of morbidity. If our intuitive observations were correct, Subject 191 was also very close to death.

To our knowledge, no similar observations of possible alcohol depriva tion effects in rodents have been reported. This is substantiated in a re- cent review by Mello (1968). There have been only a few suggestions that alcohol deprivation has produced demonstrable behavioural or phy siological changes in any animals other than man. Investigators have re- ported withdrawal symptoms in dogs (Essig and Lam, 1968) and perha a monkey (Yanagita, Deneau, and Seevers, 1965).

Our observations are only a tiny suggestion that it is possible to pro- duce physical dependence in rats, but these results are extremely encou aging. Somewhat to our chagrin, the intent of our experiments was not to produce and measure withdrawal symptoms; our intent was to mani pulate alcohol intake. Consequently, we were not prepared to documer the suggested alcohol deprivation effects with quantitative indices. We would have much preferred to have presented cumulative records and graphs rather than the lengthy verbal description above. The lack of quantitative data, however, does not necessarily detract from the impor tance of these preliminary observations. Of course, more extensive ob- servations of all types of subhuman subjects will be required in order to estimate the extent to which the observed biological processes are a rea sonable facsimile of human addiction to alcohol.

SUMMARY

The present series of water ingestion studies evaluates the effects of sev eral purportedly influential variables in the production of schedule-in- duced polydipsia. The temporal spacing of food portions, food portion size, and the type of food were found to be important determinants of polydipsia. However, on the other hand, lick-dependent delays may in- hibit the development of polydipsia. It is suggested that these studies support the position that both oral factors and reinforcement factors combine to produce the phenomenon. Procedures that produce polydip sia are also quite effective in producing high rates of alcohol ingestion. These procedures may prove to be valuable tools in expanding our knowledge of the biological processes of addiction to alcohol.

6 Drug effects upon behaviour induced by second-order schedules of reinforcement: the relevance of ethological analyses

W. WUTTKE and N. K. INNIS

SCHEDULE-INDUCED POLYDIPSIA

About ten years ago, Falk (1961a) first drew attention to the phenomenon of schedule-induced polydipsia. He observed that hungry rats working on an intermittent schedule of food reinforcement tended to drink if possible after each food presentation. In a lengthy session during which many reinforcements were programmed, a rat would ingest a volume of water far in excess of its normal daily intake. Although most of the subsequent research has involved rats, schedule-induced polydipsia has also been studied in monkeys (Schuster and Woods, 1966) and pigeons (Shanab and Peterson, 1969).

There is now an extensive literature describing the conditions under which schedule-induced polydipsia occurs and suggesting possible explanations of the phenomenon. The reader is referred to the chapters in this volume by Falk, Hawkins and his associates, and Keehn, for detailed discussions on these issues. Briefly, polydipsia occurs when small portions of food are presented to hungry animals at intervals ranging from about 30 to 300 seconds. Food presentation need not be response-contingent; however, both the type of food (dry or liquid) and the amount of food at each presentation are important variables. There is less drinking when liquid food is given and more when the portions are larger. Schedule-induced drinking is typically a post-reinforcement phenomenon. It occurs early in an interval, when the probability of another rein-

The experimental work reported here was conducted at the Department of Pharmacology, Harvard Medical School, Boston, by the first author, who also presented it at the symposium. The research was supported in part by grants MH-02094 and MH-07658 from National Institute of Mental Health, US Public Health Service. The material was revised for the present book by the second author while she was working with the Addiction Research Foundation.

forcement is either zero or very low. On short fixed-interval schedules, the time spent drinking after each reinforcement is directly related to the duration of the interval (Colotla, Keehn, and Gardner, 1970).

Many of the studies of schedule-induced polydipsia have been attempts to give support to either of two possible explanations of the phenomenon. Clark (1962) maintained that the drinking observed on temporal schedules of food reinforcement is the result of adventitious reinforcement, and that it develops in a manner similar to that of the superstitious patterns of behaviour reported by Skinner (1948). Stein (1964) implicated the thirst system and argued that prandial drinking might be expected to occur after a rat eats a dry food pellet. The data obtained so far have been equivocal, leading Schaeffer, Diehl, and Salzberg (1966) and Hawkins, Schrot, Githens, and Everett (Chapter 5) to conclude that schedule-induced polydipsia is a complex phenomenon resulting from the combined effects of reinforcement and thirst variables. Falk (1969; Chapter 7), in contrast, rejects both of these explanations and suggests a new approach to determining the underlying cause of polydipsia. He points out that schedule-induced drinking is but one of a number of activities that may occur under similar schedule conditions, depending on the options available in the experimental situation. These activities include wheel running (Levitsky and Collier, 1968), aggression (Azrin, Hutchinson, and Hake, 1966), pica (Villarreal, 1967), air licking (Mendelson and Chillag, 1970), and nitrogen drinking (Taylor and Lester, 1969). Falk considers that these activities comprise a class of behaviour to which he gives the label adjunctive behaviour and to which he relates the displacement activities studied by ethologists. When no external stimuli, such as water bottles or wheels, are available, a relatively stable sequence of motor activities (eg, pacing or turning circles) may occur in the immediate post-reinforcement period on temporal schedules. Staddon and Simmelhag (1971) have recorded such sequences, which they call interim activities, observing pigeons on both response-dependent and response-independent schedules of food presentation. They suggest that interim activities, adjunctive behaviour, and displacement behaviour are all members of a group of behaviours having similar functional properties, underlying casual factors, and adaptive characteristics.

The theories put forth by ethologists to explain displacement behaviour may assist our attempt to understand adjunctive behaviour such as schedule-induced polydipsia. Displacement activities are usually observed in situations in which, as the result of thwarting (ie, lack of a releasing stimulus) or conflict, the appropriate consummatory act cannot occur. These seemingly irrelevant activities are likely the behavioural outcome of the interaction of various motivational systems (see Hinde, 1966). The results of a study of schedule-induced drinking generated by a second-order schedule of reinforcement, to be described below, will be discussed later in ethological terms. This experiment was also concerned with the effect of certain drugs on schedule-induced drinking.

SCHEDULE-DEPENDENT EFFECTS OF DRUGS

Schedules of reinforcement produce stable and predictable patterns of responding (Ferster and Skinner, 1957) and thus have become a useful tool in studying the behavioural effects of drugs. However, the changes in responding observed on different schedules are the result of more than just the dose or chemical properties of the particular drug administered. The typical rate or pattern of behaviour generated by a given schedule is an important variable. Kelleher and Morse (1968a) present a detailed account of the problems facing behavioural pharmacology on this account. Here, we shall examine in some detail one group of drugs – the amphetamines. Amphetamines are adrenergic agents and are thus presumed to have physiological effects similar to those produced when the sympathetic nervous system is stimulated. Behaviourally, one would expect to observe increased motor activity and a reduction in food and water intake (Giarman, 1965). Dews (1958) examined the effect of several doses of amphetamine on the response rate of pigeons working under four schedules of reinforcement. Changes in response rate under the drug were systematically related to the prevailing rate prior to drug administration. Small doses of amphetamine increased the response rate if the prevailing rate was low, ie, about ten per minute. When the prevailing rate was high (one or more responses per second), however, large doses decreased the rate. Fixed-interval schedules of reinforcement, under which the first response after an interval is reinforced, usually give rise to responding at a high rate just before reinforcement and at a low rate just after reinforcement. Amphetamines can differentially affect this behaviour by increasing the low rate of responding early in the interval and decreasing the high rate of responding at the end, or both. Thus, to label amphetamines as stimulants of behaviour without regard to the situation under which they are administered is misleading.

A similar approach must be taken in considering the effects of amphetamines on drinking. In a free-drinking situation, injections of amphetamines have been found to decrease water intake in dogs (Anderson and Larsson, 1957) and rats (Teitelbaum and Derks, 1958; Epstein, 1959). However when drinking is an operant maintained by shock avoidance or food delivery, the changes in rate after amphetamine injections are similar to those observed with other operants (eg, bar-pressing in rats or key pecking in pigeons). Teitelbaum and Derks (1958) found that drinking increased when rats licking at a low stable rate to avoid shock were injected with dl-amphetamine. In squirrel monkeys, rates of licking maintained under a fixed-interval schedule of food presentation were increased or decreased by d-amphetamine, according to the rate-dependent effects of this drug discussed above (Wuttke, 1970). Falk (1964) found that schedule-induced drinking on a 1-minute variable-interval schedule of food presentation was slightly decreased by a .5 mg/kg dose of methamphetamine.

POLYDIPSIA IN A SECOND-ORDER SCHEDULE

In the experiment to be discussed here, an extension of a study reported by Rosenblith (1970), the effects of two drugs, d-amphetamine and sodium pentobarbital, were studied in rats lever-pressing for food on a second-order schedule. On this schedule, a response at the end of a 1-minute fixed-interval (FI 1) produced a 2-second flash of an overhead light followed by a click. On every third FI 1, the click was also accompanied by food. This is an FR 3 (FI 1) schedule, brief stimulus procedure (Kelleher, 1966). Rosenblith (1970) found that, initially, drinking occurred only during the first of the three FI 1 components, that is, immediately following the presentation of food. Eventually, after many sessions under these conditions, that rats also drank following the presentation of the light flash and click alone. Rosenblith distinguished two types of drinking under this schedule: 1) a steady, uninterrupted long bout of licking following the delivery of a food pellet, and 2) after an initial short bout of licking, drinking frequently alternating with bar-pressing during the second and third FI 1 components. This alternation between licking and bar-pressing may perhaps have been facilitated by the arrangement of the manipulanda in the experimental chamber — the drinking spout was mounted in the centre of one wall, the feeder was to the left on the same wall, the lever to the right. Often rats alternate between bar-pressing and approaching the feeder on interval schedules, and to do so in this situation entailed passing the drinking spout. If the water bottle were in a less convenient location, drinking might not have reoccurred once bar-pressing started (see Keehn, 1963).

This present study used the same apparatus and procedure, as well as two of the rats (R1 and R3) used by Rosenblith (1970). Readers are referred to her article for details of the apparatus and the experimental history of these rats. Rat R2 had no experimental experience prior to the study. All three subjects were male albino Charles River Farm rats. They were maintained at 70 per cent of their free-feeding weights, which ranged from 270 to 280 grams. Water was always available in their home cages. The animals were run on the FR3 (FI 1) schedule described above. Each daily session terminated after 15 food presentations, each of which comprised one 240 mg SKF pellet (Riddle, Rednick, Catania, and Tucker, 1966).

Once the behaviour was stable on this procedure (see Figure 1), several sessions were devoted to testing with the drugs. The drugs were given only on days that followed a day with normal control performance. Four doses (expressed in terms of the salt) of d-amphetamine sulphate (0.1, 0.3, 1.0. amd 3.0 mg/kg) and pentobarbital-Na (1.0, 3.0, 5.6, and 10.0 mg/kg) were administered. Each rat received each dose on either one or two occasions, except R3 who was not studied under pentobarbital. Drug doses were dissolved in saline, and administered intraperitoneally at a constant volume of 1.0 ml/kg. Pentobarbital injections were made 5 minutes before the start of a session, d-amphetamine injections 30 minutes before.

Figures 1, 2, 3, and 4 show cumulative records from representative sessions under both drug and control conditions. There are two records for each session; the upper one, labelled A, records cumulative licks, with bar-presses indicated by diagonal strokes, while the lower record, B, represents bar-pressing. A diagonal stroke occurred on this record after every 10 licks. The pen in Record A reset on the termination of each 1-minute component; the pen in Record B following food presentation (every third component). The presentations of the 2-second light flashes are marked in both records by diagonal strokes of the event pen.

Figure 1 shows the typical asymptotic performance observed on this second-order schedule. All three rats developed the same pattern of bar-pressing (B records), with a very low rate in the first component, a slightly higher rate in the second, and the highest rate at the end of the third component, the characteristic fixed-interval scallop (Ferster and Skinner, 1957). During the initial 1-minute component, when few bar-presses were recorded, most of the time was spent drinking. R3 generally began drinking at once whereas the others, especially R2, tended to pause for a short while before they started licking. Much of this time was probably spent eating. During the second component, and especially the third, licking was frequently interrupted by bar-pressing, as indicated by the diagonal strokes on the A records. Although both R1 and R2 tended to alternate between licking and bar-pressing, R3 usually continued to bar-press steadily once he completed the bout of licking initiated by the light-flash and click.

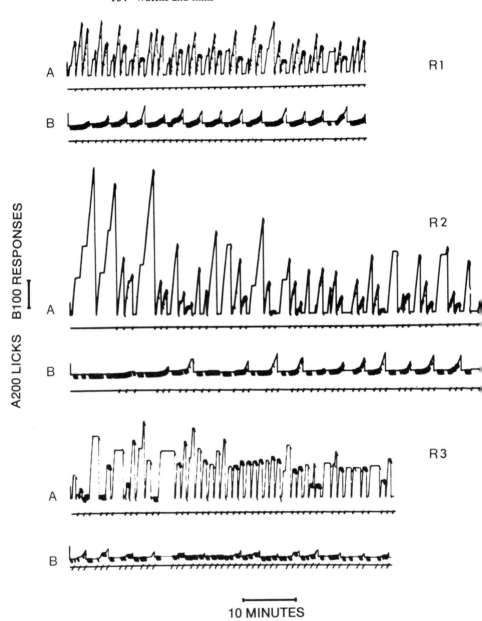

Figure 1   Representative cumulative records of performance during a control ses
sion on the FR 3 (FI 1) second-order schedule for each rat (R1, R2, R3). Record
A presents cumulative licking, with bar-presses indicated by diagonal strokes, and
Record B, bar-pressing, with every ten licks represented by a diagonal stroke. Pen
A reset after each 1-minute fixed interval; Pen B on food presentation. The termi
nation of each FI 1 component with the presentation of a 2-second flash of light
is marked in both records by a blip on the event pens.

d-AMPHETAMINE

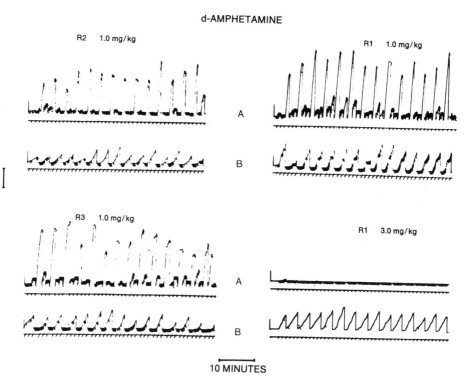

Figure 2   Cumulative records of performance on the FR 3 (FI 1) second-order schedule after administration of a 1.0 mg/kg dose of d-amphetamine for all three subjects, and after a 3.0 mg/kg dose for R1 (lower right). Other details as in Figure 1.

Figure 2 shows cumulative records for all rats at the 1.0 mg/kg dose of
d-amphetamine and for R1 at the 3.0 mg/kg dose. Comparing these records with the typical performance generated by this schedule shown in
Figure 1, two important differences may be noted: drinking was now
confined almost entirely to the first component, whereas there were
more bar-presses during the second component and early in the third
component. Both R1 and R2, who showed initial pauses following reinforcement, began drinking sooner in the interval under d-amphetamine.
At the highest dose, as the record for R1 shows, almost no drinking oc-

curred and the rat responded at a constant low rate throughout the entire 3-minute interreinforcement period. When the same dose was administered to this rat on another occasion, no licking occurred during the
second and third components, whereas,licking in the first component
was decreased to about 50 per cent of the usual rate without the drug.
Record B for this animal illustrates clearly the rate-dependent effects of
amphetamines on fixed-interval schedules, with the low rates early in the
interreinforcement interval (Components 1 and 2) much enhanced and
the higher rate in the third component almost unchanged. Clark and
Steele (1956) showed cumulative records from rats working under a multiple schedule under doses of d-amphetamine ranging from 0.5 to 4.0
mg/kg. Although three different stimuli indicated periods of extinction,
a high probability, and a low probability of reinforcement, respectively,
at the 1.0 mg/kg dose the rats responded at a steady rate from reinforcement regardless of the stimuli or schedule in effect, behaviour similar in
many ways to that shown by R3 under the 3.0 mg/kg condition.

Figures 3 and 4 show records for the rats receiving the 3.0 mg/kg and
10 mg/kg doses of pentobarbital respectively. Barbiturates such as pentobarbital also produce schedule-dependent changes in behaviour. Kelleher
and Morse (1968a) report that whereas key-pecking in pigeons on a fixed-
ratio schedule was not reduced by a 3.0 mg/kg dose of pentobarbital, responding under a fixed-interval schedule was greatly disrupted. In fact,
the pigeons rarely pecked. Dews (1958) found that a 1.0 mg/kg dose
slightly increased the rate of pecking of pigeons working under a variable-interval schedule, and Falk (1964) reports a decrease in water intake, at least early in the session, by rats showing polydipsic drinking on
a VI 1 schedule with a 2.0 mg/kg dose of pentobarbital. The cumulative
records for R1 in Figure 3 show that a 3.0 mg/kg dose of pentobarbital
had no effect on either drinking or bar-pressing. However, R2 showed
both an increase in response rate and a decrease in drinking during Components 2 and 3, that is, during intervals preceded by only the light-
flash and click. At the 10 mg/kg dose, the behaviour of both rats was
disrupted during the first 30 to 45 minutes of the session, at which point
the first reinforcement occurred. After this, the familiar pattern of
drinking and bar-pressing returned; however, drinking was depressed
while rate of bar-pressing was enhanced, especially during the last two
components.

The data from both drug and control conditions are presented in a
more quantitative form in Figures 5, 6, 7, 8, and 9. The control rates are
means of rates during 10 control sessions for R1 and R3, and during 15
sessions for R2. A session was used as a control only if the rat's perfor-

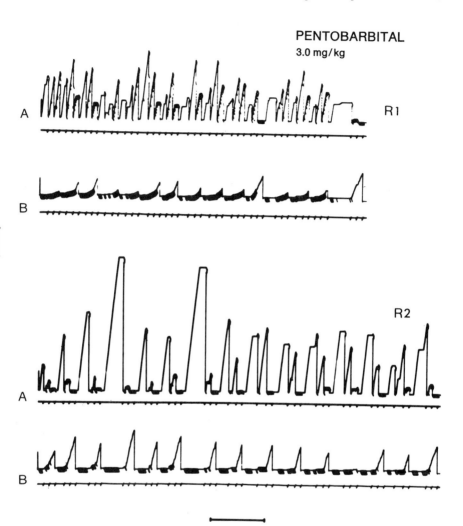

Figure 3   Cumulative records of performance on the FR 3 (FI 1) second-order schedule for R1 and R2 following administration of 3.0 mg/kg of pentobarbital. Other details as in Figure 1.

mance appeared consistent with its stable behaviour in previous sessions without drugs. The drug data are presented in terms of per cent of control rate for each rat, and are means for either one or two sessions at each dose level. Figure 5 shows the changes in the mean overall rate of bar-pressing (Figure 5A, upper graph), and licking (Figure 5B, lower

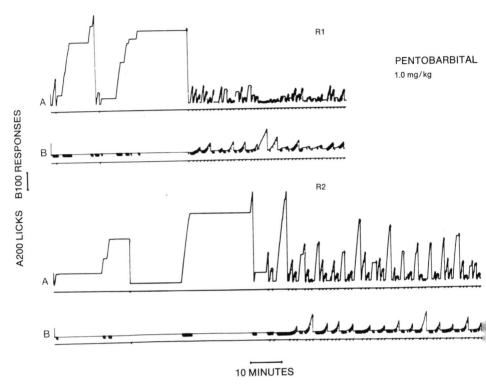

PENTOBARBITAL
1.0 mg/kg

Figure 4 Cumulative records of performance on the FR 3 (FI 1) second-order schedule for R1 and R2 following administration of 10.0 mg/kg of pentobarbital. Other details as in Figure 1.

graph) of all rats at each dose of both d-amphetamine and pentobarbital. Looking at the bar-pressing data first, the two relatively low doses of d-amphetamine produced only slight changes in rate. The 1.0 mg/kg dose produced a three-fold increase in responding for all rats, whereas the largest dose resulted in a substantial increase in bar-pressing only for R1 whose cumulative records are shown in Figure 2. Doses of pentobarbital from 1.0 to 10.0 mg/kg had little effect on the response rate of R1, whereas, except at the lowest dose, there was a substantial enhancement of bar-pressing for R2, especially at the 3.0 mg/kg level. The mean rate of licking tended to decrease slightly across successive dose levels with both drugs. The only substantial changes were at the two highest doses of d-amphetamine, as the figure shows.

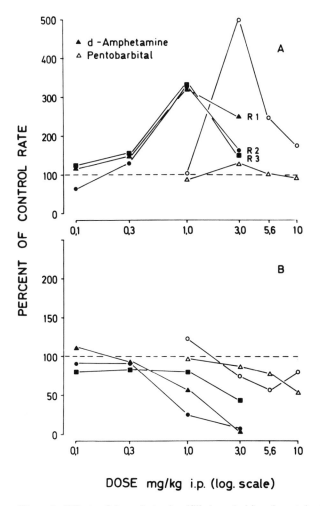

Figure 5   Effects of d-amphetamine (filled symbols) and pentobarbital (open symbols) on the overall rate of bar-pressing (A) and on the number of licks (B) during the FR 3 (FI 1) schedule. All effects are expressed as per cent of mean control rate (dashed horizontal lines). Abscissa: dose, log scale; ordinate: per cent of mean control rate. These data are based on either one or two sessions at each dose level.

Looking at the changes in overall rate may be misleading because, as was pointed out earlier, the entire pattern of responding on a fixed-interval schedule may change, with responding increasing early in an interval

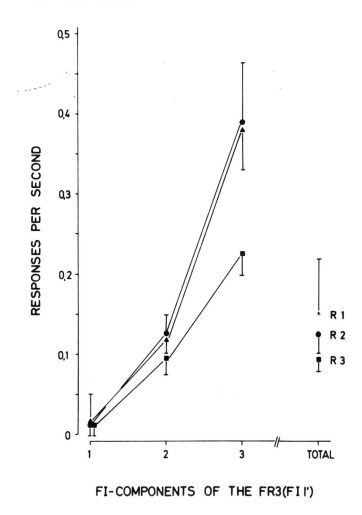

FI-COMPONENTS OF THE FR3(FI I')

Figure 6   Average control rates of responding (bar-presses) during successive FI 1-minute-components of the FR 3 (FI 1) schedule for the three rats (R1, R2, R3). (Abscissa: FI 1-minute components; ordinate mean number of responses per second averaged over n sessions; R1 and R3: n = 10; R2: n = 15.) The vertical lines indicate the range of ± two standard errors.

and decreasing towards the end, for example. If such is the case, the average output may change very little, whereas the pattern of behaviour is actually very different. Thus, the changes in bar-pressing and licking in each 1-minute fixed interval for the data shown in Figure 5 are presented in Figure 8 (bar-pressing) and Figure 9 (licking). First, however, for

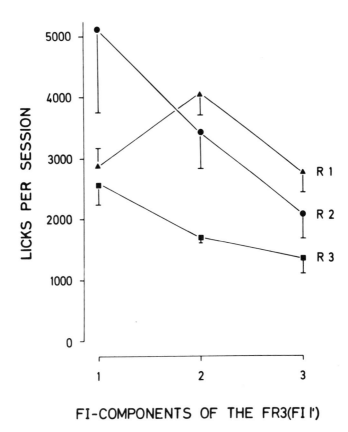

Figure 7 Mean number of licks during successive FI 1-minute components of the FR 3 (FI 1) schedule for the three rats (R1, R2, R3). Abscissa FI 1-minute components; ordinate: mean number of licks per session averaged over n sessions (R1 and R3: n = 10; R2: n = 15). The vertical lines indicate the range of ± two standard errors.

comparison purposes average rates of bar-pressing and licking during the three components under control conditions are shown in Figures 6 and 7 respectively. The rates were low but increased systematically across components. Low response rates such as these are not uncommon under second-order schedules. For two of the rats, drinking decreased across intervals, whereas R1 licked most during the second interval. The average water intake per session was 33 ml for R1, 30 ml for R2, and 27.8 ml for R3. R3 drank about twice as much per lick as the other two rats.

As Figure 8 shows, d-amphetamine had most of its effect on bar-presses during the first and second components. During the third compo-

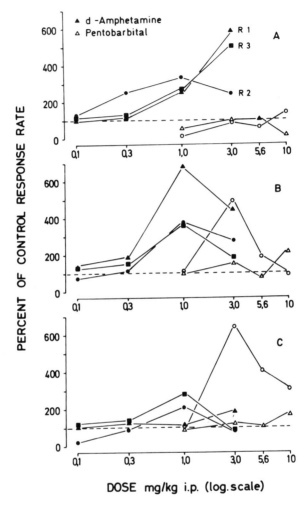

Figure 8   Effects of d-amphetamine (filled symbols) and pentobarbital (open symbols) on rates of bar-pressing during the first (A), second (B), and third (C), FI 1-minute components of the FR 3 (FI 1) schedule. All effects are expressed as per cent of mean control rate of responding (responses per second) during each FI 1-minute component (dashed horizontal lines). Abscissa: dose, log scale; ordinate: per cent of mean control response rate.

nent, only the 1.0 mg/kg dose resulted in an increase in output for two of the rats. For R2, the rat whose behaviour was altered under pentobarbital, increases in rate were observed only during the second and third

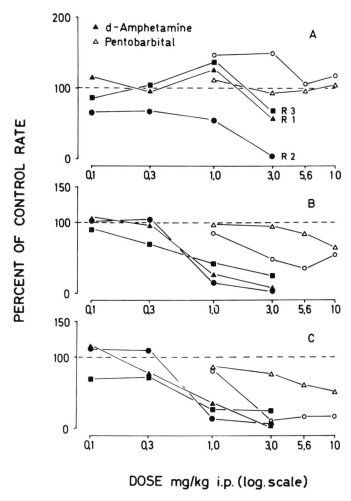

Figure 9   Effects of d-amphetamine (filled symbols) and pentobarbital (open symbols) on mean number of licks per session during the first (A), second (B), and third (C) FI 1-minute components of the FR 3 (FI 1) schedule. All effects are expressed as per cent of mean control rate during each FI 1-minute component (dashed horizontal lines). Abscissa: dose, log scale; ordinate: per cent of mean control rate.

components. In both these components, the rate was greatly enhanced at the 3.0 mg/kg dose, while during the final component the two larger doses also resulted in an increased output. As discussed earlier, with reference to the cumulative records, changes in the rate of licking occurred mainly during the last two components. Two exceptions are notable: During the first component R2's drinking was depressed at all doses of d-amphetamine and increased substantially under the two lower doses of pentobarbital, whereas R1 and R3 licked at a slightly higher rate under a 1.0 mg/kg dose of d-amphetamine. Drinking either remained unchanged or decreased systematically with increasing doses of both drugs during the second and third components.

In summary, under a three-component second-order schedule of reinforcement, schedule-induced drinking was observed to follow both food presentation and a regularly occurring stimulus that was frequently paired with food. Long, uninterrupted bouts of drinking occurred after food presentation, but shorter post-stimulus drink bouts, followed by a tendency to alternate between licking and bar-pressing, were characteristic of the behaviour observed in later components. Changes in behaviour resulting from injection of d-amphetamine or pentobarbital appeared to depend both on the dose of drug administered and the control rate of responding across the three components of the schedule. Low rates of bar-pressing during the first two components were increased by 1.0 or 3.0 mg/kg doses of d-amphetamine, whereas medium doses of pentobarbital increased response rate during the last two components. With two exceptions (see Figure 9A), rates of licking either decreased or remained about the same with all doses of both drugs.

The results of this experiment support the view that neither the 'dry mouth' nor the adventitious reinforcement explanation of schedule-induced drinking is adequate. Initially, on this schedule, drinking occurred only during the first fixed-interval component (Rosenblith, 1970), and it was only after many sessions of training that it appeared following the other stimuli (light-flash and click) when they were presented alone. This led Rosenblith (1970) to suggest that the high rate of drinking following food presentation was an unconditioned response elicited by food in the mouth. The drinking following the presentation of the light-flash and click alone may have been a classically conditioned response that developed over the training sessions. The fact that the drinking in the two situations took on a different form is not incompatible with this hypothesis; in classical conditioning situations, the CR is often distinguished from the UCR by its formal properties (Kimble, 1961). However, certain data in the literature create problems for a classical conditioning theory. Keehn and Colotla (1970b) found that under a mixed FI CRF schedule, rats began drinking only after the last of several pellets delivered on CRF, that is, at the beginning of the FI component. Moreover, the time spent drinking did not vary over a series of schedules on which the CRF component provided from one to nine pellets. If drink-

ing were an unconditioned response to food, one might expect that it
would occur after each CRF pellet, or that the duration of the drinking
bout would vary in relation to meal size. One might also expect the unconditioned response to a pellet of a given size to be of a more or less
constant duration (Keehn and Colotla, 1970a). It has been found, however, that the duration of the post-pellet drink varies directly with the
length of the interreinforcement interval on short fixed-interval schedules (Colotla, Keehn, and Gardner, 1970), a relationship similar to that
observed for post-reinforcement pauses on FI (Schneider, 1969).

ETHOLOGICAL ANALYSES OF SCHEDULE-INDUCED DRINKING

Let us now look at the behaviour generated by this second-order FI
schedule in terms of theories that have been offered by ethologists in
attempts to explain displacement behaviour. Tinbergen's (1940) original
definition of displacement activities, based on Kortlandt (1938), has
been modified by Leyhausen (1952). According to this hypothesis, all
motivations (aktions-spezifische Energien) of an animal inhibit or facilitate each other according to their momentary state of readiness or acti-
vation; in addition, they may reciprocally raise or lower their internal releasing thresholds. Thus, when the consummatory act appropriate to an
activated (motivated) instinct cannot be run off, for example, because
there is no releasing stimulus, another instinct will be secondarily activated either by facilitation of its endogenous propensity (longer lasting
effects) or by a lowering of its threshold (shorter lasting effects). If the
secondarily activated behaviour leads to a situation in which the consummatory act can occur, the secondarily activated behaviour is called
appetitive behaviour; if not, it is called displacement activity, or better,
as Leyhausen (1952) points out, alternative behaviour. The particular
type of behaviour that will occur depends largely on internal and external stimulus factors.

In a food deprived animal, the instinct, of which the consummatory
act is eating, is highly motivated. Moreover, once the animal has learned
that bar-pressing, on occasion, results in food delivery, the motivation to
press the bar will be highest just before, and lowest just after, food presentation. Thus, on fixed-interval schedules, the probability (rate) of
bar-pressing increases as time since reinforcement increases, producing
the characteristic FI scallop (Ferster and Skinner, 1957). Food induces
eating, but the small size of the pellet leads to thwarting (the bigger the
pellet, the more intensive the thwarting situation), which, by means of
the mechanism mentioned above, lowers the threshold or increases the

propensities of other instincts. At this time, if the secondary behaviour so activated is not inhibited by highly motivated bar-pressing behaviour, it will occur when some motivational energy to press the bar has already built up within the period during which the threshold for secondary behaviour is lowered by the thwarting situation. In the second-order schedule described here, the occurrence of drinking following the light-flash and click presented alone indicates that these stimuli acquired the properties of a conditioned reinforcer, which leads to a 'conditioned thwarting situation' and consequently alternative behaviour occurs. In the second FI 1 minute component of the schedule, the motivational energy for bar-pressing lifts bar-pressing over the threshold and drinking is therefore frequently interrupted by bar-pressing; from the middle of the third component, bar-pressing becomes dominant over the alternative behaviour.

Differences in the degree of polydipsia which have been observed as a function of interreinforcement time and food-pellet size (Falk, 1969) are also compatible with this theory. When the interreinforcement time is short, the tendency to bar-press is already high shortly after food presentation; therefore, despite the fact that the thwarting situation has lowered the threshold for alternative behaviour, bar-pressing soon dominates in the situation. A bigger pellet will increase the tendency to press the bar and thus shorten the time available for drinking (Rosenblith, 1970). Conversely, when the interreinforcement interval is long and the tendency to press the bar after the food pellet very low, lowering the threshold for alternative behaviour by a more intensive thwarting situation, due to a bigger pellet, will result in more alternative behaviour.

Other theories have been proposed. One account involves the 'disinhibition hypothesis' first suggested by Andrew (1956). According to this hypothesis, when two compatible drives, such as attack and escape, are both simultaneously activated in full strength, they may actually inhibit one another. Other motivational systems (drives) may then be released from the inhibition usually exerted on them by these more potent (ie, higher in the hierarchy of drives) systems. Depending on the stimuli present in the situation at the time, behaviour appropriate to another motivational system, and thus seemingly irrelevant, will occur.

Staddon and Simmelhag (1971) suggest that adjunctive behaviour and interim activities are the result of a similar mechanism. An animal working for food on an intermittent schedule of reinforcement learns that during certain periods, such as the time immediately following food presentation, food is never available. At such times, animals tend to avoid the food-getting situation and its associated responses (eg, bar-pressing), as is clearly illustrated by the post-reinforcement pause observed on fixed-interval schedules, which prescribe constant, and therefore clearly discriminable, interreinforcement periods. However, the small size of the experimental chamber does not allow the animal to leave the food-getting situation entirely, and thus a conflict situation, involving approach and avoidance tendencies, results. Early in an interval, when both these tendencies are strong, they may be mutually inhibitive resulting in the disinhibition of other motivational systems, and if the required external stimuli are available in the situation the consummatory activity appropriate to another motivational system (such as drinking when water is available) may occur.

Finally, a comment concerning the seeming irrelevance of displacement and adjunctive behaviour is required. Following McFarland's (1966) suggestion that displacement behaviour has functional significance in allowing animals to change their course of action when the activity in progress no longer has any utility, Staddon and Simmelhag (1971) argue that interim activities and adjunctive behaviour are similarly adaptive — they are a mechanism enabling an animal to 'budget his time' successfully and ensure the avoidance of places and times when reinforcement is never available.

7 The nature and determinants of adjunctive behaviour

JOHN L. FALK

The glass of water appears everywhere; it is an adjunct to every kind of sweetmeat, and even to alcohol. It has a kind of biblical significance. Lawrence Durrell, *Prospero's cell*, New York 1962.

SCHEDULE-INDUCED POLYDIPSIA: AN ADJUNCTIVE BEHAVIOUR PROTOTYPE

When a rat is reduced to about 80 per cent of its free-feeding body weight by limiting daily food intake and allowed to earn most of its food by lever-pressing on a variable-interval 1-minute schedule for 45-mg Noyes food pellets, a curious phenomenon occurs when water is con currently available. Although the animal is never water deprived, during the daily lever-pressing session (3.17 hours) for intermittent food the water intake amounts to almost one-half the body weight (Falk, 1961a The behaviour pattern is evident from the session shown in Figure 1. The upper (cumulative) channel shows the lever-pressing performance; the point at which each food pellet was earned is indicated by a short, vertical hatch mark. The lower (event) channel indicates each twelfth lick at a water tube as a pen deflection. When a food pellet was earned it was quickly consumed and immediately followed by about a 0.5 ml draught of water. Fourteen females weighing about 200 grams drank an average of 92.5 ml of water per session. Little or no water was consum ed during the almost 21 hours between sessions, although it was freely available.

This pattern of excessive drinking has been repeatedly confirmed. It i not specific to one strain of rats and has been observed in the rhesus monkey (Schuster and Woods, 1966), chimpanzee (Kelleher, personal communication), and pigeon (Shanab and Peterson, 1969).

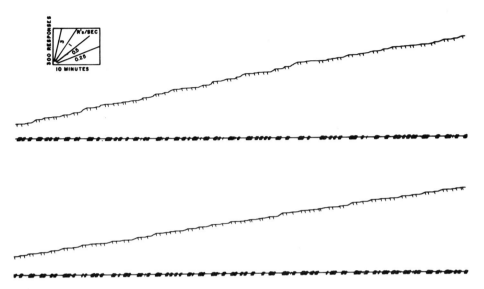

Figure 1   Polydipsia occurring concurrent with a variable-interval 1-minute schedule for 45-mg food pellets. Upper (cumulative) channel shows lever-pressing on
food schedule, and food deliveries as short, vertical hatch marks. Lower channel
shows every 12th lick on water tube as deflection.

About a decade ago, a rather fortuitous experimental arrangement en-
abled me to happen upon the phenomenon of schedule-induced polydipsia. Fortunately, I had already worked on the control of fluid intake
in the rat and from such a context knew that the production of polydipsia as a food-schedule by-product was not only an unusual finding –
it was an outrightly absurd one. It was absurd because food deprivation
in rats yields a decrease in water intake, not an increase. It was absurd
because heating a large quantity of room-temperature water to body
heat and expelling it as copious urine is wasteful for an animal already
pressed for energy stores. It is absurd for an animal to drink itself into a
dilutional hyponatremia bordering on water intoxication. But perhaps
most absurd was not the lack of a metabolic or patho-regulatory reason
for the polydipsia, but the lack of an acceptable behavioural account.
That is, the behaviour is absurd in the sense of philosophical existential-
ism. Now I do not believe that a wide variety of animals are philosophical existentialists, but perhaps we have run across a class of behaviours
in animals that was imputed to man as his exclusive, if obscure, property.
    In a previous publication, I outlined the available evidence against in-
terpreting schedule-induced polydipsia as an instance of various conven-

tional behavioural effects (Falk, 1969). To summarize briefly, the poly-dipsia is not the result of food delivery directly or adventitiously rein-forcing water intake. Nor does it serve a problem-solving, mediational, or timing function. Furthermore, drinking is not an unconditioned re-sponse to eating. It is important to note that the relation between sched-uled eating and the resultant polydipsia is not one of elicitation. The S-R relation of a salivary or pupilary reflex is relatively invariant with respect to the complex of environmental conditions and consequences. But schedules do not elicit polydipsia, or other adjunctive behaviours, in such a predetermined fashion. Given the proper environmental circum-stances, certain schedules can increase the probability of particular be-haviours enormously. But these behaviours are not elicited or generated as new responses by the schedule conditions. Polydipsia takes at least a few sessions to develop completely, unlike elicited responses, and this acquisition is not simply due to adaption to the feeding schedule (Rey-nierse and Spanier, 1968).

Thus, a decade of research has yielded no traditional physiological or behavioural explanation for schedule-induced polydipsia. Attempts to account for the behaviour as an 'emotional' side-effect of schedules, or as the animal's way of producing 'emotional pacification' are not neces-sarily wrong, but they are largely untestable notions.

SOME KINDS OF BEHAVIOUR GENERATED AS ADJUNCTS TO SCHEDULE CONTROL

The conditions that produce schedule-induced polydipsia are not com-plex. The experimental design is simple, yet the behavioural effect is strong and durable. Sidman (1960) has wisely pointed out that: 'When-ever a simple operation is found to exert a powerful behavioural effect, we may suspect that the phenomenon can be widely generalized.' I have indicated previously that another behavioural phenomenon, extinction-induced aggression reported by Azrin and his associates, stands in the same relation as polydipsia to its generating schedule (Falk, 1966a, 1966b). I suggested that when certain schedules induce extra, concur-rent phenomena strong enough to sustain scheduled behaviour in their own right, that these phenomena be called 'adjunctive behaviours.' At the New York Academy of Sciences conference on the 'Neural Regula-tion of Food and Water Intake' in 1967, I pointed out certain correspon-dences in the initiating conditions of schedule-induced polydipsia and displacement activities, suggesting that these were instances of a more general behavioural phenomenon (Falk, 1969). It is the purpose of this paper to expand further the behavioural phenomena and their correspondences in order to provide an empirical and analytic context for the recognition of the new class of behaviours termed 'adjunctive.'

One offers up a new class of behaviour with some trepidation. The multiplication of 'new' behaviour classifications has, for the most part, contributed little to the advancement of basic problems in behaviour analysis. A new classification should be more than just suggestive of new ways of viewing known facts. It must prove itself useful not only in re-organizing current data, but in making certain fresh lines of investigation compellingly obvious. Such studies should either bear out the generality of the suggested scheme or render it unconfirmed.

To this end, I will describe briefly a few behavioural phenomena that seem to me to be examples of adjunctive behaviour generated by intermittent food schedules. Then, in the following section, I will attempt to indicate certain correspondences among these behaviours.

Schedule-induced aggression and escape

While behaviourists often consider attack and escape behaviours as quite different and even antithetic responses, ethologists classify them, together with threat and appeasement postures and movements, as agonistic behaviours. This classification stems from the recognition that all of these behavioural outcomes can result from essentially the same stimulus situation and may vacillate rapidly from one to another. Behaviourists have made little headway with threat and appeasement responses, but the environmental commonalities producing both attack and escape have received recent attention in a series of experiments.

Electric shock and other forms of aversive stimulation have been used for a number of years to study escape and avoidance behaviours. Lately, several of these same aversive stimuli have been shown to produce attack in paired animals (Ulrich and Azrin, 1962). Certain ranges and parameters of unconditioned aversive stimuli can produce avoidance, escape, or attack as a function of the environmental context. Meanwhile, more complex conditioned aversive stimuli were being investigated. Ferster (1958) showed that time out from schedules of positive reinforcement could function as an aversive stimulus. Azrin, Hutchinson, and Hake (1966) found that when periods during which each key peck delivered grain to a pigeon were alternated with periods of extinction, the onset of the extinction periods produced vigorous attack on a nearby restrained pigeon. The result indicated that the onset of the extinction (time out) period was an aversive condition producing aggression just as various unconditioned stimuli did. Not only extinction, but other aspects of intermittent food schedules can produce aggression in primates and pigeons as an adjunct to the food schedule. Hutchinson, Azrin, and Hunt (1968) found that biting attacks in squirrel monkeys occurred not only after transition to an extinction component, but also as an adjunct to various fixed-ratio schedules during the pauses between completed ratios. Similar results were obtained in pigeons with a fixed-ratio 50 schedule (Gentry, 1968) and with various fixed-time schedules in which food was presented non-contingently (Flory, 1969a).

Schedules of food reinforcement can induce not only adjunctive aggression, but also escape. Both pigeons and rats will terminate certain schedules of reinforcement by producing time-out periods (Azrin, 196 Thompson, 1964). This termination (escape) behaviour appears to be produced by the aversive properties of certain aspects of schedules of positive reinforcement. I will refer to this phenomenon as 'schedule-induced escape.'

Thus, as a function of certain food-schedule parameters, both attack and escape behaviours can be induced as adjuncts to the behaviour under schedule control. It appears that the common origin of these adjunctive behaviours lies in the aversive properties of the food schedule parameters.

Schedule-induced pica

When rhesus monkeys at approximately 80 per cent of their normal free-feeding body weights were placed on a fixed-time 15-minute schedule for food pellets, pellet ingestion was quickly followed by a bout of ingesting wood shavings that lay on the floor of the living space (Villarreal, 1967). These animals did not ingest this material even though food deprived until placed on the intermittent feeding schedule. Although some of the shavings were stored in their cheek pouches, much of it was ingested. Animals were observed selecting the largest and freshest pieces available for consumption. Under extinction conditions such ingestion rapidly fell to zero.

Schedule-induced wheel-running

Rats held to 80 per cent of their normal body weights by food restriction did much more wheel-running concurrent with a variable-interval 1-minute food schedule than with fixed-ratio 1 (Levitsky and Collier 1968). The running rapidly declined under extinction conditions.

Schedule-induced air-licking

Rats held to 85 per cent of their normal body weights by food restriction were placed on a fixed-time 1-minute schedule for food pellets with a continuous airstream available from a drinking tube in place of water (Mendelson and Chillag, 1971). Protracted post-pellet licking of the airstream developed. The amount of licking was far in excess of that produced by giving an animal a comparable amount of food all at once and recording the amount of licking for a length of time equal to a normal scheduled-food session (Mendelson and Chillag, personal communication).

CORRESPONDENCES AMONG DIFFERENT TYPES OF ADJUNCTIVE BEHAVIOUR

It is one thing to assert that a group of behavioural phenomena appearing in conjunction with food schedules are analogous side-effects of schedules, but it is quite another matter to maintain that these side-effects form a class (adjunctive behaviour) the members of which yield similar dynamic properties and are functions of the same variables. In this section, accordingly, the current evidence linking various adjunctive behaviours into a functional group is reviewed by noting commonalities both in the controlling variables and the behavioural outcomes.

Effective range in consummatory rate

The adjunctive drinking phenomenon is determined by several variables, but the one of prime importance involves the length of time between eating episodes. This is specified by the interreinforcement time in schedules of reinforcement, and by the interfeeding time in noncontingent, fixed-time schedules in which the episodic delivery of food is not contingent upon a reinforced operant response. Reinforcement schedules take time to complete and produce various intermittence values in feeding. These schedule-enforced intermittences necessarily decrease the rate of consummatory behaviour and give it an episodic character when compared to similarly deprived animals allowed to consume the same daily food ration in a continuous feeding bout.

The degree of polydipsia as a function of the fixed-interval length between food pellets was systematically explored (Falk, 1966b, see Figure 2). As the fixed-interval value was increased from 2 seconds through values up to 300 seconds, the amount of water drunk increased linearly

154   John L. Falk

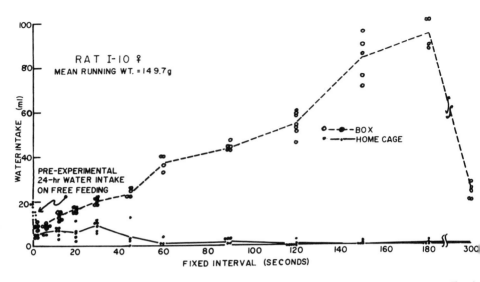

Figure 2   Polydipsia as a function of length of food fixed-interval schedule. Food limited to 180 pellets (45 mg each) for all sessions. From Falk (1966b), with permission.

up to some maximum point, but fell off at fixed interval 300 seconds to a scarcely polydipsic value. This general relation was observed again in later work (Falk, 1969). In a recent study, Flory (1969c) varied the value of the fixed-interval schedule over a range from 1 to 480 seconds and obtained a quite similar bitonic relation. Segal (1965) also noted in fixed-time schedules that the percentage of pellets followed by drinking decreased at comparably long interpellet times. Using a variable-time schedule, Hawkins (1967, see also Chapter 5) confirmed the bitonic relation found in the previously described response-contingent temporal schedule.

Flory (1969c) carefully explored short fixed-interval lengths in order to determine the intermittence threshold of polydipsia. This proved to be about fixed-interval 4 seconds for two rats and 5 seconds in the case of two other rats. At these points, the ratio of fixed-interval session water intake to baseline water intake reached a value of about 2 — unequivocal polydipsia.

It appears, then, that for rats at 80 per cent of their normal free-feeding body weight, a fixed-interval food schedule of 45-mg Noyes pellets yields a polydipsia at FI 4 or 5 seconds and this polydipsia increases up to approximately FI 2 or 3 minutes. At larger FI values the polydipsia progressively falls off to lower values. There is a range of fixed-interval values which produces a strong polydipsic effect with the effect decreasing as one approaches low or high FI values on either side of this 'effective range.' It seems likely that the critical defining feature of the effective range is not the time between the eating episodes as such, but rather the rate of consummatory behaviour determined by this temporal parameter in concert with the food portion magnitude at each reinforcement. By varying the portion magnitude as well as interreinforcement time, results obtained supported the notion that rate of consummatory behaviour was the factor determining the effective range (Falk, 1967; 1969), but Flory's (1969c) results did not entirely support this interpretation. Further work is required to clarify exactly what schedule parameters can account for the bitonic function, but all research agrees that this function exists. The region of the function where the adjunctive drinking approaches the maximal point from either side is called the 'effective range.' If the notion of a general class of 'adjunctive behaviours' is supportable, then other such adjunctive behaviours should yield similar functions with their own effective ranges.

In studies dealing with schedule-induced aggression, only the one by Flory (1969a) has specifically explored aggression as a function of interfeeding time in fixed-time schedules. As the fixed-time values were increased from 15 seconds through several values to 960 seconds, attacks increased up to 1 or 2 minutes and then fell to low levels at the longer times. The confirmation of an effective range for schedule-induced aggression in the pigeon lends some generality to this notion. Other studies have explored parts of what is probably the rising limb of the function. Hutchinson, Azrin, and Hunt (1968) found that increasing the size of food-reinforced fixed-ratios greatly increased biting attacks in squirrel monkeys, while decreasing the fixed-ratio to its former value decreased the attacks. Similarly, Flory (1969b) noted that pigeons attacked during the pause before a fixed-ratio 100, but not before a fixed-ratio 25, in a multiple FR 100, FR 25 food schedule.

In schedule-induced escape, the time spent in self-imposed time out is an increasing function of the size of the food-reinforced fixed ratio for both pigeons (Azrin, 1961) and rats (Thompson, 1964). Pigeons will escape from schedules other than fixed-ratio. Rilling, Askew, Ahlskog, and Kramer (1969) found escape occurring from the extinction component of a multiple VI 30-second extinction schedule, and from the variable-interval 5-minute component of a multiple VI 30 second VI 5-minute schedule. The data thus far do not suggest the existence of a bitonic function. Only a rising limb has been demonstrated in connection with increasing fixed-ratio size. On the other hand, I am not aware of any experiment on schedule-induced escape that was specifically designed to search for an effective range.

Deprivation Level

Because the occurrence and the degree of adjunctive behaviour is closely
related to the degree of intermittence in consummatory feeding responses, it seems reasonable to suppose that interfering with strong feeding
responses would induce stronger adjunctive behaviour than interfering
with weak feeding responses. In polydipsia studies, the animals are typically held at 80 per cent of their normal free-feeding body weights by
limiting their daily food intake. This procedure ensures that feeding-re-
sponse strength remains high throughout each daily session. Consequently, feeding intermittences imposed upon this baseline would be expected
to induce relatively strong adjunctive drinking. The strength of the feeding responses can, of course, be progressively weakened by allowing the
body weight to drift upward. If this is accomplished in a slow, controlled fashion, animals will still meet the contingencies of schedules of reinforcement and consume the delivered food with alacrity. In one experiment, bar-pressing by rats was reinforced on a fixed-interval 90-second
schedule with Noyes pellets and the usual strong polydipsic response
was induced. When the post-session food supplement was increased so
that their body weights slowly increased over a three-week period, adjunctive drinking remained at the same high level until the weights
reached about 95 per cent of the free-feeding weight. As the weights increased through the 95-105 per cent range, polydipsia decreased progressively and linearly to about 20 per cent of its original value (see Figure 3). It is important to note that whereas the adjunctive drinking was
decreasing as a function of body weight increases, the rate of bar-pressing did not decrease substantially until body weights were 104 to 105
per cent of the original free-feeding weights. Thus, animals can show
well-controlled schedule behaviour and be consuming the food pellets
in spite of slowly-instituted body weight increases, yet the adjunctive
drinking reveals marked, concomitant attenuation (Falk, 1969). There
is an important implication for adjunctive behaviour in this observation.
The maintenance of operant response rates and eating are not sufficient
conditions for inducing strong adjunctive behaviour sequences.

As body weight increases beyond the 95 per cent point, one of the required conditions for the production of adjunctive drinking becomes increasingly attenuated. This required condition is perhaps the strength
of feeding behaviour, but the experiment does not directly measure this
factor. Nonetheless, given sudden unlimited access to food, one would
expect the probability of eating to decline more quickly in the animal
starting from the higher 'per cent free-feeding weight' value. When the
post-session food supplements were omitted in the present experiment,

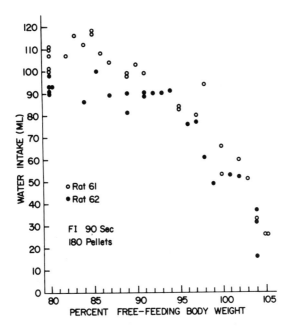

Figure 3   Adjunctive drinking as a function of body weight. Body weight allowed
to increase from 80 per cent of free-feeding weight to 104 or 105 per cent. From
Falk (1969), with permission.

driving the body weights progressively back down to 80 per cent, adjunctive drinking progressively increased and returned to its former
value.

If comparable manipulations of body weight in connection with other
schedule-induced behaviours result in similar changes in the rates of
these behaviours, it would imply that deprivation degree is one direct
determinant of a class of possible adjunctive behaviours. That is, it
would indicate that the relation between body weight alterations and
polydipsia is not peculiar to this particular adjunctive behaviour. Recently, a similar relation between body weight changes and schedule-induced
air licking has been observed (Mendleson and Chillag, personal communication). When weight changes were imposed upon rats exposed to a 1-
minute fixed-time schedule for 45-mg Noyes pellets, the degree of adjunctive air licking was an inverse function of free-feeding body weight.
The effects of varying body weight remain to be explored for schedule-
induced attack. However, Azrin *et al* (1966) showed that in food-satiat-
ed pigeons attack durations decreased to low levels. This operation is

comparable to allowing the body weight to rise to 100 per cent or grea▪
which markedly attenuates both polydipsia and air licking.

Simply imposing an effective-range intermittence value on consumma▪
tory rate is not a sufficient condition for the generation of adjunctive
behaviour. Even though the consummatory activity occurs unfailingly
and the appetitive sequence (operant pattern) remains at its customary
rate, the operations must define a rather intense deprivation state in
order for adjunctive behaviour to be induced in its fully-developed, exag▪
gerated form.

Excessive aspect of adjunctive behaviour

The amount of water drunk during variable-interval 1-minute sessions
lasting a little longer than 3 hours is almost 10 times the amount drunk
when the same number of 45-mg Noyes pellets is given all at once and
water intake over the ensuing 3.5 hours is noted (Falk, 1967). The state
of deprivation (80 per cent of the free-feeding body weight) and the typ▪
and amount of food are the same in both cases, yet the concomitant wa▪
ter intake yields about a ten-fold difference. The absolute amount and
rate of fluid intake is, of course, excessive. The bottom of the experimental chamber below the stainless-steel bars the animal stands on
is awash with dilute urine by the end of each daily session, unless this
output is minimized by a pre-session dose of vasopressin (Falk, 1964). I▪
would be interesting, but not especially noteworthy, if the animals simply took a little water after consuming each pellet but did not consume
an overall excessive amount of fluid. Such a phenomenon could be simply explained away as prandial drinking. But it is primarily the persistent and excessive aspect of the drinking that commands our attention.

The aggressive responses induced as adjuncts to various food schedule▪
also display persistent and excessive aspects. The attack topographies ar▪
strong and typically do not diminish as a function of repeated evocation▪
In the pigeon they are described as 'strong pecks at the throat and head
of the target bird, especially around the eyes. The feathers of the target
bird were often pulled out and the skin bruised' (Azrin et al, 1966).
Such attacks are strong enough to produce repeated injury to restrained
target birds. Fortunately, pigeons will often attack taxidermically-pre-
pared pigeon models used in place of live target birds. The attacks are
so forceful that Flory (1969a) found it necessary to cover the head and
throat areas of the model with closely cropped white rabbit fur.

In initial control conditions, pigeons were placed in the experimental
chamber for several daily sessions prior to any history of reinforcement

by food in order to ascertain the baseline level of attack duration (Azrin *et al*, 1966). It is important to note that on the first day most pigeons had high attack durations. On succeeding days, these attack durations decreased to near-zero levels for all birds. Thus, the initial response to the situation was a fairly high operant attack rate. This attack rate became excessively high, in comparison with even the first-session values, when the food schedule was imposed. Similar relations also held in the study by Gentry (1968).

With respect to the phenomenon of schedule-induced escape, one cannot obtain baseline consummatory rates of behaviour as in the case of drinking or attack. But this is not a serious drawback in estimating the excessive aspect of the escape behaviour. Any escape from a food or water schedule by an appropriately deprived animal is, in a real sense, excessive. Furthermore, the excessive time spent in time out from positive reinforcement was shown to increase systematically as a function of fixed-ratio size (Azrin, 1961; Thompson, 1964).

In the case of schedule-induced wheel running (Levitsky and Collier, 1968), excessive running was shown to occur in conjunction with a variable-interval 1-minute schedule compared to the running that occurred with an FR 1 schedule, or in extinction.

Schedule-induced pica, the ingestion of wood shavings, was consistently observed in monkeys on fixed-interval 15 minutes (Villarreal, 1967). It was not seen at fixed-interval 5 minutes or in extinction. Thus, the pica is excessive relative to the near-zero rates at the shorter interval and in the extinction condition.

In the schedule-induced air licking situation, the amount of air licking was much increased on a fixed-time 1-minute schedule compared to rats given the same number of food pellets all at once at the beginning of the session (Mendelson and Chillag, personal communication).

Thus, in all cases of schedule-induced phenomena, the induced behaviour occurs not only at predictable times in relation to the reinforcing events, but also in quantitative excess as a function of schedule intermittence relative to its base rate of occurrence when comparable consummatory behaviours are not paced by an intermittent schedule.

Temporal locus of adjunctive behaviour

Adjunctive behaviour occurs typically in the immediate post-reinforcement period. In the polydipsic case, a burst of drinking ensues immediately after each pellet is consumed (Falk, 1961a). This occurs on a variety of interval and ratio schedules (Falk, 1961b, 1966b). Although it is tempting to view this drinking burst as a fluid-intake response to meal termination, adjunctive behaviours other than polydipsia occur in the immediate post-reinforcement period when water is not present.

In pigeons, attack rates were high in the immediate post-reinforcement period where the schedule changed from FR 1 to extinction (Azrin et a 1966). Attack rates were a decreasing function of time from the start o the post-reinforcement period (Azrin et al, 1966; Knutson, 1970). Sim larly, squirrel monkeys on fixed-ratio food schedules showed biting attack during the post-reinforcement pause or early in the ratio run (Huc inson et al, 1968). The attack sequences in pigeons on fixed-ratio schedules also occur mainly in the post-reinforcement period (Gentry, 196&

In schedule-induced escape situations, the time-outs occur not directl after food but just before responding on fixed-ratio is initiated again (Azrin, 1961). In a mult VI 30 second ext schedule, more time-outs oc cur in the first half of the extinction component (4 minute presentatio than in the second half (Rilling et al, 1969). Likewise, most of the time outs were taken in the first half of the VI 5 minute component of a mu VI 30 second VI 5 minute schedule.

When food pellets are delivered noncontingently each minute, schedule-induced air licking is initiated shortly after pellet consumption, bu often continues throughout the entire interval (Mendelson and Chillag, 1971). In schedule-induced pica in monkeys, the consumption of wood shavings is a post-pellet event (Villarreal, 1967). Schedule-induced whe running is initiated shortly after pellet consumption (Levitsky and Collier, 1968).

Thus, in most cases, the adjunctive behaviour occurs as an event following rather closely upon reinforcement. The main exceptions to this seem to involve attacking or escaping close to the initiation of large fixed-ratios, or in the early segments of such ratios. The initiating facto for the adjunctive behaviours in such cases may involve certain aversive properties of large fixed-ratios (Thompson, 1965). Rather long interfood times do not in themselves seem to relocate the attack period awa from its usual immediate post-feeding position (Flory, 1969a).

There are, however, certain cases that do not fit the above descriptio These cases constitute interesting exceptions to the general observation that adjunctive responses occur in the immediate post-reinforcement period. A trivial case of this is where a second pellet can be obtained shortly after a first pellet is earned, such as an FR 5 always following a DRL 30 second component (Falk, 1969). Here adjunctive drinking occurs after the second pellet and not the first, because a favourable food contingency successfully competes with the drinking response. Of great er importance are cases in which the adjunctive behaviour migrates awa from the immediate post-reinforcement period. With large fixed-ratio components (FR 60 and 120), attacking occurred in episodes such that the ratio performance was interrupted, perhaps as a function of ratio strain (Knutson, 1970). With fixed-interval schedules on the order of 3 minutes or so, I have noticed that the drinking is sometimes distributed throughout the interval in a series of shorter drinking bursts, rather than in the typical sustained single burst. Also, drinking is not initiated in the immediate post-reinforcement period on these longer fixed-interval schedules. Segal *et al* (1965) have noted quite similar effects for fixed-time (noncontingent) schedules. In a recent paper, Segal (1969b) described the case of one rat in which the usual polydipsic pattern on FI 3 minutes gradually changed its time distribution and when the schedule was changed to FI 4 minutes the drinking pattern took on FI scallop characteristics. In spite of the complex experimental history of this animal, it is entirely possible that given the proper sequence of conditions schedule-induced polydipsia can be transformed into operant drinking as Segal suggests. In fact it would be surprising if adjunctive behaviours, which monopolize such a large amount of session time, did not sometimes make contact with the programmed contingencies. Perhaps one of the most striking ways in which this takes place is in the modulation of elicited behaviour, first demonstrated by Morse, Mead, and Kelleher (1967), that is described in detail by McKearney in Chapter 1.

Response contingency not crucial to the generation of adjunctive behaviour

Because it is conceivable that the excessive degree of schedule-induced polydipsia could be a displacement from an operant system that is momentarily at low probability (lever pressing) to another activity, it is worth ascertaining whether the omission of a response contingency makes a major difference. To this end, I used a noncontingent variable-interval 1-minute schedule (viz, a variable-time 1-minute schedule) to deliver pellets to animals irrespective of their behaviour (Falk, 1961b). This made no appreciable difference in the amount of polydipsia (see also Falk, 1969).

Likewise, Azrin *et al* (1966) found that the typical attack responses occurred when a period of free feeding was interrupted by a no-food period in pigeons that had never been reinforced for key pecking. These results showed 'that the pecking attacks were not simply a "displacement" of the conditioned key-pecking responses' (Azrin, *et al*, 1966). The study by Flory (1969a) also used fixed-time schedules of food presentation.

Both the schedule-induced pica and the schedule-induced air licking experiments were done with fixed-time schedules (Villarreal, 1967; Mendelson and Chillag, 1971).

Thus, given an appropriate deprivation level, various schedule-induced phenomena seem to be determined primarily by the rate of food delivery, rather than by some feature of response contingency defining a schedule of reinforcement. Accordingly, the major determinant of schedule choice is the rate of food delivery, independent of whether or not responses are necessary to acquire the food (Killeen, 1968). The rate of consummatory behaviour defined by a schedule determines both its relative preference and the degree of adjunctive behaviour it generates. But the schedule preference, as well as response rate (Herrnstein, 1970) are both direct functions of reinforcement rate, whereas the rate of adjunctive behaviour is a bitonic function.

Adjunctive behaviour can sustain a schedule of reinforcement

If water is not freely available from a drinking tube concurrently with a food schedule, but is available in small portions contingent upon the completion of a fixed-ratio schedule, polydipsia is acquired and will sustain large fixed-ratios (Falk, 1966a). This establishes the polydipsia as a reinforcing activity capable of sustaining scheduled behaviour. It also implies that the animal is not simply engaging in some arbitrary, time-filling response, or that drinking is just reflexly elicited by eating.

Azrin (1964) has reported that extinction-induced aggression will also support a fixed-ratio schedule. Pigeons will respond on a second key with the onset of extinction, the reinforcing relation being the provision of a target bird, which is then attacked.

Schedule-induced escape, in the form of 30 seconds of time-out from a fixed-ratio schedule for water, was sustained when a FR 3 was required to produce the time-outs (Thompson, 1964). Again, this showed that the escape behaviour functioned as a reinforcer.

Environmental control of the adjunctive behaviour manifested

Relatively little research has tested the extent to which one adjunctive behaviour may be substituted for another. This would be an obvious direction for research on adjunctive behaviour to take since the link between the food schedule and the particular adjunctive behaviour manifested is probably not one of high specificity. That is to say, the linkage is probably amenable to stimulus facilitation by the environmental situation.

When access to a running wheel in place of water was provided for rats showing schedule-induced polydipsia on a variable-interval 1-minute food schedule, wheel-running activity was approximately double the level associated with an FR 1 food schedule (Levitsky and Collier, 1968). When both water and the wheel were provided, drinking occurred post-pellet and running occurred throughout the interreinforcement interval. This intermittent food schedule produced excessive drinking or running when either one or the other of these commodities was provided. When both were provided, both were engaged in excessively relative to their respective baseline rates. Clearly, the excessive, adjunctive behaviour is to a large extent a function of the environmental opportunities provided.

It became evident early in polydipsia research that if paper towels or other absorbent material were placed beneath the bars forming the floor of the experimental space, some rats pulled such material up through the bars, shredding and manipulating it. This behaviour attentuated the level of drinking, especially in the latter portions of a session. Our solution to this, as we were primarily interested in studying the polydipsia, was to build deeper catch pans and place only a thin layer of Sanicel on the bottom. Freed and Hymowitz (1969) made similar observations and emphasized the substitutability of these chewing-manipulatory behaviours for polydipsia.

A somewhat similar relation holds with respect to schedule-induced polydipsia in the rhesus monkey. These monkeys can show a high level of polydipsia (Schuster and Woods, 1966). They also show schedule-induced pica, consuming wood-shavings in the post-pellet period (Villarreal, 1967). When both water and shavings are present, some animals engage in polydipsia preferentially, while others alternate between these two activities (Villarreal, personal communication).

An indication that responses other than attack can occur as adjuncts to food schedules in the pigeon is the recent finding that fixed and variable-interval 2-minute food schedules produced polydipsia (Shanab and Peterson, 1969). Also, fixed-ratio food schedules result in attack (Flory, 1969b; Gentry, 1968; Knutson, 1970) or escape (Azrin, 1961) in pigeons, probably as a function of the behaviour possibilities afforded the animal in the situation. There is obviously a need to compare the substitutability of attack and polydipsia, as well as attack and escape, on the same animals using the same food intermittence as a generator schedule for these adjunctive behaviours.

The strategy of testing for substitutability of behaviours with respect to intracranial-stimulation-induced behaviours (so-called 'stimulus-bound' behaviours) and peripheral-shock-induced behaviours has revealed some unsuspected nonspecificities. Valenstein, Cox, and Kakolewski

(1968) have shown that when eating, drinking, or gnawing is produced by electrical stimulation of the hypothalamus, one of these behaviours can substitute for the one originally and consistently produced by changing the options available to the animal while holding the hypothalamic stimulation parameters constant. Peripherally-administered electric shock results in a highly-predictable and immediate attack response in rats and other animals (Ulrich and Azrin, 1962). Yet, such stimulation when applied to virgin male rats paired with receptive females results in a much higher incidence of copulatory behaviour than in non-shocked controls (Caggiula and Eibergen, 1969). Male-male pairings resulted in fighting.

Not only can changing the available environmental options exercise critical control over the behaviour induced by electrical stimulation, but also the historical sequencing of these options and contingencies can apparently alter the sign of a reinforcer. Thus, shock-elicited responses can be modulated so as to produce the shocks on a FI schedule (Morse *et al*, 1967), and a shock-avoidance performance can be altered into a maintenance of responding under an FI electric-shock-presentation schedule (McKearney, 1968, Chapter 1; Stretch, Orloff, and Dalrymple, 1968).

The environmental controls exercised by stimulus facilitation and the sequencing of options play a major role in determining the behaviours induced not only by feeding schedules but also by centrally and peripherally administered electric stimulation.

THE PROXIMAL EVENTS CONTROLLING ADJUNCTIVE BEHAVIOUR

Some of the major determinants of adjunctive behaviour have been discussed, such as feeding schedule and deprivation level. In the present section, the possible environmental events controlling the temporal locus of the behaviour will be considered.

First, I believe that interpretations of the bouts of adjunctive behaviour based upon notions about the animal being confused, disappointed, harassed, teased, or frustrated by an intermittent food schedule are untenable. There are methodological problems concerning the confirmability of such notions. But, more cogently, it is difficult to maintain that a rat subjected to a fixed-interval 90-second schedule for several months is still reacting with innocent disappointment and incredulity, and consoling itself with post-pellet drinking bouts. Rather than being a response to an uncertain feeding situation, the behaviour seems to be a precise product of the imposed controlling conditions. Adjunctive behaviour, then, is a result of schedule control, not a transition state into, or a confusional state concerning such control.

Adjunctive behaviour is not elicited by the schedule conditions. In the first section I have already outlined certain reasons for not viewing the relation as an unconditioned reflex. The striking regularity and exaggerated level of adjunctive behaviour gives the appearance of an elicited response. Nonetheless, the schedule conditions probably do not generate such behaviour as new responses, but as large increases in the base rate of a behaviour already present as a response to the current situation. An ethologist might say that the schedule-environment context releases an adjunctive behaviour. This would be a fair characterization providing one realizes that a releaser is not an elicitor, but has functions more analogous to a discriminative stimulus than to an unconditioned or conditioned stimulus. 'Like the discriminative stimulus, it [a releaser] increases the probability of occurrence of a unit of behaviour but does not force it' (Skinner, 1966).

The notion that adjunctive behaviour is an increase in behaviour already present in the situation at a lower base rate does have some empirical support. When rats eat following a deprivation period, a few draughts of water usually occur in conjunction with the feeding (Falk, 1966a, 1967). In accordance with this, when the base rate of drinking is suppressed by pre-session stomach loads of water each day, animals can be prevented from acquiring polydipsia (Chapman, 1969). Comparable loads given to rats with *established* polydipsia leave the drinking mainly intact (Falk, 1969). In aggression research, the initial responses of animals to the restrained, target animal provide a fair base rate of attack (Azrin *et al*, 1966; Gentry, 1968). The wheel-running base rate of food-deprived rats is quite evident under ordinary laboratory conditions and can be seen under the fixed-ratio 1 and extinction conditions imposed by Levitsky and Collier (1968). Under conditions where water-drinking is probable, air-licking was shown to be probable (Hendry and Rasche, 1961). The base rate for wood-shavings pica in monkeys is quite low, but not zero (Villarreal, 1967). It is also a case of what the ethologist would call a 're-direction activity' since the motor pattern is quite similar to that of the activity interfered with, namely eating. The motor pattern, then, does have an appreciable base rate in the situation.

The stimuli producing the base rates of adjunctive behaviour are largely unknown. Attempts to account for post-pellet drinking bursts in terms of a response to a dry mouth have been dealt with previously and found wanting (Falk, 1967; 1969). For example, polydipsia occurs when the food used is a liquid, one-third water by weight. Chapman (1969) has shown that wetting the rat's mouth post-pellet by means of an intra-oral tube does not stop the polydipsia unless the amount administered approximates the amount that would have been ingested. By contrast, a ten-times smaller post-pellet, intra-oral injection of water normalizes the post-prandial drinking pattern of free-feeding, desalivate rats (Kissi-leff, 1969). Attempts to vary or give accounts of the initial base rates of other adjunctive behaviours have been minimal.

The pattern of drinking typical of effective-range polydipsia is a bout of drinking that follows food pellet consumption with short latency. This temporal locus is characteristic of other adjunctive behaviours and was discussed previously. A few attempts have been made to ascertain the significance of this temporal relation using schedule-induced poly-dipsia. The post-reinforcement occurrence of drinking on a fixed-interval schedule militates against a simple 'violation of expectation' account of the behaviour. At this time the lever-pressing rate is low, it is the usual FI pause period, when any 'expectation' of a pellet would also be low. The initial portion of this characteristic pause period is precisely when reinforcement probability is lowest. When it is not low, as in the post-DRL component of an alternating DRL 30 seconds, FR 5 schedule, post reinforcement drinking does not occur (Falk, 1969). There are two no-tions involved here. One is that the drinking burst is an event controlled by the recency of pellet consumption unless another pellet is imminent. The other notion is that the low probability of reinforcement is the cru-cial event in the immediate post-pellet period, rather than any recency effect of the pellet consumed.

The role of recent pellet consumption has been explored by using schedules involving conditioned reinforcement and chaining. Richard Bryant and I explored the possibility that drinking bursts would occur after a conditioned reinforcer. We paired pellet delivery with a 3-second buzzer for rats on an FI 60-second schedule. This was later changed to a sequence in which the FI 60-second schedule resulted in the pellet and buzzer, as before, or with 50 per cent probability yielded the buzzer a-lone. The FI 60-second schedule resulted in polydipsia, and the second schedule resulted in a much higher level, since the inter-reinforcement time was lenghtened to 120 seconds on the average. But relatively little post-buzzer drinking occurred. The major portion of the drinking still occurred as post-pellet events. A more successful procedure for attaining drinking after a conditioned reinforcer was used by Rosenblith (1970). A second-order FR 3 (FI 1-minute) schedule was used with rats in which every completion of an FI 1-minute yielded a 2-second light flash and every third completion also yielded a pellet. Considerable control of drinking in the immediate post-light-flash period was demonstrated. Wolfgang Wuttke (see Chapter 6) has obtained similar results with the same schedule.

Randall Flory, Richard Bryant, and I worked on the problem of ascer-taining whether transition to an S^Δ (no reinforcement) component, which also required a zero response rate to terminate (DRO), would produce drinking. Such a component comprises a low probability of reinforcement and also an enforced period of no operant lever responses. The basic schedule we used was a chain with a short FR as the initial member. This led either to a discriminative stimulus for the DRO component or one for an FI of the same length. The DRO was followed by the initial FR member, whereas completion of the FI was reinforced with a food pellet and followed by the FR member. Although various parameters of the schedule were changed, at no time did we obtain appreciable drinking except following pellet delivery. Transition to, or completion of, the DRO period never produced appreciable drinking, nor did completion of the initial (FR) member leading into the FI component. The drinking was polydipsic, and entirely post-pellet in locus. At this time, there is not yet enough research to make a definitive statement concerning the proximal controlling events for adjunctive behaviour.

DISPLACEMENT ACTIVITIES AS ADJUNCTIVE BEHAVIOURS

For several decades, ethologists have produced a considerable empirical and theoretical literature on behaviours that are characterized as 'irrelevant,' 'incongruous,' or 'out-of-context.' These 'displacement activities' aroused continuing interest because they were puzzling and difficult to predict. For example, two skylarks in combat might suddenly cease fighting and peck at the ground with feeding movements. Or, in a similar situation, two starlings might stop, preen their feathers, and then resume fighting. In the midst of courting behaviour, ducks are often observed to engage in short bouts of preening. The black-headed gull can be observed to commence nest-building behaviour when its brooding is interrupted (Moynihan, 1953). In all these examples, the displacement activity seems to be inappropriate to the stimulus situation and the behaviour 'immediately preceding or following' (Tinbergen, 1952).

The most widely-accepted definition of displacement activity is Tinbergen's (1952): 'A displacement activity is an activity belonging to the executive motor pattern of an instinct other than the instinct activated'. If instead of 'instinct activated' the major deprivation operations or stimulating conditions are substituted in the definition, it can be provisionally rephrased. The 'displaced' behaviour can be referred to as a response sequence that is ordinarily a function of variables other than those that presumably dominate the current situation.

Displacement activities are described as arising from various kinds of situations, but one such situation is the 'thwarting' of consummatory behaviour. For most ethologists, a typical thwarting situation is not one in which a physical barrier is placed in the way of the consummatory behaviour, but one in which the necessary releasing stimuli are not present. Thus, the thwarting of a drive is said to occur when one or more eggs are removed from the nest, effectively removing a portion of the releasing stimuli for incubation behaviour in the brooding bird (Moynihan 1953). This results in displacement nest-building or preening. Fanning (egg-ventilating movements) that occurs in the male three-spined stickle back during courtship has been interpreted as displacement fanning due to the inadequate releasing stimuli presented by the female, eg, failure to follow the male toward the nest (Tinbergen and Van Iersel, 1947). These investigators also observed that displacement activities occur when 'an external stimulus, after having activated a drive, suddenly stops.' The emphasis here is not upon the simple absence of an appropriate releasing stimulus in the presence of a strong drive, but upon the dynamic change in the situation. Tinbergen (1952) cites the observations of Kortland on the cormorant in which aggressive behaviour changes suddenly to a sexual displacement activity when the opponent flees.

Thus, displacement activities are described as occurring in situations where an animal under high drive conditions is engaged in a phase of the consummatory behaviour and for some reason is prevented from continuing this behaviour. These are also the conditions producing adjunctive behaviours: a lean animal engaged in eating is prevented from continuing this behaviour by the intermittence imposed by the feeding schedule.

We have already described the important role played by environmental controls in determining the type of adjunctive behaviour manifested. Similar considerations apply to displacement activities. In the older literature, displacement activity was assumed to be determined by a kind of 'sparking-over' from one internal energy state subserving one instinct to another. In recent research, the importance of current facilitating stimuli in determining what particular displacement activity will occur has been recognized. Morris (1954) pointed out that the male Zebra finch can show different displacement activities depending upon the current stimulus situation. When threatened, it will feed if food is nearby, sexually mount a female if one is present, and, if neither food nor a female is available, it will preen or assume a sleeping posture. Further detailed analyses of the importance of stimulus facilitation in determining the displacement activity manifested are provided by Rowell (1961) and Sevenster (1961).

In both adjunctive behaviour and displacement activity situations, the interruption of a consummatory behaviour in an intensely motivated an imal induces the occurrence of another behaviour immediately following the interruption, which is facilitated by environmental stimuli.

ADJUNCTIVE BEHAVIOUR: ADJUSTIVE, TOXIC, OR CREATIVE RESPONSE?

Certain values of variables that compose contingencies of reinforcement yield behavioural effects in unexpected directions and magnitudes. These behaviours are not ineluctably elicited by the contingencies. However, under certain contingency-environment combinations, rather protracted sequences of adjunctive behaviour occur with high probability. The contingency relation alone is not sufficient to induce the adjunctive behaviour in the absence of certain supporting environmental conditions. The particular environmental circumstances that exist will determine which adjunctive behaviours are generated by a given contingency. But there is no necessity to assume that if a particular contingency gives rise to sequences of one adjunctive behaviour under one environmental condition it will necessarily induce some other form of adjunctive behaviour under a different environmental condition. Since the contingency-environment combination is regarded as the main stimulus condition generating an adjunctive behaviour, there is no reason to assume that if the environment is altered so that a certain adjunctive behaviour cannot occur a substitute behaviour will necessarily emerge. Such a notion would be reminiscent of 'symptom substitution' which attributes the major stimulus control of symptoms to variables other than the immediate environmental situation. The extent to which one form of adjunctive behaviour may be replaced by another one under changed environmental circumstances is an empirical question. But there is no theoretical necessity for some other intrusive behaviour to supervene if, for instance, the water source is removed from a polydipsia situation.

Because adjunctive behaviour is such a conspicuous aspect of the behavioural output in those situations that produce it, several possible theoretical and interpretive notions quite naturally arise. We have already set aside those explanations framed in terms of simple, physiological bases, mediating functions, or adventitiously reinforced behaviours. But there remain certain categories that, while not giving an account of the genesis of the behaviour, nonetheless favour a particular evaluative context for interpreting it.

Adjunctive behaviour as adjustive

It is highly probable that when a psychologist observes intense and pro-

longed consummatory behaviour he will assume that it serves some func
tion for the organism. Eating is said to serve certain hunger or tissue
needs. If the organism is demonstrably obese, and without other specifi
nutrient needs, the eating is presumed to be either a regulatory or a me
bolic maladjustment. It is a pathological condition of the adjustment
mechanism. By this view, behaviour is either adjustive or the outcome c
disordered adjustive mechanisms. In cases where an input-output exchange appears to work to the detriment of that relation, an alternate a
justive reason is sought or assumed. For example, if body water is evapo
rated in the heat, it is not in the interest of fluid adjustment, but for th
regulation of body temperature. Assuming this general species of adjustive model, eating that does not serve tissue needs or that is not a demo
strably regulatory or metabolic disorder of adjustive mechanisms is said
to be a functional disorder. Even this type of malfunction is also assum
ed to serve certain adjustive ends. It is said to discharge impulses or re-
lieve tensions that cannot for other reasons obtain motor expression.
Thus, what might appear to be maladaptive behaviour in terms of energ
exchange is claimed to have an alternate adjustive function: the relief o
tensions that otherwise would be debilitating.

Given the above general orientation, it is not surprising that attempts
have been made to account for adjunctive behaviour within a framewor
of adjustment. With regard to adjunctive drinking, it has been claimed
that it maintains the mouth in a condition to swallow dry food, that it
maintains the food/water ratio in the stomach, that it decreases the bod
temperature that is increased by eating, and so on. As these explanation
in adjustive terms have been found wanting, there has been no lack of
alternative suggestions along the lines of functional disorders. For exam
ple, polydipsia has been said to be a frustration reaction to the food
schedule.

If all behaviour is assumed to be either adjustive or pathological dis-
tortions of adjustment, by definition adjunctive behaviour must either
be directly adjustive (which it seems not to be), serve an ancillary adjustive role (which has not been demonstrated and seems highly improbable), or be a disordered adjustive reaction. This last would have to reduce to a functional disorder in that no pathological alterations have
been instituted. While the neurotic may derive certain 'secondary gains''
from his neurotic behaviour, the case for interpreting adjunctive behaviour in this regard is rather opaque. Nor does adjunctive behaviour seem
to have the functional properties of neurotic behaviour. It develops
rapidly rather than slowly, and it is characteristically predictable of all
members of the species rather than idiosyncratic as to occurrence and
form.

Adjunctive behaviour: toxic or creative response?

When one loses heart in searching for the adjustive ends served by adjunctive behaviour, it is perhaps understandable that the quest could turn toward darker interpretations framed in terms of behavioural toxicity. Certain combinations of drug and schedule parameters have been described as behaviourally toxic (Thompson and Schuster, 1968) in that performance outcomes are disrupted relative to undrugged behavioural baselines. The same drug dosage levels may leave behaviour controlled by other schedule parameters intact. Just as certain drug and schedule parameter combinations exhibit behavioural toxicity, certain environment and schedule parameter combinations also might be viewed as yielding another mode of toxic response: adjunctive behaviour. According to this notion, adjunctive behaviour is the manifestation of a maladaptive response to an unfavourable environmental situation similar to the stereotypes shown by institutionalized retardates and caged animals.

The question as to whether adjunctive behaviour is a toxic manifestation or a creative deviation cannot be answered by a description of the topography of the response. If the adjunctive behaviour results in the organism failing to adjust to environmental contingencies, or if the behaviour itself leads to damaging consequences, then it can be considered as maladaptive or as a toxic response. If the behaviour results in a new behavioural emphasis working to the benefit of the organism, then it can be viewed as a powerful mechanism for adaptive cahnge. Whether the result is toxic or creative will be a function not only of the generator schedule but also of the environmental circumstances — the ecology of the situation. Adjunctive behaviour may be toxic and intrude upon possible adaptive responses in one environment or have adjustive or creative results in an environment with more prosthetic possibilities (Lindsley, 1964).

ON THE NATURE OF ADJUNCTIVE BEHAVIOUR

Having come this far in indicating certain functional correspondences among adjunctive behaviours, even to the territorial borders of ethology, I would be remiss if I did not attempt to provide a working definition of adjunctive behaviour, if only to serve as a summary.

Adjunctive behaviour is a stable increase in behaviour probability not attributable to variables that directly affect the unconditioned, conditioned, or operant probability of that behaviour, but which is a function of variables primarily determining some other class of behaviour with respect to 1) its unconditioned probability, 2) its consummatory rate, or 3) the operant probability sustained by it.

Less explicitly, but more succinctly, adjunctive behaviour is behaviour maintained at high probability by stimuli whose reinforcing properties in the situation are derived primarily as a function of schedule parameters governing the availability of another class of reinforcers.

The behaviour is referred to as 'a stable increase' to distinguish it from behavioural contrast phenomena and other more transitory effects. Clearly it should not be attributable to unconditioned or conditioned determinants, otherwise it could not be considered as adjunctive. The 'operant probability' could, of course, be strengthened in many other ways such as making water intake a shock-avoidance operant. This too is scarcely adjunctive. The 'unconditioned probability' of some other class of behaviour refers to such variables as 'per cent free-feeding body weight' as a determinant of feeding probability. The 'consummatory rate' refers to variables that control the rate of eating. These are primarily schedule considerations, but other variables can certainly affect this rate: desalivation, local muscle relaxants, punishment contingencies, etc. The 'operant probability sustained by it' takes into account those schedule factors that give rise to pauses in the operant performance. Such pauses perhaps favour change-overs to the adjunctive behaviour. For example, with ratio strain, the pigeon engages in attacks during portions of the pause (Knutson, 1970).

With respect to the second, short definition, those with interests in the area of motivational theory should note the implication that 'schedule of reinforcement' can be considered as a drive operation. Catania (1968, p. 334) has defined 'drive operation' as 'any operation that changes the effectiveness of a stimulus as a reinforcer ...' In accordance with this definition, certain food schedules are drive operations for adjunctive behaviours.

When the environmental conditions producing adjunctive behaviour are maintained, the behaviour tends to persist and remain in its exaggerated form. It is difficult to satiate. In preliminary work, Richard Bryant and I have found that polydipsia is relatively difficult to discourage by punishment contingencies compared to deprivation-induced drinking. Likewise, relatively large quatities of highly-hypertonic NaCl are ingested adjunctively (Falk, 1964; 1966c).

The reinforcement intermittence and thwarting conditions that yield adjunctive and displacement behaviours increase the organism's probability of responding in strength to other possibilities in the environmental context by increasing the gain on operant units receiving relatively low, but appreciable, facilitation from current environmental stimuli. In this regard, Armstrong (1950) comments that 'a species which is able to modify its behaviour to suit changed circumstances by means of displacements, rather than by the evolution of *ad hoc* modifications starting from scratch, will have an advantage over other species. Therefore, *ceteris paribus*, a displacement-prone species will be more adaptable, and consequently more successful, than a species not so equipped.' But he also ironically observes: 'No doubt many dysgenic displacements have been eliminated with their performers in the course of evolution.'

8 Schedule-independent factors contributing to schedule-induced phenomena

R. R. HUTCHINSON and G. S. EMLEY

Behavioural by-products may frequently occur during ongoing programmes of contingent response control. An experiment often produces major secondary effects that are not to be understood in terms of the contingent relations between the events manipulated by the experimenter and the primary performance. As more research has produced these behavioural by-products, certain of their principal characteristics have been established. Thus, the regularity of schedule-induced phenomena has been firmly established in the last several years. In addition to our greater understanding of these performances, we have begun to appreciate that knowledge of such collateral behaviours may also be crucial to a full understanding of the primary performances themselves.

The explanatory potential of this knowledge of secondary behavioural effects has been recurrently demonstrated. For example, several workers have either speculated upon, or actually experimented with, the possibility that transitions to nonreinforcement for previously reinforced operants were 'noxious,' 'aversive,' 'frustrating,' or 'negatively reinforcing.' Ferster's (1958) work on contingent timeout from reinforcement in both pigeons and monkeys attempted to demonstrate that such transitions were in fact punishing. Several experiments followed these initial demonstrations in attempting to support the notion that extinction was a negatively reinforcing condition in the traditional sense of such a term. For example Appel (1963b), Azrin (1961), and Thompson (1964; 1965) each illustrated that certain features of positive reward schedules produce 'escape' or timeout responses. Such effects were used to support the notion

Preparation of these materials was supported in part by the Office of Naval Research Contract N00014-70-A-0183, the National Science Foundation, Grant GB-18413, the National Aeronautics and Space Administration Grant NGR-23-010-004, and the Michigan Department of Mental Health. Our thanks go to S.C. Betteridge and N.J. Murray for their assistance.

that the absence of reward was, in some way, more than the mere absence of reward and in fact was the presence of some noxious or aversive state of affairs. These results, however, were fraught with difficulty in that they were generally interpretable in terms of an organism's simply behaving so as to maximize reinforcement. The demonstration, however, by Azrin, Hutchinson, and Hake (1966) that the transition to conditions of nonreward can produce attack behaviour in pigeons, and the subsequent experiments by Hutchinson, Azrin, and Hunt (1968) showing that certain portions of a fixed-ratio schedule occasioned attack behaviour by monkeys towards a rubber hose, each provided additional support for the earlier tests. Here extinction, at least in its initiation, was more than simple absence of response strengthening, because its onset directly produced an independent novel (and collateral) behaviour, similar or identical to the behaviour produced by the direct delivery of a painful electric shock. Another example of knowledge of a collateral behaviour providing assistance in understanding other behaviours lies in the findings of Azrin, Hutchinson, and Hake (1967) that nonperformance of avoidance or escape reactions, if resulting in shock, could lead directly to attack by rats and monkeys, and that, in turn, these reactions often proved suitable as avoidance or escape responses, and would thus be learned especially rapidly. Similar findings have been made in the area of polydipsia, where an understanding of the collateral behaviour and the contingently-controlled baseline behaviours have each been instructive in knowing more about the other.

Though these findings have been helpful to us and to others interested in the effects of schedules of response contingent stimulus control, their principal merit may not depend upon a preoccupation with schedule processes. The work on aggression has made it apparent that such behaviour is not to be viewed solely or primarily as a schedule-induced effect. Ulrich and Azrin (1962) showed that attacks were produced directly by the application of electric shock. Azrin, Hutchinson, and Hake (1966) have demonstrated that attack resulted directly from termination of response-independent food presentations. During the last several years we have been conducting experiments in which we have studied various effects of the direct response-independent application of events such as electric shock and food upon different behaviours. The results provide basic information about environmental influences on a number of reaction tendencies, and may hopefully serve as important observations for comparison with other experiments where such events are manipulated in a response-contingent fashion.

Many of us are products of the operant tradition, and possess a set of psychological knowledges and skills that have been shown to be of exceptional technological power. In such a comfortable condition, we tend, however, to neglect the continuing necessity for certain critical experimental tests. For example, if a particular response is strengthened during the contingent delivery of food or shock termination, we usually accept the simple response-strength increase as a sufficient demonstration of the contingent control relation. Yet we know that numerous unlearned effects may also develop over time. In a more conservative mood each of us would suggest that a more thorough test of whether a particular condition was or was not 'reinforcing' would be to study response tendencies in the absence of such conditions, then in the presence of contingent events, and again in the absence of the contingent events. This ABA design or, as it is often termed, baseline, reinforcement, and extinction, is a powerful series of manipulations that we have come to respect as a reasonable test of the claims of contingent control. If a performance is suitably affected, that is, moves from a low level to a higher level in the B condition, then down again when we remove those variables, we may be convinced that the response-contingent event is responsible for the behavioural increases noted. But is it? We all appreciate that the contingent application of a stimulus variable is actually the simultaneous arrangement of two factors: 1) the establishment of contact between the organism and the agent such as food or shock, and 2) the contingency arrangement between some unit of behaviour and that stimulus event. This additional factor of the contingency is the essence of operant conditioning and serves to distinguish as 'learned', or operantly conditioned, response strength so generated from many other performances. Yet, again, our methods are so powerful that we often, and in fact typically, are convinced that response strength results from the contingent application of an event, even though the contingency itself is very frequently not manipulated. Comparison between the contingent and the noncontingent application of 'biologically-relevant' or 'primary reinforcer' type events is, it seems to us, a crucial but presently underdeveloped experimental concern within the experimental analysis of behaviour. The work reported here makes some attempts at such comparisons. In the experiments reviewed most completely here we have been studying the effects of the experimental manipulation of painful electric shocks, delivered independently of a subject's ongoing performances, upon several distinct response classes.

METHODS

If the work reported here has been successful to any degree, it is a result of the combined efforts of a number of persons who have worked over the years to produce experimental methods incorporating several highly desirable features. The subject paradigm is that originally developed by Dr Hake at Anna, Illinois, for his thesis work on punishment with the squirrel monkey. The method provides the partial restraint of the subject by an ingenious chair, waist-lock, and tail-yoke assembly (Hake and Azrin, 1963). This chair permits relative freedom of the torso, upper extremities, and head, while severely restricting the general mobility of the animal, and particularly the tail. The latter factor is important as it allows continuing, precise contact with the subject for the purpose of delivering a regulated painful electric shock. This predictable and specifiable shock delivery system seems to us a very marked improvement over most other shock application systems. In the procedure employed, the distal 4 to 5 inches of the tail is shaved and, each day prior to running, cleaned with alcohol. The tail is then placed under the electrodes to make contact at two points. Electrode cream is rubbed into the tail for one minute and then additional paste is applied over these points of contact. Only by such methods is subsequent stimulation predictable and rigorously controllable. As an additional control, tail resistance is monitored both at the beginning and end of each session, and series resistances are employed to further minimize any variation that might yet occur. Such specifiable contact between the environment and the organism becomes mandatory when one is interested in the frequent contact with a precise stimulus condition. Such requirements are certainly found in studies of punishment, escape, and elicited behaviours; perhaps more often than in the study of avoidance behaviour, where environmental factors immediately controlling performance are those other than the infrequent shock. In many behavioural studies, there is scope for choosing, strengthening, and manipulating any of a variety of response topographies. This flexibility, afforded through the process of successive approximation and contingency control, is not available when studying the effects of response-independent events. Instead, one must be prepared to arrange the delivery of events independently of any experimentally desired behavioural outcome. Further, the researcher must passively record the behavioural actions that result. For these reasons, it is necessary to develop response sensors that make contact with performances in ways that do not detract or punish, or in any other way arbitrarily delimit, behavioural expression. In our studies of biting attack, it has been necessary to choose rubber hose types and dimensions that can withstand frequent tearing and ripping. Similarly, in other studies of manual manipulation, it has been necessary to choose sensors, such as chains to be pulled or levers to be depressed, that are not so lightly counterweighted as to allow continual depression, but instead produce frequent release and subsequent redepression by the subject. The arrangement of these sensors in

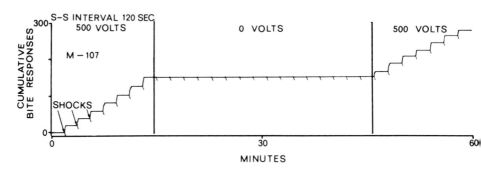

Figure 1   Representative record for one subject showing the relationship between shock exposure and biting attack on a rubber hose. During the shock period, 500-volt tail-shock deliveries are indicated by vertical deflections of the cumulative record.

space is highly important. If concurrent performances are occurring, response sensors, by their spatial location and physical construction, must provide for the reliable and sensitive, but selective, contact with behaviour.

BEHAVIOUR PRODUCTION BY AVERSIVE STIMULI

Unconditional effects

Upon initial exposure to painful electric shock, a squirrel monkey restrained in a chair engages in a number of measurable reactions. Typically the shock produces a high-pitched scream and violent struggling, which appear to be an intense effort to escape from the restraint chair. If a rubber hose is suspended in front of the subject's face, the animal will, after several shocks, grasp the hose with both hands, lean forward, and bite for some number of times. This behaviour, referred to as biting attack behaviour, has been reported by us previously (Hutchinson, Azrin, and Hake, 1966; Hutchinson, Azrin, and Renfrew, 1968) and follows closely the general pattern of reactions initially described by Ulrich and Azrin (1962). Figure 1 illustrates a cumulative record of such behaviour over a 60-minute session for one subject during three successive experimental tests. Initially the animal was exposed to a 100-millisecond shock each two minutes, independently of ongoing behaviour. Each shock produced a flurry of biting responses for some seconds, which then subsided until the next shock. In the second condition, the voltage generator was disconnected and biting attacks were immediately eliminated. In the third experimental condition the subject was exposed again

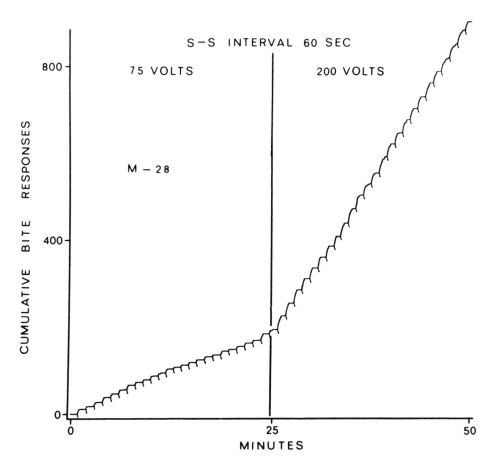

Figure 2 Representative record for one subject showing frequency of biting attack at the two shock voltages indicated. Shock deliveries are indicated by vertical deflections of the cumulative record.

to shocks every two minutes and the biting behaviour occurred in the original pattern. This illustration shows that the biting performance is caused explicitly and directly by the painful electric shocks. As with all of our work on elicited behaviour, very large individual subject differences exist in the absolute magnitude of behaviour produced by the stimulus events studied. All, however, have shown the basic pattern illustrated in Figure 1.

The absolute frequency of biting attacks in response to an individual shock was in part determined by the intensity and furation of each shock (Hutchinson, Azrin, and Renfrew, 1968). In Figure 2, a transition from a lower to a higher shock intensity is illustrated. The subject was

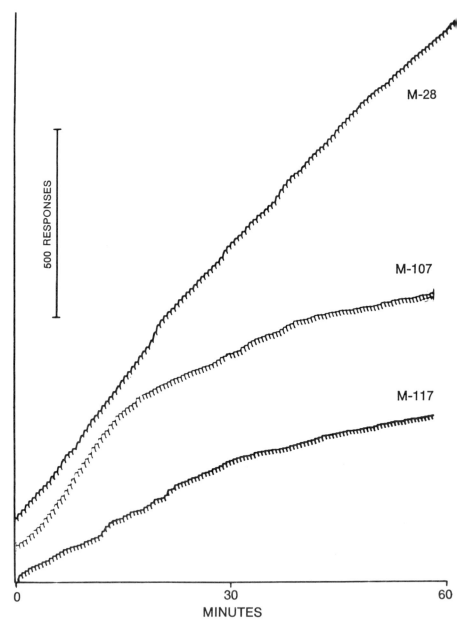

Figure 3   Cumulative records of biting attack of an entire experimental session for three subjects, showing decrements in responding within the session. M-28, M-107, and M-117 received 400-volt, 300-volt, and 200-volt shocks, respectively, where indicated by vertical deflections of the cumulative record. The shock-shock interval was 30 seconds.

S – S INTERVAL 240 SEC.

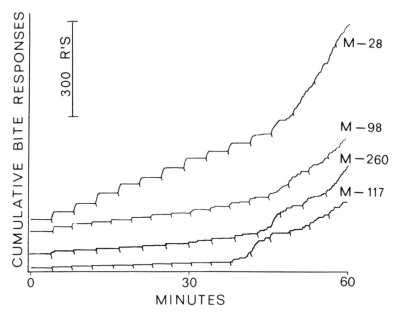

Figure 4   Within-session increases in responding for four subjects exposed to consecutive previous sessions of noncontingent tail shock. 400-volt shock deliveries are indicated by vertical deflections of the cumulative record.

receiving 75-volt shocks every 60 seconds, and then 200-volt shocks were presented at the same frequency. All shocks were delivered independently of behaviour. The transition in response frequency occurred immediately upon introduction of the higher voltage. The direct relation between magnitude of biting behaviour and intensity of shock led to the assumption of a simple and direct relation between biting attack and stimulus magnitude. After additional studies, however, it became clear that the relation is anything but simple. In most of our earlier work, subjects were exposed to only brief episodes of electric shock. In later work, as subjects accrued histories of a wider variety of shock conditions, several major processes not initially observed became evident.

First it was discovered that lower shock intensities did not produce a smaller and unchanging degree of biting attack. At lower shock intensities attack often occurred at modest levels initially, declining rapidly over a single session and even more drastically over subsequent sessions. Again, there was considerable variability between animals. In Figure 3, the performances for an entire session for three subjects are illustrated. Each of these subjects showed varying degrees of response decrease upon suc-

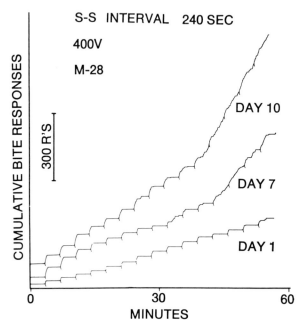

Figure 5   Cumulative records of biting attack for one subject showing development of increased responding over successive sessions.

cessive shock deliveries. Several studies indicated that these response de-creases might be fully dissipated over a period of one or two days with-out testing or shock delivery Thus it became evident that biting attack behaviour demonstrated response habituation much as do other elicited phenomena. The experiments are reported completely in Hutchinson, Renfrew, and Young (1971).

With some of our subjects, however, effects quite the opposite of ha-bituation gradually developed. For these subjects, under the experimen-tal conditions to which they were exposed, biting attacks became pro-gressively more frequent upon successive minutes and sessions of shock exposure. Again, large individual differences appeared in the amount of biting attack to similar or identical shock parameters. In Figure 4, the performances for an entire daily session for four subjects showing this effect are illustrated. These performances are not transitory, but reflect the steady state assumed after some days or weeks of exposure to the experimental conditions. Shocks were delivered every 4 minutes and shock intensity was 400 volts. Each subject showed a fairly constant number of bites after each shock for the initial 20 to 40 minutes of the experimental session. Gradually, a greater number of bites occurred af-ter each shock until, in some instances, biting occurred continuously, at

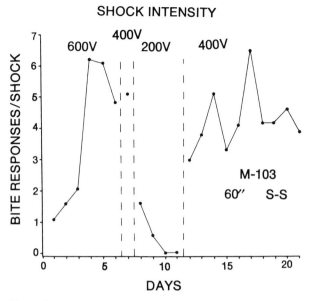

Figure 6   Records for one subject showing increases and decreases in biting attack upon tail shock at the intensities noted. Each point is an average of the total day's bites divided by the number of shocks delivered during that session. No correction for within-session response increments or decrements is provided.

a rate of 2 or 3 per second, independently of specific shock deliveries. It must be emphasized that these were not performances observed initially, but they are typical of terminal performance under these conditions. For example, each of the subjects illustrated showed performance identical to that shown in Figure 4 on the following day. Thus the response elevations appeared recurrently upon repeated exposure to conditions similar to those here illustrated. In Figure 5, the development of such performance is shown for one of the four subjects. Subsequent to 10 days of exposure to the conditions noted, performance assumed the same progressively increased pattern as shown in Figure 4. The performance illustrated on Day 10 is essentially identical to that seen on Day 12, Day 15, and thereafter until the conditions of the experiment were altered. Numerous additional experiments clearly showed us that the conditions necessary for these effects, which we have named facilitation, include the delivery of intense, infrequent electric shock. Stated more precisely, increased shock intensity was shown to produce greater response facilitation effects; additionally, shock frequency must be reduced enough so as not to produce the counter-effect already discussed, that is, response habituation. These experiments are described more thoroughly in Hutchinson, Renfrew, and Young (1971). It was quite

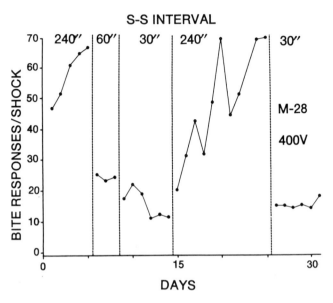

Figure 7   Data from one subject showing increases and decreases in biting attack at the shock-shock intervals noted. Each point is an average of the total day's bites divided by the number of shocks delivered during that session. No correction for within-session response increments or decrements is provided.

clear at this point that two major long-term changes in biting attacks would result upon continued exposure to shocks of certain intensities and frequencies. The effects noted often required several days or weeks to develop. Figures 6 and 7 illustrate this gradual development of increased or reduced responding as a function of both shock intensity and shock frequency. It should also be noted that termination of shock did not produce an immediate reduction in biting: subjects often continued to bite for hours, days, and, in some instances, weeks after shock removal.

These effects are not unique to this response system alone. About three years ago we had the good fortune to observe the occurrence of other behaviour, also produced by electric shock. A small response lever had been installed in one of the removable front panels of the restraint chair. The lever was to be used with other subjects in studies of avoidance behaviour, but was accidentally in place one day during the experimental session for Monkey M-34. This subject was being exposed to electric shocks that were not contingent upon any performance, and biting attacks were being measured. In the left hand portion of Figure 8, the progressive increase in biting attack produced by shocks (response facilitation) is illustrated over a 5-day series of shock deliveries. The lower

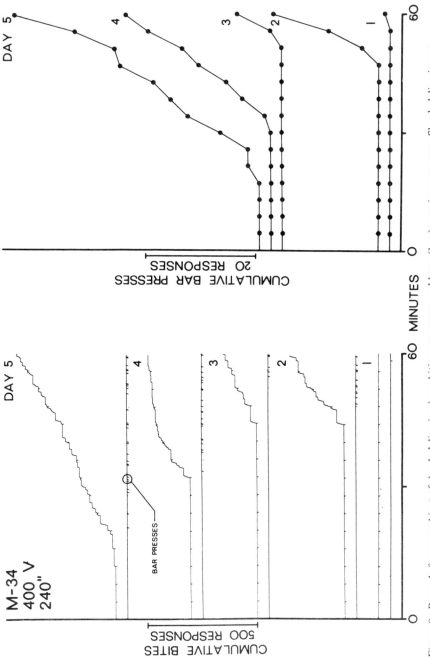

Figure 8 Records for one subject of shock deliveries, hose-biting responses, and lever-(bar-) pressing responses. Shock deliveries are indicated by vertical deflections of the cumulative bite record. Development of increased responding in both modes is shown over five consecutive daily sessions.

of each pair of tracings in this portion of the figure shows the records obtained of lever-pressing concurrent with biting attacks. This lever-pressing is replotted cumulatively in the right portion of the figure, which shows that the same facilitation of responding occurred with lever pressing as with biting attacks. During the subsequent three years, this instance of serendipity led to a number of studies designed to elaborate more fully the conditions of shock delivery that promote lever-pressing. We now know that, in general, the conditions necessary for the continued production and facilitation of this manipulative behaviour are the same as those necessary for the production and facilitation of biting attack, ie, the intermittent delivery of intense electric shocks. Again, we have found large individual differences in the magnitude and temporal pattern of behaviour generated by these conditions. In Figure 9 the performance of subject MC-23 over a period of 43 days of shock exposure is illustrated. It may be seen that this particular subject developed a progressively higher rate of reaction over successive days of exposure until, by Day 43, the overall response rate often exceeded 50 responses per minute. Upon continued shock application, manual lever pressing gradually assumed a characteristic temporal distribution within the intershock interval. These patterns will be discussed in subsequent sections.

Conditional effects

In our earlier studies of biting attack, and in the work with manual manipulative responses, we frequently encountered temporal patterns of behaviour suggesting that the conditions of the experiment associated with shock delivery, that is, the passage of time, might be capable of producing reactions independently of shock delivery. Several studies were initiated to determine whether the classical conditioning of biting attacks was possible. In Figure 10, the average performance for one subject within the intershock interval for an entire session is illustrated. Ten seconds prior to shock, flashing white light was presented. The light and electric shock were coterminous. Subject M-254 came to bite rapidly at the onset of the flashing light and continued, though at a decreased rate, until shock delivery, when the large burst of biting attack responses occurred. Other stimuli, not associated with shock, did not produce the effects seen in Figure 10. Other studies with lever-press and chain-pull responses indicated that these reactions could also be produced by stimuli associated with shock delivery. Figure 11 portrays the results of an experiment, subjects were exposed to 80 seconds of a continuous 1500-Hz tone followed immediately by 80 seconds of continuous light. The light and shock were coterminous. Eventually, Subject MC-13 responded

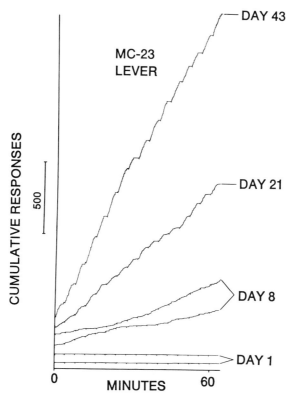

Figure 9 Cumulative records from one subject showing development of increased lever-press responding over successive daily sessions of 400-volt, noncontingent tail shock. Shocks, at 240-second intervals, are indicated by vertical deflections of the cumulative record.

at a higher rate toward the end of the tone stimulus. Responding would decrease briefly in the light stimulus, but increase rapidly as the moment of shock delivery approached. Just before shock however, behaviour tended to decrease or be suppressed. Subsequent to shock, no responses were evident. The effects upon biting attack and manual manipulation responses by stimuli associated with electric shock have in common the characteristics of response production prior to shock delivery. Attack and manipulative responses, however, appear dissimilar immediately subsequent to shock, when biting attacks tend to occur at a high rate very little manual manipulative behaviour is evident. These differences will be discussed more thoroughly in subsequent sections.

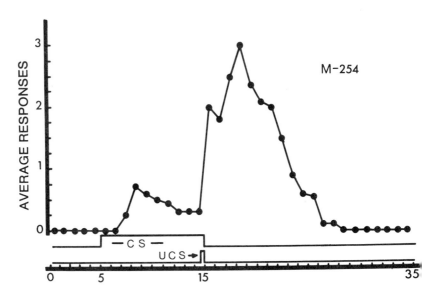

Figure 10   Average bite responding during the inter-shock intervals by one subject in one 60-minute session. The CS was a flashing white light and the UCS was tail shock.

An additional feature was a progressive increase in responding up to slightly before the moment of shock delivery, but with a response reduction or cessation immediately prior to shock. This decrement in responding immediately prior to noncontingent shock delivery is characteristic of the process referred to as conditioned suppression. The suppression phenomenon is a general one, observed in the large majority of cases, in spite of the fact that the decreased performance itself is generated by the same or highly similar stimulus conditions, as is the responding that occurs immediately prior to the suppression. Thus the stimuli associated temporally with shock delivery come to produce both biting attacks and manual manipulative responses, but stimuli even more intimately associated with shock delivery can suppress these same performances.

Responding of the type illustrated in Figure 10 and 11 did not occur only during the delivery of explicit external stimuli. Often, as mentioned earlier, performance came to show a temporal pattern that strongly suggested the same phenomena experimentally illustrated in these tests. For example, in Figure 12 the biting performance of a single subject is shown for an entire experimental session. Shocks were delivered every 4 minutes. During the inter-shock interval, a characteristic pattern of performance was evident. Subsequent to shock, a burst of biting attack respon

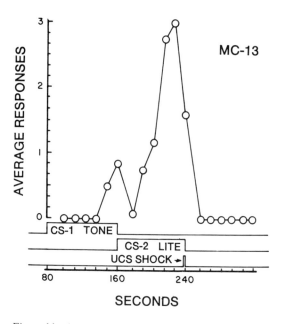

Figure 11   Average lever-press responding prior to shocks during inter-shock intervals/stimuli by one subject during one 60-minute session.

ses occurred for some seconds. Following a period without behaviour, and gradually as the time of next shock approaches, attacks increased in frequency until shortly before shock, when behaviour was absent. A sample segment of this performance is magnified in the lower right-hand section of the figure. In Figure 13 the temporal pattern frequently seen of lever-press responding is illustrated for one subject for an entire experimental session. At this point it is crucial to remember that all shocks were delivered without regard to performance of the subject. That is, they were not contingent upon behaviour. The figure illustrates quite clearly the progressive increase in response frequencies up to slightly before the moment of shock delivery, with suppression occurring immediately prior to shock. Subsequent to shock little behaviour was evident. Three separate inter-shock intervals have been chosen. It can be noted that the lengthened intervals contributed to higher overall response rates.

Differential influences of stimuli upon different response classes

So far, we have shown that the direct delivery of electric shock can produce biting attacks and/or manual manipulation responses, and that each

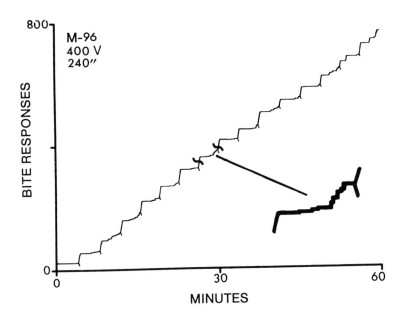

Figure 12 Cumulative record of biting attack by a single subject during one session of noncontingent shocks, indicated by vertical deflections of the record. A characteristic segment of inter-shock responding, showing a burst of biting as shock time approaches, is shown magnified in the lower right.

of these phenomena may habituate to continuing exposure to high frequency, low intensity shocks or may show progressive facilitation if high intensity, infrequent shocks are delivered. Further, we have seen that both of these classes of behaviour may be produced by stimuli associated temporally with shock deliveries. Also, even in the absence of external stimuli, temporal conditioning develops. Additionally, these performances each illustrate an additional complexity in that they frequently reflect a suppression immediately before shock delivery. Though not discussed explicitly so far, several comparisons between Figures 10 and 11, and between Figures 12 and 13, clearly illustrate separate and dissimilar temporal patterns of biting attack and manual manipulation.

In fact, when both responses are simultaneously available, predictable but dissimilar concurrent performances develop. Figure 14 provides examples of concurrent biting attack and manual chain-pulling or lever-pressing by four subjects for an entire experimental session. The left panel of this figure illustrates the actual cumulative records. The overall pattern of performances was characterized by high-frequency biting im-

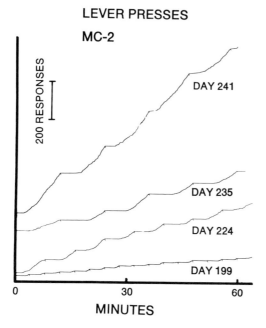

Figure 13   Cumulative records of lever-press responding by a single subject exposed to one-hour daily sessions of non-contingent shock for a prolonged period. The inter-shock interval was 4 minutes on Day 199, 8 minutes on Day 224, and 12 minutes on Days 235 and 241.

mediately following shock, with a reduction in biting until later in the interval. Response frequency for the manual manipulative responses was low immediately subsequent to shock and became progressively higher as the next shock approached. Occasionally, even when both manual manipulation and biting attack responses were available, some subjects showed a measurable degree of attack prior to shock delivery. For example, Subjects MC-28 and MC-13 each showed some biting prior to shock. Immediately subsequent to shock, however, manual manipulative responding was absent and the relative frequency of behaviour shifted towards biting attack. These performances are summarized in the right-hand portion of Figure 14.

It may be noted that responding immediately prior to shock was less compared with responding earlier. Thus the suppression phenomenon was evident even in the concurrent response situation. The data in Figure 14 illustrate that the response classes of biting attack and manual manipulation are separable, not only on the basis of topographical con-

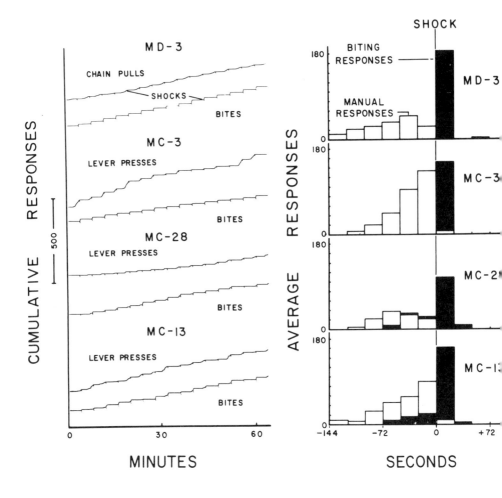

Figure 14   Concurrent biting-attack and manual responses by four subjects during single, 60-minute sessions of noncontingent tail shock at 240-second intervals. Actual cumulative records are shown on the left, and entire session averages of pre- and post-shock responding are summarized on the right.

sideration, but, perhaps more importantly, on the basis of the differential influences of shock. Manual manipulative responding by all subjects did, at some point prior to shock, exceed the performance of biting attack in relative probability, whereas subsequent to shock delivery, the relative probability of biting attack exceeded that of manual manipulation for all subjects. This shift in the relative probabilities of the two concurrent performances serves to argue strongly that the effects are no

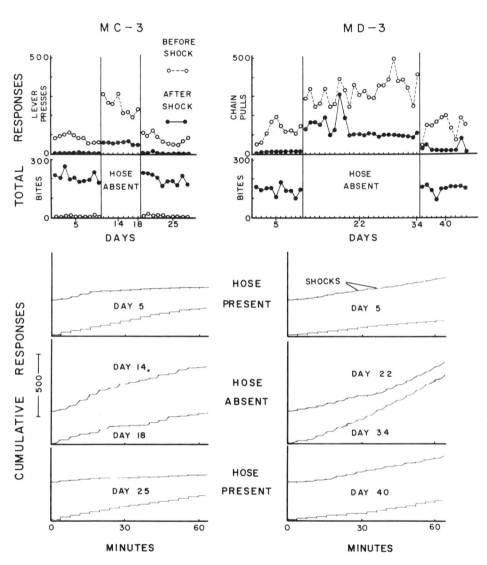

Figure 15   Manual responding by two subjects, each with and without access to a rubber bite hose. On Days 5, 25, and 40, the upper cumulative record is of manual responding and the lower record is of biting. On Days 14, 18, 22, and 34, the cumulative record is of manual responding. On all cumulative records, shock deliveries are indicated by vertical deflections.

due to idiosyncratic elements of chamber design or response sensor dimensions. In fact, the data suggest that the class of performance character-

ized as movement through, and manual manipulation of, the environment is the class of response that strongly predominates prior to the oc
currence of a noxious event. Alternatively, the data suggest that movement through, and biting attack upon, the environment predominates
over other reaction tendencies subsequent to the occurrence of a noxious event. In addition, both reaction patterns show a general suppression immediately before the noxious event.

What of a situation in which both responses are not possible? More re
cently we have conducted several experiments designed to assess the in
fluence upon manual manipulative responding of the presence and absence of the opportunity for biting attack. These data are reported by
Hutchinson and Emley (1971). In Figure 15 the performance of two re
presentative animals is illustrated. The upper figures demonstrate the
total daily emission of both manual manipulation and biting attack responses before and after shock over successive days of testing. During
this series of tests the rubber hose was removed from the chamber for a
period of days and the effect of such removal upon the lever-press and
chain-pull responses for the two subjects was assessed. The conditions c
before shock and after shock represent an arbitrary bisection of the inter-shock interval into a first and last half. This has been found suitable
for differentiating the anticipatory responding ordinarily shown in the
manual manipulative mode from the biting attack reactions seen after
shock. The upper portions of Figure 15 show that the large majority of
manipulative responses occurred before shock, whereas biting attacks
occurred almost exclusively after shock. After removal of the rubber
hose marked changes occurred in the manual response performances.
Now, both subjects showed response flurries on the chain and lever sub
sequent to shock. It can be seen that this post-shock manipulative responding was raised considerably in the absence of a hose. In one case
(MD-3), the post-shock manipulative responses approximately equalled
the previous post-shock biting reactions when a hose had been available
An additional and more intriguing result was the marked elevation of
before-shock manipulative responding during the hose-absent condition
In the lower portion of Figure 15, sample cumulative records are show
for typical days during each of the three conditions. In the centre most
plots, two separate days of manipulative responding are illustrated. It
may be seen that the frequency of pre-shock manual manipulations was
considerably increased during hose absence. These responses in no way
represent the additional accrual of biting attacks toward the response
lever. Observations confirmed that these did not occur. Furthermore,
for several tests, a neck-yoke restraint device prevented the head from
contacting the lever or chain.

The data of Figure 15 suggest that the absence of the opportunity to engage in biting attack markedly elevates the tendency to engage in anticipatory manual manipulations prior to shock and, additionally, fosters the production of post-shock manual response bursting. The increments in both pre-shock and post-shock manipulative responding by removal of the hose seem to mimic rather closely the effects often observed upon manipulative responding subsequent to the increase in shock intensity, providing strong presumptive evidence that biting actually serves to reduce certain of the effects of shock delivery.

SOME DIFFERENTIAL EFFECTS OF SEVERAL DRUGS UPON DIFFERENT
RESPONSE CLASSES

In the experiments described so far, each of two grossly different topographical performances was controlled by the same event, the response-independent delivery of electric shock or stimuli associated with shock. As this work has progressed and we have come to understand a little more about pre-shock performances, it appears more likely that the manual manipulative behaviours prior to shock might reflect certain basic motivational or 'emotional' processes normally interacting with contingency programme during punishment or escape and avoidance conditioning. We came to suspect that these anticipatory performances represented a reinforcement-free index of the strength of unconditional and conditional noxiousness or aversiveness.

In recent experiments, discussed in detail in Emley and Hutchinson (1970), several pharmacological agents have been administered to subjects exhibiting shock-maintained behaviour. In Figure 16, representative performances from four subjects, each exposed to a separate pharmacological compound, are illustrated. The dose-response curves for the four compounds, as they have influenced biting-attack and lever-press performances, are given separately. It may be seen that morphine produced progressive decreases in both biting attack and lever-pressing. Chlorpromazine progressively suppressed biting-attack performance but actually enhanced pre-shock lever-pressing throughout the range of its suppressive effect upon biting attacks. The usual effect of chlordiazepoxide was to enhance pre-shock lever-pressing in dosage ranges that had relatively little effect upon biting attack. At a higher dosage, however, both biting attacks and lever-presses were suppressed. With amphetamine, both biting attack and pre-shock lever-pressing were progressively elevated until biting attacks were abruptly suppressed, even at dosages that maintained an exceptional degree of pre-shock lever-pressing. At yet higher dosages, le-

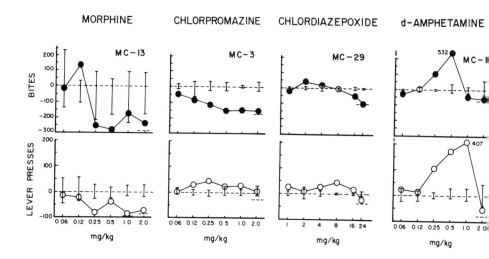

Figure 16   Relative biting attack and lever pressing by four subjects under the influence of the compounds and dosages indicated. The full-width dashed lines indicate the average saline-control behavioural levels for each subject and response, while ranges are shown by the vertical lines. Zero-level behaviour is indicated by the short dashed lines at the right of each frame.

ver-pressing was also depressed. The control ranges indicated in Figure 16 were those for the preceding saline control days. Drug testing was conducted each Wednesday of a five-day experimental week.

It has been exciting to have two concurrent performances of a subject differentially affected by the same drug at the same dosage during the same experimental session. The exceptional experimental power attendant upon such built-in control procedures warrants consideration in further investigations by others interested in the effects of chemical compounds on such indices of aversive-stimulus motivated behaviours.

DISCUSSION

Prolonged exposure to intense, infrequent electric shock has been shown to produce two distinguishable response patterns. The behaviours of both attack and manual manipulation were shown to increase progressively, not only over successive instances of shock, but also over successive sessions. The temporal and intensive properties of this facilitation process suggest that the effect is, at least in part, humourally mediated. This seems possible because the accelerated responding typically occurs between 20 and 40 minutes after shock exposure commences. Others working with the avoidance paradigm, have reported similar response changes (Hoffman, Fleshler, and Chorny, 1961). In the present work, the effects are shown not to be limited to performances maintained momentarily by consequence control. Rather, the faciltation process appears general to at least several different response systems.

Progressive increases in both manual manipulation and biting attack up to the moment of shock occur in a temporal conditioning situation, or during explicit instatement of discrete shock-paired stimuli. With both of these conditioning effects, however, stimuli most closely associated with the shock produced response suppression or reduction. Thus a progressive increase in some aspect of conditional stimulation results in a general progressively heightened tendency toward action until, at maximal levels, a major inversion to suppression occurs.

An analysis of the temporal and intensive interactions between biting attack and manual manipulation demonstrated a characteristic pattern of interaction between performances for all subjects. Generally, manual manipulative responses became progressively elevated toward the moment of shock. Additionally, there was some biting attack, though to a relatively lesser degree, which also increased toward the moment of shock. Each of these response classes was often reduced or absent immediately before shock. Subsequent to shock, biting attacks predominated over both behaviours and progressively decreased over succeeding seconds.

In the past, we have attempted to provide a rationale for viewing biting attack behaviour as a sensitive and valid index of more naturalistic attack reactions. The anticipatory manipulative responding seems likely to be our index of escape or flight tendency free of contingency influences through shock reduction or elimination. Though this is a speculative and largely unsupported assumption, if eventually supported it will allow data from the present discussion to form the basis for an important, experimentally based statement of the temporal and intensive relations between escape and attack performances. We may then have a suitable model for the study of the temporal and intensive interactions between 'fleeing,' 'freezing,' and 'fighting.'

Evidence does exist to suggest that the anticipatory manual responding described is closely related to escape or avoidance behaviour. The facilitation process already discussed closely parallels the 'warm-up' effects during Sidman avoidance performance, reported and discussed by Hoffman, Fleshler, and Chorny (1961). The temporal pattern of respond ing seen here bears a close similarity to that shown by Anger (1963), Sid man (1966), and Hoffman (1966) for avoidance performance. The tendency towards response suppression or reduction immediately before shock, though only infrequently observable in the situation where a response terminates or postpones shock occurrences, has nevertheless been reported and discussed previously (Hoffman, 1966). Thus, the patterns of performance during both initial and terminal conditions, as illustrated in the present paper, bear a striking and consistent similarity to performances that are in part dependent upon the contingent control of shock reduction or removal, that is, escape and avoidance performance. Though in no way constituting proof, such regularities provide additional reason to pursue the possibility that the manual behaviours observed under free shock conditions are in fact an accurate index of escape or avoidance 'motivation'.

The similarities reported here between response-independent, shock-produced behaviours and behaviour attributed to contingent shock control, place a constraint on estimates of the nature and/or degree of control actually exerted by the contingency itself in such situations (Morse and Kelleher, 1966; Kelleher and Morse, 1968b; McKearney, 1968, 1969). In fact, free-shock testing subsequent to avoidance has produced performances like those reported here (Kelleher, Riddle, and Cook, 1963; Sidman, Herrnstein, and Conrad, 1957; Sidman, 1960; Byrd, 1969). A more detailed discussion of this point may be found in Hutchinson, Renfrew, and Young (1971).

To the extent that the performances studied here actually index general reaction tendencies occurring in the natural repertoire of organisms, the experimental paradigms may be helpful in other studies of theoretical and practical interest. For example, we have illustrated reliable differences between the effects of different, commonly employed psychotropic compounds upon these several shock-generated performance baselines. Hopefully, results of other studies similar to these will be available in the near future.

To this point we have illustrated how we came to discover several features of and interactions between anticipatory manual responses and the more 'reflexive' attack reactions to the intense shock stimulus. What would be the effect of other powerful recurrent stimuli, perhaps even of a positive reinforcing type? About a year ago we put this and related questions into experimental terms. Squirrel monkeys were partially restrained as described earlier in this paper except that tail electrodes were not applied. They were food deprived and tested for 1 hour daily. Bana-

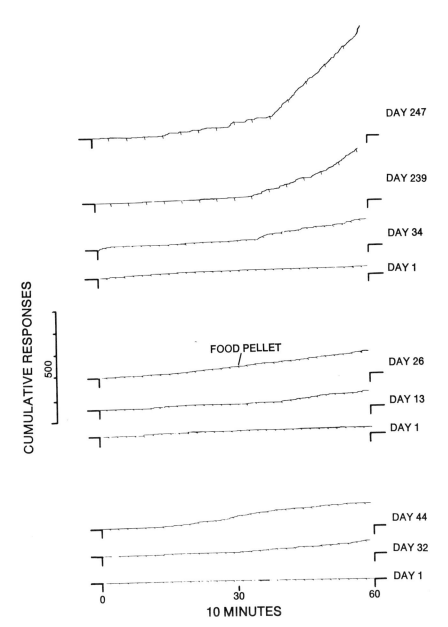

Figure 17   Sample cumulative records of performance of three squirrel monkey subjects over successive days of exposure to the response-independent delivery of food pellets. Each subject was food deprived and maintained at 70-80 per cent of its free feeding weight. Pellet deliveries are indicated by the downward vertical deflections on the response pen tracing.

na and regular-flavoured Noyes food pellets of various sizes from 45 to 300 mg were then delivered on a response-independent fixed-time schedule. Within the chamber was a small rodent response lever, and/or an overhead chain mounted similarly to that used for the shock studies. We were amazed to discover that the recurrent delivery of food pellets gradually produced more and more manual responding. Figure 17 presents some of the data for three of six subjects thus tested. Each subject showed a gradual increase in responding over subsequent test sessions. Each subject showed also a characteristic gradually developing pattern of responding within the inter-pellet interval. Shortly after pellet delivery a burst of responding occurred. Response rate was low until later in the interval when it again increased until slightly before the time of the next pellet delivery, when responding was again suppressed. Thus the pattern of manual responding generated by the response-independent delivery of positive reinforcement is similar, if not identical, to behaviour shown to have evolved in an identical environment upon the delivery of response-independent electric shock. (Refer to Figure 15 during those days when no hose was available.)

We are exploring these effects and how they may relate to patterns of performance generated by response-contingent schedules of the same reinforcers. We are certain, at least at the present time, that in schedules of positive reinforcement there are powerful eliciting and other response-generating effects that are not directly or indirectly the result of the contingency but, rather, the direct effect of simply arranging contact between the organism and a powerful stimulus. What is the true topographic and functional breadth of reactions generated following food pellet delivery during deprivation, an electric shock, or other strong 'biologically relevant' stimuli? Similarly, what breadth of reaction topographies and what functional interrelationships occur in anticipation of strong events such as food and shock? These are questions that we are only now beginning to answer. Our findings on these and related questions will almost certainly provide assistance toward a greater understanding of a variety of individual and social behaviours.

COMMENTS

Hutchinson and Emley conclude their account of behaviour maintained by response-independent electric shocks by describing informal observations of a similar phenomenon occasioned by response-independent schedules of *positive* reinforcement. We can supplement these observations with more formal data collected from pigeons in the laboratory of Dr C.G. Miles.

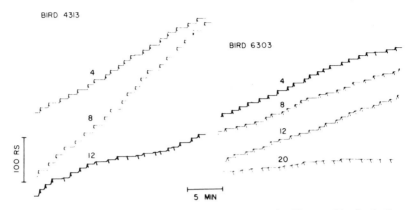

Figure 1   Characteristic segments of cumulative records of key-pecking for both birds from a session on each of the three or four non-contingent schedule conditions received. Each food presentation (marked by a blip of the recording pen) was preceded by the onset of the key-light (not marked.) The duration of this pre-food stimulus (4, 8, 12, or 20 seconds) is indicated for each record.

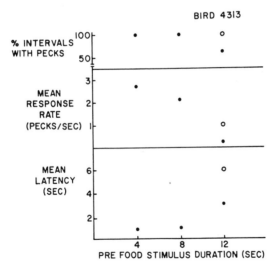

Figure 2   Bottom, mean latency (time to first response following stimulus onset); middle, response rate during stimulus; and top, per cent of stimulus intervals in which keypecking occurred. Open circles represent data from the response-contingent schedule.

Stimulated by the study of Brown and Jenkins (1968) on autoshaping in the pigeon, we have examined differences in pigeons' pecking behaviour on contingent and non-contingent (response-dependent and response-independent in Hutchinson and Emley's terms) schedules of grain-reinforcement. Our procedure was similar to the fixed trial condition (Experiment 4) reported by Brown and Jenkins, in which the pre-food stimulus remained on for eight seconds prior to food presentation, even if key-pecking occurred. Several of their birds developed high rates of pecking in this stimulus.

We examined the relationship between the duration of pre-food stimulus (a white key-light) and the pecking maintained by it. In the non-contingent conditions grain was delivered on a 64-second variable-interval schedule, with the key-light coming on 4, 8, 12, or 20 seconds before food presentation and remaining on until the 4-second reinforcement period ended. At other times the key was dark. One response-contingent schedule, corresponding to the 12-second pre-food stimulus condition, has been examined (a multiple EXT FI 12-second schedule).

Figure 1 shows cumulative records of key pecking during the pre-food stimulus for the two birds studied. In Figure 2 are average data for one of these birds, and despite considerable individual differences, the changes in behaviour for both birds were similar. Three measures are of interest — the number of intervals (out of 60 per session) in which pecking occurred; the number of pecks made during the stimulus; and the time to the first peck (latency) following the onset of the key-light. As well as the recorded changes shown in the figures, other differences in behaviour were observed. On the non-contingent schedules, 'pecking' behaviour was maintained throughout the pre-food stimulus; however, only when the interval was relatively short was this pecking on the key and therefore recorded. On the response-contingent schedule, pecking on either topography (on or off the key) did not always begin as soon as the stimulus came on; in other words, more typical FI behaviour seemed to develop.

Comparing the data from the contingent and non-contingent conditions shown in Figure 2, we find that response rate increased when the contingency was added even though the time to the first key peck had increased as well, indicating that now more of the pecking during the later part of stimulus intervals was on the key.

9 Side-effects of aversive control

R. ULRICH, S. DULANEY, T. KUCERA, and A. COLASACCO

A FUNCTIONAL DEFINITION OF AGGRESSION

One of the most noteworthy side-effects of aversive control is aggression. Although some early investigations of aggression were conducted under controlled laboratory conditions (O'Kelly and Steckle, 1939; Daniel, 1943; Miller, 1948), most of the information gained from an experimental analysis of aggression has been collected over the past decade. This research has led to the identification of several causes of aggression that occur as a result of various environmental conditions.

For purposes of laboratory and naturalistic observation and experimentation, aggression may be defined as behaviour associated with the presentation of aversive stimulation to another organism. Associated is emphasized because many behaviours fall under the category of being associated with presenting aversive stimulation to another animal but, in fact, never result in injury. Both ritualized fighting and attack against an inanimate object fall into this category, and thus may be termed aggressive. This definition avoids referral to motivational factors such as an intent to injure or a deliberate action. With this definition, behaviours that may be primarily instinctive could be termed aggressive. In fact, a form of aggression first extensively examined under laboratory conditions appears to have many instinctive or unconditioned characteristics.

The research reported in this paper was conducted at the Behavior Research and Development Center at Western Michigan University and was supported by the Office of Naval Research (#N00014-67-0421-0001), the National Institute of Mental Health (#R01-MH18036-01), the Western Michigan Univeristy Research Fund, and the Michigan Department of Mental Health. The authors wish to thank Darwin Stier, Jim Scherrer, Bob Pierce, Madolyn Lewis, Lynn Peters, and Jack Orr for their assistance in conducting this research and Lois Speck and Marie Harris for their help in the preparation of the manuscript.

UNCONDITIONED AGGRESSION

A series of experiments described in 1962 by Ulrich and Azrin identifie
and labelled a particular class of responses as 'pain-elicited aggression.'[1]
This was not the first report of such a phenomenon, however. Other ex
perimenters have observed individual cases: O'Kelly and Steckle (1939)
reported that when long sequences of intermittent shock were delivered
through the floor to six rats, they would pair off and fight. Except for
one attempted replication (Daniel, 1943) this research was not pursued
Scott (1946) noted that as soon as young mice have teeth they will attempt to bite anything that pinches their tails. He also observed (Scott
and Fredericson, 1951) that the painful stimulation received by a peace
fule male mouse when attacked will produce fighting.

The experiments of Ulrich and Azrin revealed a more general phenomenon: when animals are paired and presented with certain levels of nc
contingent, aversive stimulation, the animals immediately and reliably
begin to fight each other. For the species studied, the fighting was topo
graphically similar to fighting and attack behaviours observed in natural
environments, occurred whether the subjects were of same or different
strain, species, or sex.

Most of the research reported by Ulrich and Azrin (1962) used electric shock as the aggression producing stimulus; however, this report
and subsequent experiments have shown that other stimuli also produc
pain aggression reactions. These stimuli include externally delivered
shock through the feet or tail, back shock through implanted electrode
heated floors, and tail pinches. These data have been reviewed by Ulrich
(1966) and Ulrich, Hutchinson, and Azrin (1965). Subsequent investiga
tions of pain-aggression reactions employed electric shock as the agres-
sion-producing stimulus because it allowed more versatility and accurac
as an independent variable than other stimuli.

Two experimental procedures

Before discussing the general results of pain-aggression investigation, it
may be valuable to explain the two most common methods of experimentation.

1 / Since that time the terms 'pain' or painful events have been used as a description of a particular level of aversive stimulation capable of producing aggression.
Thus, the class of painful stimuli is included in the larger class of aversive stimuli
(ie, some stimulus intensities will produce and maintain escape or avoidance behaviour through the termination or postponement of the stimulus, but will not
produce aggression).

Paired-subject designs

Initial experiments of pain-aggression involved the placement of two rats in an enclosure equipped to deliver foot-shock through a grid floor. When shocked, the rats typically assumed a 'stereotyped fighting posture' by rearing on their hind legs, facing each other, and directing striking or biting movements toward each other. Lunging at the other from the stereotyped posture frequently caused one or both rats to tumble to the floor. (Jumping may have been primarily a function of the particular aversive stimulus used to elecit fighting, and not necessarily an actual component of the fighting response. In our laboratory, it has not been observed when paired rats are shocked through a tail shock apparatus. Baenninger and Grossman (1969) reported no jumping as part of an aggressive exchange when tail pinches were used to elicit fighting and stereotyped postures instead of grid-shock to the feet.) When the interval between shocks was long, the rats returned to their normal positions (all four feet on the floor) and ceased fighting. When another shock was delivered, both rats moved from their 'relaxed' position into the stereotyped fighting posture. When the interval between shocks was short, rats often remained facing each other, standing on their hind feet for most of the session. As shocks were presented, the upright rats began to strike and bite each other. Although this behaviour ceased shortly after shock termination, the rats remained 'prepared' for the next shock. In each case the aggressive response observed in these experiments is topographically very similar to the aggressive behaviour of wild rats in natural settings (Eibl-Eibesfeldt, 1961; Lorenz, 1966).

Although this basic experimental design has been used primarily in studies of aggression with rats as subjects, it has also been used to study the occurrence of pain-aggression reactions in other paired animals, including cats, snakes, hamsters, squirrel monkeys, turtles, mice, and chickens (Ulrich, Hutchinson, and Azrin, 1965). In addition to pairs consisting of two like species, pain-aggression reactions have been observed when pairs where of different species. Cats, rats, hamsters, snakes, squirrel monkeys, opossum, and raccoons have all been observed to attack a member of another species when shocked (Ulrich, Hutchinson, and Azrin, 1965; Ulrich, Wolff, and Azrin, 1964).

Single-subject designs

Shortly after the first results of paired-subject pain-aggression research were reported, another method for the study of aggression was developed.

In 1964 Azrin, Hutchinson, and Sallery reported that squirrel monkeys would attack inanimate objects as well as live animals. This information was vauluable for several reasons. Previous research indicated that squirrel monkeys would indeed attack each other when shocked in paired-subject experiments, but, unlike rats, they continued to fight each other well past shock termination and had to be physically separated by the experimenters to avoid the serious injury that inevitably occurred when fighting was allowed to continue (Azrin, Hutchinson, and Hake, 1963). When an inanimate object was used, the attack responses of the single monkey were closely tied to the presentation of the aversive stimulus. Thus, the excessive amount of fighting observed in paired situations was probably related to increased aversive stimulation generated by reciprocal attacks or counter aggression.

Azrin, Hutchinson, and Sallery (1964) reported an automated method for the study of aggression. By placing a squirrel monkey in a restraining chair equipped with a tail-shock apparatus (Hake and Azrin, 1963) and an attackable inanimate object, attack behaviour could be recorded automatically, thus alleviating some of the necessity for constant observation and manual recording of aggression. A tennis ball suspended from the top of the restraining chair could be bitten by the monkey by grasping the ball and pulling the ball to its mouth. This movement of the ball closed a microswitch and recorded the occurrence of a biting attack.

This method, using a restraining chair and tennis ball, was also used to study the effects of another type of aversive stimulus – a tail pinch (Azrin, Hake, and Hutchinson, 1965). Hutchinson, Azrin, and Hake (1966) discussed some of the technical problems this design failed to eliminate. They reported that the tennis ball design could automatically 'determine the existence or non-existence of attack but could not measure frequency, duration or intensity.' For example, the amount of time the monkey held the ball near its face was not an accurate measure of the amount of biting attack. To gain information on the duration or frequency of biting, experimenters were still obliged to observe the subjects.

In place of the tennis ball assembly, Hutchinson et al (1966) proposed a bite-hose apparatus. When the monkey bit the hose the volume of air in the hose was displaced. By attaching different sensing devices to the bite-hose assembly, it was possible to record frequency, duration, and intensity of biting attacks accurately. This recording method is still used in most of the experiments designed to study pain-aggression ins squirrel monkeys.

The single-subject design has not been extended to the study of pain-aggression in other animals, with the exception of a recent report of an apparatus for the measurement of the biting attack of a restrained rat (Azrin, Rubin, and Hutchinson, 1968).

Some general results from the two designs

Using shock (though other stimuli have produced similar effects) and employing one of the two basic designs (usually paired subjects are rats, and single subjects are squirrel monkeys), many parametric and quantitative differences have been observed, but both designs have demonstrated generally similar effects of different variables on the pain-aggression reaction.

Scheduling influences

Shock frequency

The number of aggressive responses recorded is a direct function of the frequency of shock presentation: the more frequent the shock, the higher the probability of aggression, both in foot-shocked paired rats, (Ulrich and Azrin, 1962) and tail-shocked restrained monkeys (Hutchinson, Azrin, and Renfrew, 1968).

Also relevant to shock frequency is the temporal relationship of aggression to shock presentation. Ulrich and Azrin (1962) noted that rats would assume a stereotyped fighting posture would upon shock presentation and that the fighting episode rarely lasted longer than one second. Subsequent experiments have verified the fact that probability of attack (Azrin, Hutchinson, and Sallery, 1964), frequency of biting or number of bites (Hutchinson, Azrin, and Renfrew, 1968), and percentage of time spent biting (Azrin, Rubin, and Hutchinson, 1968) all decreases with time since the last shock. Thus, aggression is inversely related to the time since shock delivery.

Shock duration

Within certain bounds, shock duration also has a direct effect on the amount of pain-induced aggression. Optimal shock duration for producing aggression in paired rats has been found to be approximately 0.5 to 3 seconds. Within this range the longer durations decreased in effectiveness over continued shock deliveries, with slightly less initial effectiveness, shorter durations has the opposite effect (Azrin, Ulrich, Hutchinson, and Norman, 1964). By using various shock intensities and shock-

shock intervals, Hutchinson, Azrin, and Renfrew (1968) showed biting attack of squirrel monkeys to increase as shock duration increased from 0.1 seconds to 0.8 seconds.

Shock intensity

Increasing intensities of shock have produced increasing aggression in paired rats (Ulrich and Azrin, 1962), paired cats (Ulrich, Wolff, and Azrin, 1964), and squirrel monkeys (Hutchinson, Azrin, and Renfrew, 1968). In all cases, this direct functional relationship occurs within limits: very weak intensities produce no attack, whereas very strong intensities debilitate subjects, and also produce no attack. A similar functional relationship has been reported when a tail pinch served as the aggression-producing stimulus. As the intensity of the tail pinch was delivered to restrained squirrel monkeys was increased from 10 to 60 pounds per square inch, the probability of attack also increased (Azrin, Hake and Hutchinson, 1965).

Degree of contact with the target of aggression

If the probability of contact between the subject and the object of attack (animate or inanimate) is high, the probability of attack is also high. Ulrich and Azrin (1962) found that decreasing the floor space alotted to paired rats increased the amount of fighting to shock, primarily because the closeness of quarters assured that the rats would be in physical proximity at shock onset. When floor area is held constant but the number of rats in that area is increased, more fighting also results (Antal and Kemeny, 1964; Ulrich and Azrin, 1962).

Another method of altering the degree of contact between paired rats is to impair sensory receptors. When rats were blinded and then shocked the amount of fighting was less than before. Rats blinded by eye removal fought more than rats who were merely hooded; this was related to the fact that the hoods also covered the rats whiskers. Actual removal of both the eyes and whiskers further decreased fighting (Flory, Ulrich, and Wolff, 1965).

Although initial research indicated that previous familiarity of paired rats had no obvious effect on pain-aggression reactions (Ulrich and Azrin, 1962), later investigations showed the amount of aggressiveness in paired rats to be related to their degree of social contact and interaction (Hutchinson, Ulrich, and Azrin, 1965). Rats that were socially isolated until mature showed less frequent aggressive reactions to shock than rats raised under community conditions. Also, when rats (even those raised in isolation) were exposed to many daily sessions of shock presentation, they fought more often and more intensely than rats of the same age that had not had the experience. Thus, the authors acknowledge 'the extensive influence exerted by a prior history of elicited aggression upon the current probability of elicited aggression' (Hutchinson, Ulrich, and Azrin, 1965).

The degree of contact with an inanimate target of aggression is frequently controlled by the design of the apparatus. Original designs of a restraining chair-bite hose assembly insured the subject's orientation and proximity to the object of attack (Hutchinson, Azrin, and Hake, 1966). A more recent record apparatus design for study of shock-induced biting attack of rats also forces the subject to face the target (Azrin, Rubin, and Hutchinson, 1968). In the case of restrained squirrel monkeys, the occurrence of biting attack is not dependent upon this control. Tail-shocked squirrel monkeys will bite a rubber hose or a tennis ball without the restraint of the neck yoke. No published data allow comparison of hose biting performances with and without the neck yoke, thus the effect of the controlled orientation is not available.

Other data show that if an attackable object is not immediately available, a squirrel monkey will, when shocked, emit an operant response to gain access to such an object. Further, a monkey will make necessary discriminations to emit the correct operant response (Azrin, Hutchinson, and McLaughlin, 1965). Thus, when aversively stimulated, contact with an attackable object may assume the role of an operant reinforcer.

RESPONDENT CONDITIONING OF PAIN-AGGRESSION

The first investigators to report the occurrence of pain-aggression reactions were also the first to report (though indirectly) the classical or respondent conditioning of that phenomenon. In 1939 O'Kelly and Steckle found not only that rats would pair off and fight when shocked, but also that these rats eventually began to pair off and fight in response to the sound of the motor operating the timer that regulated shock presentations.

Ulrich, Hutchinson, and Azrin (1965) discussed an early, unpublished study that also obtained what might be interpreted as respondent conditioning of pain-aggression. In that study, two rats were isolated at eighteen days of age and brought together only for daily sessions. Thus, the only time these subjects saw another rats was during a daily period in which aggression-producing shock was delivered every three seconds. Not only was shock always associated with the presence of another rat, but, because of the frequency of shock, any of the other animal's movements always closely preceded another shock. Later, both subjects were placed in a shock free situation with two naive rats. For two days after the subjects were placed in this situation, any movement or noise by another rat immediately produced a fighting posture and occasional striking responses. Apparently, the presence of another rat had itself become capable of producing some aggressive reactions.

In more recent studies, experimenters have been able to classically condition pain-aggression reactions in paired rats (Creer, Hitzing, and Schaeffer, 1966; Vernon and Ulrich, 1966). Creer *et al* (1966) found the stereotyped fighting posture easier to condition than actual fighting responses, though both were observed. They also noted the importance of the intensity of the conditioned stimulus: a 45-db, 60-Hz buzzer was insufficient to elicit a fighting response, even after many CS-UCS pairings. When an 80-db, 4000-Hz buzzer was repeatedly paired with the UCS, fighting responses did occur to the buzzer. Creer *et al* also demonstrated that pain-aggression reactions could be conditioned using either a simultaneous conditioning procedure (CS and UCS began and terminated together) or a delayed conditioning procedure (CS preceded UCS, both terminated together). Using a 60-db, 1320-Hz auditory stimulus, Vernon and Ulrich (1966) demonstrated the importance of the UCS intensity. Eighteen rats were paired and randomly assigned to one of three groups (three pairs in each group). The pairs in each group were exposed to the same delayed conditioning procedure except for the intensity of the UCS. The shock intensities used were 2.0 mA, 2.5mA, and 3.0mA. Consistent with previous data (Ulrich and Azrin, 1962), pairs in the 2.0 mA, group fought more often to shock (UCS) than did the 2.5-mA group, who in turn fought more often than the 3.0 mA group. These results were expected because it had been shown that 2mA is the optimal intensity for producing pain-aggression reactions. The same relation also held for the CS alone trials. When the CS was presented alone, rats from the 2.0-mA group still fought more often than did the 2.5-mA group, who fought more than the 3.0-mA group.

OPERANT CONDITIONING OF AGGRESSION

Thus far, various functional relationships have been reviewed that are relevant to certain antecedent environmental events and the resulting behaviour, specifically, aggression. Some of these environmental events have a direct influence, such as various shock intensities, durations, and schedules of presentation. Other events have a more indirect influence, such as a history of contact with either the aversive stimulus or the object of attack, or a history of prior association with aggression-producing situations, as in classical conditioning of aggression.

Aggression, like most other complex behaviours, may also be influenced by consequent environmental events. Operant conditioning of aggression represents another casual relationship between environmental events and aggressive behaviour. Several experimenters have been able to shape and maintain aggressive behaviour through positive reinforcement, but some of these also report the occurrence of what appears to be unconditioned aggressive reactions that interact with and sometimes temporarily outweigh the operant response. For example, Reynolds, Catania, and Skinner (1963) established aggressive responding in food-deprived pigeons by making food available upon successive approximations to pecking the head of another pigeon. By selective reinforcement during different environmental conditions, stimulus control of aggression was established. When the chamber was illuminated with a blue light, one pigeon of the pair attacked its partner, and when the chamber was illuminated with a green light the other pigeon attacked. During a 'neutral' white light, however, one pair of subjects often engaged in violent unconditioned fighting. Although this behaviour was not specified in the reinforcement schedule, and appeared to be elicited by the behaviour of the other subject, it was still possible to control it by operant techniques. When Reynolds *et al* reinforced going to opposing corners when the white light came on, unconditioned fighting ceased. The experimenters noted another possible occurrence of unconditioned aggression. When one pigeon attacked the other to gain food reinforcement, the target of attack retaliated with more aggression or with vigorous defensive responses to the extent that the two birds continued to fight even after food was made available. Recognizing the interaction of several variables, the authors drew the following conclusion regarding conditioned and unconditioned aggression: 'The aggression shaped by the experimenter does not take on the characteristics of the instinctive pattern. It simply brings the bird into a situation which may release unconditioned fighting ... The experiment seems to show that aggressive patterns can be shaped and maintained by reinforcement, and that the frequency of both conditioned and unconditioned patterns may be controlled by presenting or withholding reinforcement' (Reynolds, Catania, and Skinner, 1963, p. 74).

Ulrich, Johnston, Richardson, and Wolff (1963) selected a comparatively docile strain of rats (Sprague-Dawley) and shaped aggressive responding in a water-deprived experimental rat toward his partner (a control animal that was not water deprived) by making water contingent upon attack. When the experimental rat made the required attack, the control animal remained submissive, often moving away and occasionally squeaking. When two experimental animals were paired, attack responses increased in duration and intensity. Like the pigeons, a similar relationship was observed between the conditioned and unconditioned fighting of rats: 'The experimental animals would often grapple with each other and continue to fight and did not respond immediately to the buzzer [that signaled water availability] by drinking. It appeared that the attack movements initially conditioned through operant reinforcement eventually resulted in the elicitation of apparently "innate" aggressive reactions.' In fact, the unconditioned aggression not only interacted with conditioned aggression, but to some degree outweighed it. When the two experimental animals were paired, their preoccupation with fighting resulted in their receiving fewer reinforcements than when they were paired with submissive controls. The amount of unconditioned fighting did decrease 'after many pairings' when one of the experimental subjects assumed a more submissive role, thus establishing a pattern of dominance. During these sessions, the behaviour of the paired experimental rats resembled that observed in earlier sessions when an experimental subject was paired with a submissive control animal. Even when the amount of unconditioned aggression did decrease, there was no increase in responses reinforced. In a final phase, the paired experimental subjects were placed on an extinction procedure in which fighting and attack no longer produced water reinforcement. The authors report a slight initial increase in aggression that preceded a final cessation of all aggressive behaviour.

Based on two different procedures (Reynolds *et al* − extinction during $S^\triangle$ periods, Ulrich *et al* − extinction phase), both reports suggest a possible relationship between extinction and aggression, a relationship later subjected to experimental analysis (Azrin, Hutchinson, and Hake, 1966).

Aggressive responding can also be conditioned by using intracranial stimulation as the reinforcer (Stachnik, Ulrich, and Mabry, 1966). In addition to being very effective in shaping and maintaining operant behaviour, intracranial stimulation (ICS) offers several other advantages over consummatory reinforcers. First, it can be presented to the subject without disrupting the behaviour being conditioned. When either food or water was used, presentation required that the subject cease fighting in order to obtain and consume the reinforcer. Another advantage cited by Stachnik *et al* (1966) is the fact that ICS does not appear to introduce confounding variables caused by satiation and deprivation. Stachnik, Ulrich, and Mabry (1966) showed that ICS could cause a rat to attack not only another rat, but also a cat or a squirrel monkey. The rat attacked these animals with such vigour that counter-aggression ultimately resulted.

These studies show that aggression can be produced and controlled by operant reinforcement procedures, but that unconditioned aggression, though not specified in the experimental procedure, is likely to develop and interact with the originally conditioned operant response. The unplanned aversive stimulation resulting from the reinforced operant was capable of producing unconditioned aggression.

INTERACTION OF UNCONDITIONED AGGRESSION WITH AVERSIVELY CONTROLLED OPERANTS

Because unconditioned aggression can be produced by such unplanned events as the accidental occurrence of aversive stimulation that creates instinctual counter aggression, it is quite probable that planned use of aversive control may well have the predictable effect of producing unconditioned aggressive behaviour. As recent investigators have pointed out, however (Azrin, Hutchinson, and Hake, 1967; Ulrich, 1967a), very few experiments are conducted to determine what possible effects aversive control procedures might have on the occurrence of aggression. Conversely, most of the literature on unconditioned aggression does not allow for study of escape or avoidance responses. In studies of fighting, subjects are typically allowed no escape; in studies of escape and avoidance, subjects are not placed in social situations that permit physical contact or the occurrence of aggression.

One side-effect of aversive control might be the possible creation of environments that produce aggression. Even if the results of procedures employing aversive stimuli are proven to be affected or altered when aggression is also possible, this still has no particular relevance to future single organism research of aversively controlled operants. In a human situation, however, the experimenter using aversive control finds it more difficult to avoid social settings that allow aggression to occur. In fact, in applied work it is exceedingly difficult for the experimenter or modifier to divorce himself from the subject's environment. Thus, as attempts are made to apply basic animal research findings to human control, all possible effects of procedures should be analyzed.

A few experiments exemplify some procedures that have been used to study the interactions of unconditioned aggression with aversively controlled operants. Ulrich and Craine (1964) trained rats individually to bar-press to escape and/or avoid shock on a continuous avoidance schedule with a warning signal preceding shock. After stable avoidance responding had developed, subjects were exposed to daily 4-hour avoidance sessions. During the last half hour of each of these sessions, either a small dummy or a naive rat was placed in the chamber with the subject. Introduction of the dummy into the chamber produced no change in the subject's escape-avoidance performance, and produced no attack behaviour. When a live rat was introduced, escape-avoidance responding was replaced with shock-induced fighting and attack. In fact, during the first two sessions when the other rat was present (social situation), the two rats fought after almost every unavoided shock. In later sessions, the amount of fighting decreased but, owing the subject's continued preoccupation with the naive rat, avoidance responding did not return to the previous single-subject level. During the single-subject phase the subject remained near the bar and was able to respond efficiently. In the social situation, after making a bar-press, the subject retruned to the naive rat, assumed a fighting posture, and remained in that position until the pre-shock warning stimulus occurred, at which time he would approach the bar, press it, and then return again to the other rat. These additional movements did result in a decrease in responding, but, because the amount of fighting also decreased, a lower response rate may reflect an increased efficiency of avoidance responding. In single-subject avoidance responding, the subject made more responses than were necessary (averaging slightly less than 5 per minute) to successfully avoid all shocks (approximately 3 per minute). During later sessions of the social situation when fighting responses decreased, the subject was averaging slightly less than 3 per minute. It is not possible to ascertain whether avoidance responding was actually made more efficient by the preoccupation with the naive rat in a social situation, because the authors do not report the number of shocks actually received – a critical variable when aggression during avoidance responding occurs (Azrin, Hutchinson, and Hake, 1967).

Although the study by Ulrich and Craine did not show clearly that a social situation is detrimental to avoidance responding, a later study showed that avoidance and escape performances were affected adversely when the environment included the presence of another rat (Ulrich, Stachnik, Brierton, and Mabry, 1966). Naive rats were placed in a chamber that was programmed for Sidman avoidance (S-S= 1.5 sec, R-S = 20 sec, S = 1 mA). They acquired the avoidance response without shaping. Eventually avoidance behaviour was established whether rats were placed in the chamber singly or paired. Single subjects always performed better; they received fewer shocks, responded at higher rates, and learned the avoidance response more quickly than paired subjects. After acquisition of the avoidance response, subjects were re-grouped. Single subjects were paired with naive rats, and paired subjects were separated and became individual responders. When single subjects were paired the response rate dropped its lowest value by the second session after pairing, and decreased even further before increasing again. With the exception of the first session after being paired, avoidance responding never reached its pre-pairing level. The number of shocks received showed a similar effect. When efficient single rats were paired with naive animals, the number of shocks received showed a similar effect. When efficient single rats were paired with naive animals, the number of shocks received quickly increased. Like response rate, the number of shocks received never returned to the pre-pairing level.

During the acquisition of avoidance, rats that were initially paired were observed to develop into two types of responders. Of each pair, one rat typically became the avoider while the other became a non-avoider spending his time attacking his partner as he tried to terminate shock by bar-pressing. When the pairs were separated, avoiders became better avoiders (as reflected in an increased response rate and a lower number of shocks received). Non-avoiders received many shocks on the first session after being separated, but soon they too acquired the bar-press avoidance response. Both procedures showed that social situations where aggression is possible do in fact interfere with the acquisition and maintenance of escape-avoidance responding. Based on these data, Ulrich *et al* (1966) concluded: 'The present finding that shock-induced fighting noticeably interferes with avoidance behaviour suggests that the use of aversive stimulation as a controlling technique, where more than one subject is involved, may quite probably have the added effect of causing aggression.'

Ulrich (1967a) investigated the interaction of shock-induced aggression with shock-controlled escape behaviour. Some rats were individually conditioned to escape periodically recurring, pulsating shock by pressing a bar located in the left half of a chamber, and others learned to escape by pressing a bar in the right half. Following stablization, 'left-side rats' were paired with 'right-side rats' and placed in the chamber, which, as in the training sessions, was equipped with a clear Plexiglas partition that separated the chamber into its two halves (right and left). When the animals were paired, one bar-press no longer terminated shock. Shock was terminated only when both rats responded on the bar in their half of the chamber within 15 seconds of each other. Two responses, one on each bar within 15 seconds, were defined as 'cooperative escape.' Either of the pair could make the first bar press, but shock was terminated only after the other also responded. When the cooperative contingency remained, but the partition separating the two animals was removed, cooperative escape responding was almost entirely replaced by shock-induced fighting. The disruption of escape responding did not occur as a function of increased floor space alone, or when a moveable toy was used instead of another rat.

Ulrich (1967a) reported that when the partition was absent, one subject sometimes attempted to press both bars, but was usually unable to do so because his partner would assume a sterotyped posture and block the way. Azrin, Hutchinson, and Hake (1967) used a modified single-subject design to avoid this variable when they studied the interaction between aggression and escape-avoidance with rats. The experimental chamber was equipped with an escape-response bar in one cornder, and a target rat in the opposite corner. The target rat was restrained in an upright posture and protected from grid shock by a small plastic platform. The distance between the response bar and the target rat was about eleven inches, which made it impossible for an unrestrained experimental rat to emit attack and escape responses simultaneously. By the same token, the choice of which response occurred was controlled by the experimental procedure and the behaviour of an individual subject, not the interacting behaviours of two subjects as in Ulrich's (1967a) experiments. During each session rats were presented with shock that they were unable to avoid, but were able to shorten by pressing the bar. Single subjects (no target rat in the chamber) acquired the escape response quicker and better than rats in the social situation (target rat available). In fact, four of the ten rats tested in the social condition never learned to escape and spent almost all of their time attacking the target rat. (When one of these four was given additional training without the presence of the target rat, he did acquire the escape response, and when again tested in the social situation, previous attack behaviour was replaced by escape responding.) Records of escape or attack probabilities of the six subjects that did learn to escape in the social situation showed an inverse relation. As the session progressed attack probabilities decreased and escape probabilities increased. When the number of responses necessary to escape shock was increased and effective escape became difficult, the probability of attack also increased, and the probability of escape responding decreased.

Azrin *et al* (1967) further examined the interaction of aversively controlled operants and aggression using restrained squirrel monkeys. The studies using a restrained target rat showed that one of the chief determinants of escape or attack interactions was the fact that the design of the apparatus made the escape and attack responses mutually exclusive, mainly as a function of spatial incompatibility. The use of restrained squirrel monkeys allowed for both responses to occur simultaneously or in rapid succession. These experiments included study of hose-biting attack and bar-press avoidance (continuous or discrete trials) interactions, and avoidance when hose-biting served as the avoidance response. In view of the data collected from these experiments with rats and monkeys, Azrin, Hutchinson, and Hake (1967) proposed the following general rule: 'The amount of attack during a shock escape or avoidance procedure is determined by the frequency and duration of the shocks actually received under that procedure' (p. 145).

This rule, however, would seem to apply mainly to experiments that use a single-subject or a modified single-subject design to study escape-avoidance and aggression interactions. When non-restrained subjects are paired, many more variables enter into the determination of the amount of aggression that occurs. Unconditioned aggression is affected (and effected) by many variables, planned and unplanned. For example, in paired situations, the efficiency of avoidance or escape is not a function of an individual alternative, nor is the occurrence of aggression.

Recent research from our laboratory has explored several cooperative escape and avoidance schedules that allow either joint (cooperative) responding or an individual alternative. With these schedules, paired, unrestrained rats may be used to study escape-avoidance and aggression interactions. The procedures used in these experiments were similar to the Ulrich (1967a) experiments except for variations in the actual escape response procedure during shock. Shock parameters, shock scheduling, and the apparatus were the same. These experiments mainly examined the effects of various schedules on the maintenance of joint escape, which in turn reduces the occurrence of aggressive responses when subjects are placed in social situations.

The procedure used by Ulrich (1967a), termed cooperative escape, required a single depression of each of two response bars with a certain time to terminate shock. Colasacco (1970) investigated two schedules, termed alternative schedules, that provided the possibility of either individual or joint (response requirement shared between two bars) escape on any single trial during an escape session. They were:
1) Division alternative — where the total of responses required was more than one, represented by X. Individual escape was accomplished by emitting X responses on one of the bars. Joint escape was accomplished by emitting any number of responses less than X on one bar and the remainder on the other. Values of 2, 4, and 6 were examined. For example, if the response requirement for shock termination was 4, the division alternative escape schedule could have been completed in the following ways:

	Subject 1	Subject 2
Individual alternative	4	0
	0	4
Joint alternative	3	1
	1	3
	2	2

2) Cooperative alternative — where the total response requirement was more than one, represented by X. Individual escape was accomplished by

emitting X responses on one of the bars. Joint escape was accomplished as soon as at least one response occurred on each bar. The only response requirement for shock termination examined so far has been 6, when the cooperative alternative escape schedule could be completed in the following ways:

	Subject 1	Subject 2
Individual alternative	6	0
	0	6
Joint alternative	$1 \leqslant n < 6$	1
	1	$1 \leqslant n < 6$

If, during the cooperative alternative escape schedule, one animal began a series of responses to complete the individual alternative for escape and at any time during that series, the other animal responded on his bar, shock was immediately terminated.

Briefly, these procedures produced the following effects:

Animals were trained individually to escape shock, paired (with a partition separating them), and exposed to an alternative schedule which allowed for division of the ratio across two bars as a joint alternative to individual escape (division alternative schedule). In general this division alternative did not maintain joint escape behavior of paired subjects. One subject typically assumed the entire response requirement. When a cooperative alternative was intoduced, one of the three pairs who had been exposed to the division alternative schedule did develop effective joint escape responding under the new schedule. Three naive pairs exposed to the cooperative alternative for the first time all demonstrated a high percent of joint terminations. When the division alternative was presented following high levels of joint escape under the cooperative alternative conditions, all pairs showed a drop to zero or near zero levels of joint escape (Colasacco, 1970, p. ix).

Because attack probability has been shown to be inversely related to the probability of effective escape (Azrin, Hutchinson, and Hake, 1967), the development of a cooperative alternative schedule of escape demonstrates one method for arranging environments to decrease the probability of aggression in paired or social situations when aversive stimulation is used as a major controlling device.

A short experiment from this same thesis lends some support to the hypothesis that the general statement, 'the amount of attack during a shock escape or avoidance procedure is determined by the frequency and and duration of the shocks actually received under that procedure' (Az-

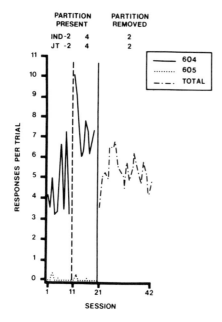

Figure 1 Paired response rate of S604 and S605 with partition present and re-moved during total response requirements of 2 and 4 with the division-alternative schedule in effect. See text for details of the schedule.

rin, Hutchinson and Hake, 1967) is not adequate to describe the control-ling variables in paired situations.

A pair of rats with a history of exposure to different response require-ments of a division alternative schedule (total response requirement, first two — Phase I, and then four — Phase II) was returned to a division alter-native schedule requiring a total of two bar-presses. When returned to this condition, the partition separating them was removed, thus allowing the opportunity for aggression to occur.

Figure 1 shows that throughout the experiment almost all escape re-sponding was assumed by Subject 604. (Visual observation revealed that Subject 604 also did most of the responding during the partition re-moved phase; however, this could not be recorded with available equip-ment and only total responses are shown in the final phase). Removal of the partition did not seriously affect response rate per session (Figure 1), and may have slightly increased the mean time to terminate shock per session (Figure 2).

Figure 3 shows the percent of fighting that resulted during the last ten sessions of the partition-removed division-alternative escape schedule

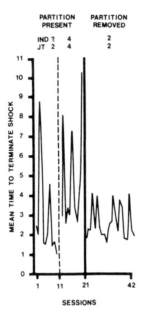

Figure 2   Mean time to terminate shock for S604 and S605 with the partition present and partition removed during total response requirements of 2 and 4 with the division alternative schedule in effect. See text for details of this schedule.

(Session 33-43 of Figures 1 and 2). As can be seen, very little fighting occurred. This is consistent with the other measures in showing little decrease in response rate, and little increase in the time required to terminate shock.

Following the partition-removed phase, subjects were exposed to an additional ten sessions during which the partition was removed but responses were no longer effective in terminating shock. Instead, each shock trial consisted of a single 0.5 second shock pulse. The delivery of shock was the same as during the partition-removed division-alternative schedule, as subjects could never avoid the first shock. Often they received more than one shock per trial before completing the escape requirement, and so during the phase when bar-pressing was ineffective, the subjects proabably received less than the number of shocks received during effective escape situations. As can be seen in Figure 3, however, the amount of aggression was greater when the bar-press contingency was removed, even though shock frequency and duration decreased. Many previously explored variables can help to explain this phenomenon. For example, when the bar-press had no effect on the schedule of

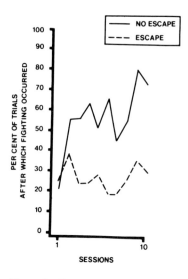

Figure 3   Per cent of fighting under escape and no escape conditions for S604 and S605. Dotted lines represent the per cent of fighting responses to escape trials during the last ten sessions of the partition-removed phase, division-alternative schedule (Sessions 33-42 in Figures 1 and 2). Solid lines represent ten additional sessions when only one inescapable shock was delivered on each trial regardless of responding.

shock presentation, both subjects may have moved away from their stations near the response bars, providing increased contact, and increased aggression. At any rate, the amount of aggression in this un-restrained social situation was not determined chiefly by the frequency and duration of the actual shocks received.

PUNISHMENT-AGGRESSION INTERACTIONS

Punishment of pain-induced aggression

In recent studies, pain-induced aggression was suppressed when additional aversive stimulation was made contingent upon each aggressive response (Baenninger and Grossman, 1969; Ulrich, Wolfe, and Dulaney, 1969). Baenninger and Grossman used tail pinches to elicit aggression in paired rats, and grid shock, either to fore- or hind-paws, to punish it. Although only actual biting attack was punished, the occurrence of stereotyped fighting postures and expression of dominance were also

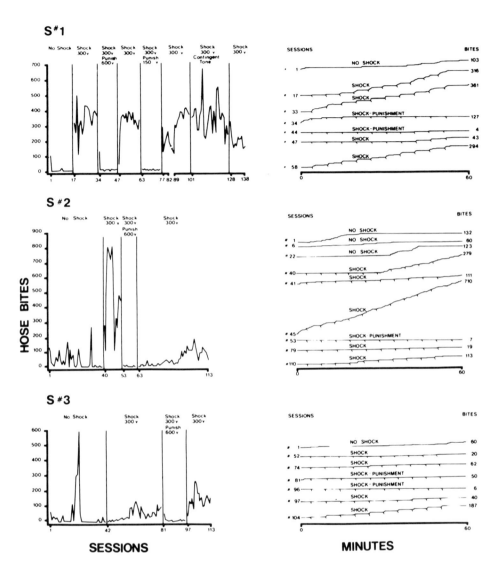

Figure 4   The rate of hose biting between and within sessions for Subjects 1, 2 and 3. The left side of the figure shows the total number of hose bites recorded during each session. The experimental conditions are labelled at the top of each of the individual graphs and the first session of every phase is numbered. The corresponding cumulative records on the right show the rate of hose biting within selected sessions for the same subject. The number of each session from which the cumulative record was taken is listed at the beginning of each record, and the total number of hose bites per session is given at the end. The experimental phase is indicated above each cumulative record. Diagonal marks indicate delivery of a scheduled shock. From Ulrich et al (1969), with permission.

suppressed, suggesting 'an essential unity of the three aggressive behaviours measured in this experiment.'

Using a single-subject design, Ulrich, Wolfe, and Dulaney punished the shock-induced hose biting of squirrel monkeys with tail shock — the same stimulus served both functions: to elicit and to suppress. An initial no-shock phase was terminated when spontaneous biting reached a near zero level. During shock phases, subjects received regularly scheduled (eliciting) shocks causing biting to increase. When punishment phases were initiated, scheduled shocks continued to be delivered and every hose bite produced another shock. A punishing shock twice the intensity of the scheduled shock suppressed hose biting in all subjects to a near zero level. A punishing shock half the intensity of the scheduled shock also suppressed biting in the one subject tested, whereas a contingent tone did not. Figure 4 summarizes the results of this experiment.

Ulrich *et al* also reported some other observations. Although contingent shock did suppress hose biting, some indication of an initial facilitation was noted. Often subjects bit the hose a few times in the 5-minute period before the first scheduled shock; when this occurred during the first punishment session, however, many more bites resulted. This initial increase can be seen for Subject 1 in the cumulative record of Session 34, and for Subject 3 in the cumulative record of Session 81 (See Figure 4). Although this increase was merely temporary, it follows that the punishment cannot be considered entirely effective in light of these possible initial facilitative effects.

The authors also noted that observations of the subjects during different phases of the experiment indicated certain behavioural side-effects resulting from punishment:

During the major portion of the no-shock phase, the monkeys generally appeared at ease, although they frequently bit the hose. The scheduled shocks during pre-punishment sessions caused obvious violent skeletal muscle activity and increase in biting. However, when not engaged in hose biting, the behavior did not appear to differ greatly from the behavior observed during the no-shock phase. In both phases, the monkeys generally sat in an upright posture with one or both hands resting on the bite hose. In the punishment phase, however, particularly in the later sessions, the subjects' behavior was dramatically different. When scheduled shock was delivered, all subjects exhibited a general 'apprehension' in relation to the bite hose. Upon delivery of a scheduled shock, the subject would jerk, move rapidly toward the bite hose, and then move away again in a whirling motion. Although much activity was observed upon shock delivery, this activity seldom included hose biting. During the inter-shock interval, behavior was typified by either self-abuse (finger biting, face clawing, side biting, etc.) or by a general freezing of posture. This freezing of posture was characterized by a crouched or slumped position that was quite dissimilar from the upright posture observed in the non-punishment phases. When the punishment contingency was removed, the additional behaviors observed during the punishment phase ceased (Ulrich, Wolfe, and Dulaney, 1969, P.1013).

Two questions arose from this experiment.
1 To what extent can shock-induced aggression be controlled by operant punishment procedures?
2 Can the side-effects resulting from punishment of shock-induced aggression be quantified?

Intermittent punishment of shock-induced aggression

Several experimenters have shown that operant procedures (or the use of consequences in the control of behaviour) can be employed to control unconditioned aggression. Reynolds, Catania, and Skinner (1963) reinforced aggression in paired pigeons, and, when unconditioned aggression resulted, they were able to eliminate it by requiring that birds move to opposite corners during 'neutral' periods, reinforcing the movement with food. Unconditioned aggression can also be reduced if subjects are allowed an opportunity to escape, to avoid, or to shorten the aversive stimulation (Ulrich, Stachnik, Brierton, and Mabry, 1966; Azrin, Hutchinson, and Hake, 1967; Ulrich, 1967b; Colasacco, 1970).

If unconditioned aggression could be suppressed with one schedule of punishment, would a different punishment schedule produce similar results? To what degree is punishment effective in the suppression of aggression? Is it necessary that each aggressive response be followed by the punishing stimulus, or, as in the punishment of operant behaviour, will an intermittent schedule also suppress (perhaps to a lesser degree)?

Two subjects with a long history of shock-induced aggression and a history of punishment of aggression have been used to study the effects of one schedule of punishment on unconditioned aggression. (Subjects are #2 and #3 from Ulrich *et al* (1969), see Figure 4 in this text). Neither subject had been exposed to shock or to the experimental environment for one month, and had not been punished for hose biting (or any other response) for more than six months. After the 1-month lay-off, subjects were placed in the experimental environment and exposed to scheduled shock during daily 1-hour sessions. Sessions were procedurally identical to sessions in the shock-alone phases of the Ulrich *et al* (1969) experiments. Ten, 300-Volt scheduled shocks were delivered, one every 5 minutes. The same restraining chair and bite apparatus as in the previous experiments were used. Aggression was measured in terms of the number of times subjects bit a hollow rubber hose mounted approximately one inch away from the wall in front of the monkey's face. During the second phase of the experiment, an intermittent schedule of punishment was introduced. During intermittent punishment, the first bite following the start of a new interval was followed by a 600-Volt shock. The first interval began when the session started, the second interval began 5 minutes later when the first scheduled shock was delivered, the third began upon the delivery of the second scheduled shock, and so on. The last interval began when the tenth and final shock was delivered, and lasted for 10 minutes (rather than 5) until the session ended. In the third phase, the punishment contingency was removed and subjects received only ten, 300-Volt scheduled shocks. Subject 3 completed one additional intermittent-punishment phase and one additional scheduled-shock-alone phase (no punishment).

Figure 5 shows total bites per session during all phases for Subject 2. The session numbers along the abscissa are the total number of sessions the subject had accumulated at the start of this particular study and give a rough indication of the length of the subject's exposure to the experimental environment and tail shock.

The 1-month lay-off is perhaps the chief reason for the lack of responding by Subject 2 during the first few sessions of the scheduled-shock-alone phase because after three sessions biting behaviour returned. When hose biting was punished intermittently, the initial effect was a partial suppression of biting. This may have been closely related to the subjects previous history of punishment. As seen in Figure 4, Subject 2 never returned to his pre-punishment level for the duration of that experiment. In fact, of the three monkeys reported by Ulrich *et al* (1969), Subject 2's hose biting behaviour was the most quickly suppressed, showed no initial facilitation, showed the least variability during punishment, and took the longest to recover after the punishment contingency was removed. Based on these data, the initial decrease in biting during the intermittent punishment phase might have been mainly a function of the subject's history rather than the schedule itself. As intermittent punishment sessions progressed, any suppressive effect of intermittent, bite-contingent shock disappeared. During the last half of the intermittent punishment phase, response rate was extremely variable and unusually high (compare Subject 2's graph in Figure 4 to Figure 5). Removal of the punishment contingency produced no obvious change in hose biting.

Figure 6 shows cumulative records of biting during typical sessions of each phase for Subject 2. (In most cases, records with a large number of bites are shown. The distribution of bites during sessions where fewer bites were recorded is the same; the records showing more biting are pre-

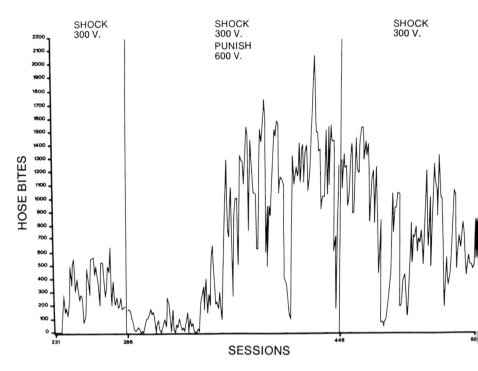

Figure 5   Total hose bites per session for Subject 2. Experimental conditions are labelled at the top of the graph, and the first session of each new phase is number-ed at the bottom. See text for details of schedules of shock presentation and pun-ishment.

sented to show that effect.)

The top cumulative record (Session 281) is typical of the pre-punish-ment, scheduled-shock-alone sessions. Subject 2 always bit directly after shock presentation, and often bit several times during the interval. The next cumulative records were taken from the earlier part of the intermit tent-punishment phase (Sessions 349 and 351), when some suppression was observed. As can be seen, the subject sometimes refrained from bit-ing immediately after the scheduled shock, but often in the middle of the interval, the subject would bite, get a 600-Volt shock, and continue biting. Cumulative records of Sessions 431 and 434 (late intermittent punishment) show the distribution of biting after prolonged exposure to intermittent punishment. Initially, intermittent, 600-Volt, bite-con-tingent shock may have partially suppressed biting, but after many ses-sions it not only became ineffective as a punisher, it even seemed to fa-cilitate or to elicit more biting attack. Figure 5 shows that during later sessions of the intermittent punishment phase the amount of bites per

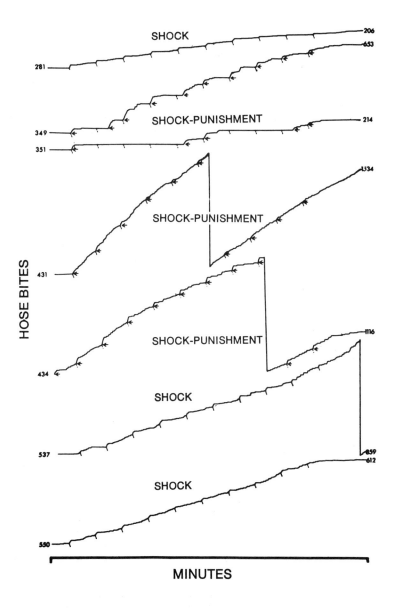

Figure 6   Cumulative records showing the rate of biting by Subject 2 during se-lected representative sessions. The experimental conditions are labelled above each cumulative record. The number of each session is given at the beginning of the re-cord, and the total bites per session is given at the end. Diagonal marks indicate delivery of a scheduled shock. Arrows indicate when a 600-volt punishing shock occurred as a consequence of the first bite during a new interval.

session once rose to over 2000 — a record in our laboratory.

Some evidence of facilitation can be seen in the cumulative record of Session 434. During that session, Subject 2 bit during the first interval (the 5-minute period before the first scheduled shock). Because it was the first bite in that interval, it was immediately followed by a 600-Volt shock. In this instance, the bite-contingent shock obviously served to produce rather than eliminate biting. In these later intermittent sessions, when Subject 2 received a 300-Volt scheduled shock, he would bite the hose without hesitation, and, receiving the 600-Volt, bite-contingent shock, would continue biting.

Also of interest are the two different effects of continuous punishment (Ulrich *et al*, 1969) as opposed to intermittent punishment on post-punishment responding. Figure 4 shows that Subject 2's pre-punishment total hose bites per session was high and variable. Sample cumulative records show that pre-punishment biting was not obviously related to shock presentation and that Subject 2 exhibited a 'tendency to bite throughout the inter-shock interval with little regard to shock presentation ... ' (Ulrich, Wolfe, and Dulaney, 1969, p.1012). Continuous punishment was effective immediately, almost to the point of total suppression. When punishment was removed 'most hose biting tended to occur immediately after presentation of a scheduled shock. Thus, biting differed from that observed during the first shock phase (pre-punishment) not only in amount, but also in respect to its occurrence in relation to shock presentation' (Ulrich *et al*, 1969, p.1013). Almost the opposite effect occurred when an intermittent punishment procedure was used as a consequence of hose biting. Subject 2 went from a fairly stimulus-bound pattern of biting before intermittent punishment (see Session 281) to a pattern of biting throughout the session with little regard to scheduled shock presentation or intermittent bite-contingent shock presentation during the intermittent punishment phase. During post-intermittent punishment the total amount of biting remained extremely variable from session to session. Within sessions a higher rate of hose biting did tend to occur directly after scheduled shock presentation, but much more biting was recorded during the inter-shock interval than during the pre-intermittent-punishment phase.

Thus, perhaps the only general effect of intermittent punishment in this case was that it reversed some of the effects of continuous punishment. In comparison to continuous punishment, intermittent punishment seemed to have an overall facilitative effect that is reflected in total hose bites per session.

Figure 7 shows total bites per session for Subject 3 during each phase of the experiment.

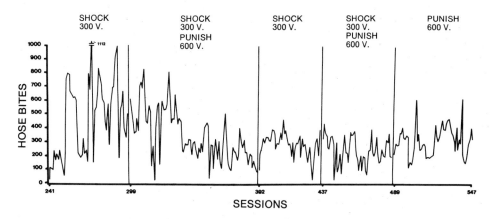

Figure 7   Total hose bites per session for Subject 3. Experimental conditions are labelled at the top of the graph, and the first session of each new phase is numbered at the bottom. See text for details of the schedules of shock presentation and punishment.

Unlike Subject 2, Subject 3 bit the hose directly after scheduled shock presentation rather than completely through the interval. Cumulative records (see Figure 8) demonstrate this pattern. Whether the total number of bites per session was high (see cumulative record of Session 272) or low (Session 292), biting attack was reliably initiated by scheduled shock presentation. When the intermittent punishment phase begun, the first effect of this procedure was to disrupt the pattern of hose biting during sessions. Instead of stimulus-bound hose biting, Subject 3 tended to bite throughout the interval (as did Subject 2). The cumulative record of Session 300 shows this effect.

As with Subject 2, some suppression of hose biting did result when Subject 3 was exposed to intermittent punishment. This suppression did not occur during the first few sessions of the suppressing effect of punishing the first bite in each interval. During this session, Subject 3 often did not bite directly after scheduled shock, but sometimes bit later in the interval, at which time the bite-contingent shock elicited for more biting. This suppressive effect lasted only four sessions. During the rest of the first intermittent-punishment phase, patterns of hose biting were stimulus bound and appeared similar to pre-punishment patterns (see the cumulative record of Session 387). During subsequent phases in which the intermittent punishment contingency was removed and reinstated, little difference can be seen in either the total amount of bites per session or the pattern of biting within sessions (see Figure 7, Sessions

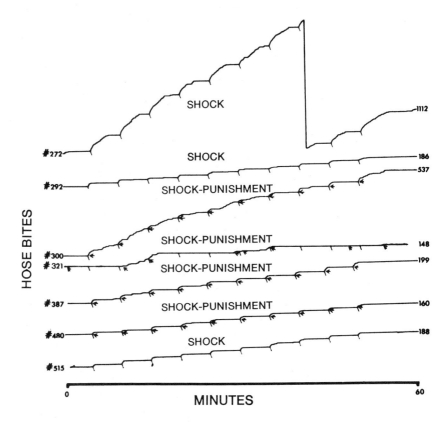

Figure 8   Cumulative records showing the rate of biting during selected representative sessions of each phase for Subject 3. The experimental conditions are labelle above each cumulative record. The number of each session is given at the beginning of the record, and the total bites per session is given at the end. Diagonal marks indicate the delivery of a scheduled shock. Arrows indicate when a 600-volt punishing shock occurred as a consequence of the first bite during a new interval.

393-547, and Figure 8, cumulative records of Sessions 387, 480, and 51ᵉ In all cases Subject 3 recieved a scheduled shock and bit the hose with decreasing frequency as the time since scheduled shock presentation increased. This pattern resulted whether or not the first bite was followed by a 600-volt shock.

   In summary, this particular schedule of intermittent punishment of shock-induced aggression did produce a lowered rate of hose biting for Subject 2 during the ealry portion of the punishment phase. This effect was short lived, however, and later it appeared that the additional shock produced a facilitation of biting. The effects of intermittent punishment on the biting of Subject 3 were not clear. Obviously, at some point an intended punishing shock serves an eliciting function, and a history of punishment or shock may affect further aggressive behaviour. Further research can help to establish schedules of punishment (or reinforcement) that may aid in the prediction and control of unconditioned aggression.

Displacement of shock-induced aggression

The second question that arose from the experiment reported by Ulrich *et al* (1969) involved the possibility of quantifying some of the observed side-effects of punishing shock-induced aggression. Ulrich *et al* reported that monkeys acted abnormally during punishment sessions, either by engaging in self-abusive behaviours or by becoming motionless. An apparatus modification allowed more than one measure of behaviour change resulting from punishment. This modification involved removing the single bite hose assembly located directly in front of the seated subject and installing two semicircular bite hose assemblies (Orr, in preparation) on either side of the monkey. Thus, instead of leaning slightly forward to bite the hose, the subject turned slightly to either the left or the right. The pressure switches were adjusted so that only bites, not pinches or blows, were recorded.

With this apparatus, it was possible to punish aggressive responses on one hose while measuring the effects of such procedures on aggression towards the other. This rationale and general procedure have been used in experiments termed the Displacement of Aggression. Sessions lasted for 1 hour, daily, and conditions were one of the three below.
1) No-shock: subject was simply placed in the chair and a free-operant rate of biting on each hose recorded during the session.
2) Scheduled-shock-alone: subject received ten, 300-Volt tail shocks, one every 5 minutes. The number of bites on each hose was recorded.
3) Punishment: as in the scheduled-shock alone condition, the subject received ten, 300-Volt shocks, one every 5 minutes. Each bite on the preferred hose (the hose the subject bit the most per session during the preceding phase) was immediately followed by a 600-Volt shock. Bites on the other hose produced no additional shock.

The conditions were like those of the Ulrich, Wolfe, and Dulaney (1969) experiments, except that a second attackable object was added to the environment.

Subject 101 was experimentally naive when placed in the restraining chair under scheduled-shock-alone conditions. Except for a greater frequency of biting during the first three sessions, Subject 101 maintained

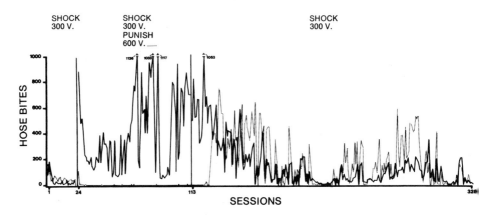

Figure 9   Total bites on the preferred (dotted line) and non-preferred (solid line) per session for Subject 101. Experimental conditions are labelled at the top of the graph, and the first session of each new phase is numbered at the bottom. See text for details of the schedules of shock presentation and punishment.

a very stable rate of biting on both hoses (see Figure 9). In Session 24 a punishment phase was begun. During this phase, every bite on the pre-ferred hose (dotted line) produced a 600-Volt shock. This procedure caused a sudden increase in biting on both hoses. Not only did bites on the non-punished hose increase, but Subject 101 also bit more than 100 times on the punished hose, and thus received over 100, 600-Volt shocks. This increase in the amount of shocks received may have been one of the reasons for the great amount of biting on the non-punished hose (solid line), except that increased level of hose biting continued af-ter biting on the punished hose had ceased. After Session 24, the subject never bit the punished hose more than ten times, and usually did not bite it at all. As can be seen in Figure 9, however, biting on the non-pun-ished hose remained very high and extremely variable. This change in the amount of biting cannot be attributed to an increased number of shocks received and may rather be a function of the actual schedule of punishment. On Session 113, the punishment contingency was removed. This change in contingencies did not cause an immediate change in be-haviour owing to the almost total suppression of biting on the preferred hose during punishment. In later sessions, Subject 101 began to bite on the preferred hose (dotted line) again, and eventually the total number of bites per session decreased and approached the level recorded during the pre-punishment, scheduled-shock-alone phase.

In addition to causing a change in total biting, punishment of biting on the preferred hose caused a disruption of the pattern of biting within

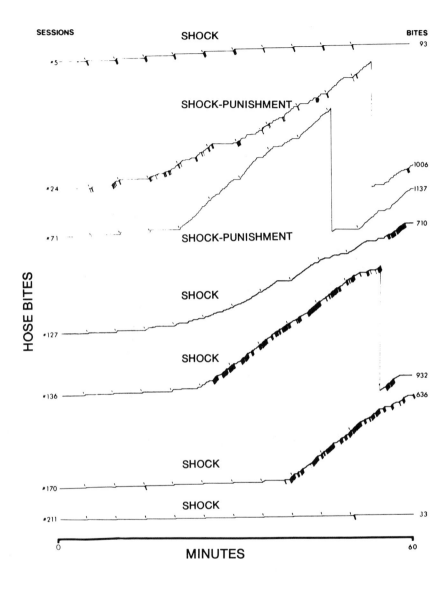

Figure 10   Cumulative records showing the rate of biting during selected representative sessions on each phase for Subject 101. The experimental conditions are labelled above each cumulative record. The number of each session is given at the beginning of the record, and the *total* bites per session (bites on both hoses combined) is given at the end. Small pointers above each cumulative record indicate the delivery of scheduled shock. Diagonal marks indicate bites on the preferred hose. All bites are recorded cumulatively.

sessions. Figure 10 shows typical biting patterns from sessions in each phase. During the pre-punishment phase the subject bit the hose directly following shock presentation. Although one hose was preferred, bites were typically recorded on both during most of the sessions. Bites on the non-preferred hose followed no pattern, and were interspersed through out the session. The cumulative record of Session 5 shows the typical pattern of biting during the pre-punishment, scheduled-shock-alone phase. Scheduled shocks are indicated by the small marks occurring above the cumulative record. All bites are recorded cumulatively: bites on the preferred hose are marked with diagonal lines, bites on the non-preferred hose are not marked.

The pattern of biting shown in Session 5 (Figure 10) was disrupted when the punishment phase was begun. On the first session of this phase (Session 24) biting on both hoses increased. During later punishment sessions, biting on the preferred hose decreased, and the pattern of biting changed. When the total number of bites per session was low, the cumulative record looked like the record of Session 5 (except that biting was on the other hose). When the number of bites per session was high, the increase was caused by a 'take-off' in biting toward the end of the session. The cumulative record of Session 71 shows this 'take-off.' This change in the pattern of biting cannot be attributed to any eliciting characteristics of the 600-Volt punishing shock, because during these sessions few were received, although much biting occurred. Similarly, on days when little biting occurred, there was also no relation between the rate of biting and the number of punishing shocks received. A lower rate of biting occurred mainly when and if a take-off occurred during the session. After the punishment contingency was removed, and the subject began to bite the preferred hose again, another pattern of biting developed. During each session the subject continued to bite the non-preferred hose in response to the first few scheduled shocks, but at some point later in the session began to bite the preferred hose, biting it at more than twice the rate (reflected in the slope of the cumulative record) observed during the first part of the session. As in the take-off that occurred during the punishment phase, this pattern of responding was not directly related to scheduled shock presentation and continued at a steady rate until the session ended. The phenomenon can be seen in the cumulative records of Sessions 127, 136, and 170. Over many, many sessions the amount of biting during the post-punishment, scheduled-shock-alone condition began to approximate the amount of biting recorded during the pre-punishment condition. Sudden increases in the number of hose bites per session (as in Sessions 210-300) are caused by recurrences of a take-off at the end of the session. During these later sessions, some biting on the preferred hose was observed to occur earlier in the session; however, any-take-off at the end of the session was exclusively due to an increased attack on the preferred hose.

Punishment of non-aggressive operants

Initial research into punishment-aggression interactions led to another research topic. Ulrich *et al* (1969) pointed out the differences between studying punishment *of* aggression, and studying punishment in *relation to aggression:*

The effectiveness of punishment in reducing the frequency of some arbitrarily chosen operant response is well documented (Azrin and Holz, 1966; Boe and Church, 1968). Critical variables involving the presentation of the punishing stimulus are the intensity, frequency, scheduling and immediacy of the punishing stimulus. The effectiveness of the punishment procedure is related also the deprivation level of the organism and the schedule of reinforcement involved in maintaining the operant response. The present investigation [i.e., those involving the punishment *of* aggression] differed from other punishment studies in two aspects: (1) the punished response appears to have many respondent characteristics, and (2) whereas other studies were concerned with the suppression of behaviors conditioned and maintained by positive reinforcement, this study investigated the suppression of behavior produced and maintained by the same stimulus used to punish it (p. 1014).

With this in mind, some pilot experimentation has been completed in this laboratory to study these differences by designing a traditional punishment experiment but allowing the opportunity for aggression. To further eliminate some of the interaction with the punishment procedure, both the aggressive response and the operant response could be emitted simultaneously.

The apparatus was a standard squirrel-monkey restraining chair with one semicircular bite hose located at eye level in front of the monkey. In addition to the bite hose, the front panel of the restraining chair was equipped with a response lever (below and to the right of the hose) and a food cup (below and to the left of the hose).

A naive squirrel monkey was deprived of food to 80 per cent of his body weight, and then conditioned to respond (by lever-pressing) on a VI-30 second schedule with standard food pellets serving as reinforcers. Throughout the experiment, the bite hose and the lever were available to the monkey and frequency measures were taken of the occurrence of each response. When both response rates showed some stability, lever

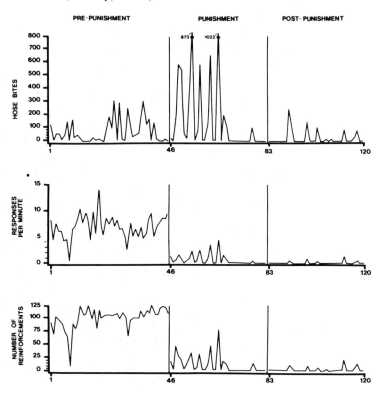

Figure 11 Three measures of the behaviour of Subject 206. Hose bites (top), lever-press responses per minute (middle), and number of reinforcements per session (bottom) are presented. Experimental conditions are labelled at the top of the figure, and sessions labelled at the bottom of each graph.

pressing was punished with shock. Although lever pressing was still rein-forced on the same VI-30 second schedule, every lever press, regardless of whether it produced a reinforcer, was followed by shock. A final pro-cedure was a return to baseline conditions (no shock for lever pressing).

Figure 11 shows the effects of these procedures on three dependent variables: hose bites (top), lever press per minute (middle), and number of reinforcers (bottom).

During the pre-punishment phase, some biting did occur. This biting was not directly related to the rate of lever pressing, or the number of re-inforcements received. When punishment was introduced, a predicted change occurred in the response rates of the monkey. Lever presses de-creased in frequency, and hose bites increased. When punishment was re-moved, an interesting pairing of hose bites and bar presses occurred.

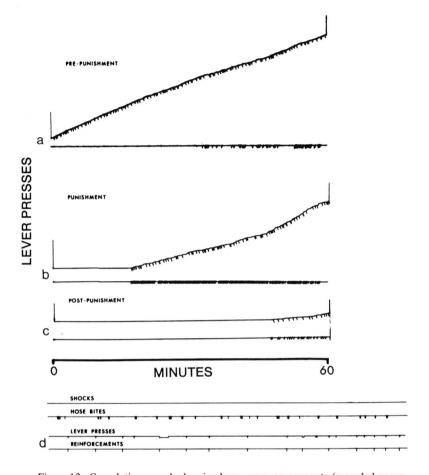

Figure 12   Cumulative records showing lever-press response rate (recorded cumulatively), reinforcements (diagonal marks on cumulative record), and hose bites
(marks on event pen of cumulative recording) for Subject 206. Experimental conditions are labelled above each cumulative record. At the bottom of the figure is
an event recording of shocks received, hose bites, lever presses, and reinforcements
for Subject 206 during a portion of a post-punishment session.

There was biting in each session where the monkey pressed the lever.
This was not related to the delivery of shock as in the previous phase,
for, during this phase, the monkey received no shock for lever pressing.
Figure 12 shows sample cumulative records of each of these phases. It
also contains a sample event recording of one of the post-punishment
sessions. All three cumulative records show that when biting occurred it

occurred toward the end of the session. During pre-punishment sessions this biting was not related to lever pressing (see Record a). During punishment, lever pressing did not begin at the start of the session, but both lever pressing and hose biting began simultaneously. After punishment was removed, the pattern of responding did not return to pre-punishment patterns, instead, the subject still did not begin to lever press when the session was begun, and lever pressing and hose biting continued to occur simultaneously (see Record c). The event record (see Record d).shows that this pairing did not occur in any particular sequence, that is biting did not always precede specific lever presses, nor did lever presses always occur before hose bites. There was, however, a short interval of time between the occurrence of either of these responses.

SIDE-EFFECTS OF AVERSIVE CONTROL

From the data reviewed and from recent experiments on pain-induced aggression, certain conclusions can be drawn to some side-effects of aversive control. First, pain produces aggression. Data collected over the past decade indicate that the pain-aggression reaction is a reliable and predictable phenomonon. In fact, this phenomenon is so consistent that it presents several difficulties when aversive stimulation or painful events are used in the control of behaviour. When pain is present in the environment, the occurrence of unconditioned pain-aggression reactions must not be underemphasized.

Second, environments or events frequently associated with pain can produce aggression. The successful classical conditioning of pain-aggression reactions has many implications for human control. In fact, one experiment of the classical or respondent conditioning of aggression alludes to this possibility: 'The finding that organisms respond aggressively to what outwardly appear to be neutral stimuli, in accordance with their past-experiences of pain, suggests a possible explanation for some cases of "apparently unprovoked" aggression' (Vernon and Ulrich, 1966). Beyond the possibility of apparently unprovoked aggression, lies a potentially more serious problem. The control of human behaviour, particularly in applied settings, requires some sort of interaction between the experimenter (or modifier) and the controllee, or between the controllee and some other individual. Few behaviours that are considered to be social problems, and thus require modification, do not involve another individual. When aversive control is used in the control of human behaviour the stimuli associated with specific aversive events may come to elicit reactions similar to pain-produced ones. At best, the use of aversive control carries with it the possibility that stimuli present when aversive events occur will also assume certain aversive properties. In human situations it is unfortunate if the 'neutral stimulus' that produces 'apparently unprovoked aggression' happens to be another human. Rachman and Teasdale (1969) indicate how pain-aggression reactions may arise during aversion therapy employing shock. To alleviate such reactions they suggest administering the noxious stimuli remotely, and isolating the patient, especially from the therapist.

Third, aggressive behaviour can produce more aggressive behaviour. When rats (Ulrich *et al*, 1963) or pigeons (Reynolds *et al*, 1963) were trained to fight each other, unconditioned aggression developed, although not specified by the reinforcement schedule that maintained fighting. Again, the occurrence of learned aggression produced sufficient aversive stimulation for the other organism that unconditioned aggression soon occurred, and in some cases displaced control by the reinforcement schedule that originally maintained aggressive behaviour. When methods used to control another organism's behaviour are aggressive (that is, behaviour associated with delivering aversive stimulation to another organism), one must expect the possibility of counter aggression, perhaps of a more unconditioned variety. In natural situations of human control, this is not often observed to be a problem. Usually the controller is bigger or stronger (that is, has more powerful consequences at his disposal) than the controllee, and any counter aggression is quickly suppressed. In such situations, overt or immediate aggression may not be observed. For example, a recent behaviour modification experiment employed shock to control the undesirable behaviours of an 11-year-old girl. Regarding the use of shock and its effects on the girl's behaviour, the experimenter stated, 'Although strong escape and avoidance behaviours were produced with the shock, both intentionally and inadvertently, no general avoidance of or attempts to escape from the room or the experimenter were seen' (Risley, 1968). Regarding the use of shock as it relates to aggression, the experimenter further stated. 'No aggressive behavior toward any person or object occurred in the laboratory. When the aggressive behavior toward her little brother (which antedated this study) was punished with shock, no evidence of pain-elecited aggression was noted, only a systematic decrease in the behavior.' The author concluded by saying, 'These findings do serve to limit the generality of extrapolations from past research with contraindicates the use of punishment.' It is our contention that this type of evidence, based on observations in an applied setting, cannot be equated to past basic research. Instead, the generality of basic aggression and punishment research is limited only by the lack of equivalent experimental control in applied settings.

In any event, the pain-aggression reaction does exist, and the possibility of its occurrence should be considered in any situation in which aversive control is employed. A fourth conclusion lends further support to this issue: when aversive control is used to maintain operant behaviour (such as escape and avoidance), unconditioned pain-aggression reactions may interfere with the performance of the operant response. It should be noted, however, that careful scheduling of contingencies and other environmental events can reduce the possibility of an actual occurrence of aggression. For example, whether or not aggressive behaviour develops in such situations is related to factors such as the subjects' conditioning history and the difficulty of the escape or avoidance response.

Fifth, when aversive control is used to suppress aggression, other behaviours occur that make such practices inadvisable. Whether or not this conclusion is valid depends upon the criteria used in the evaluations of 'advisability.' Based on the data on the punishment of aggression that are available to date, the following points seem relevant to the issue of advisability.

1 During continuous punishment of shock-induced aggression, Ulrich *et al* (1969) reported that the punishment schedule initially facilitated aggression on the first session of the punishment phase for two of the three subjects. In this experiment, a slight facilitation at the beginning of the punishment phase caused no particular problem – the subject was a small, restrained squirrel monkey. If some other organism is involved, for example, a very large unrestrained human, or a gorilla such facilitation might have other implications.

2 In later punishment sessions, although a continuous schedule of punishment was effective in suppressing one aggressive response (hose biting), other forms of behaviour took its place (for example, self-abuse or freezing postures). Again in human situations, the occurrence of such atypical behaviours might be more detrimental than the response that was initially the target of the punishment procedure.

3 Thus far, only one other schedule of punishment has been used when the subject was allowed no alternative response. This intermittent schedule was, however, generally ineffective in the suppression of aggression, and at times actually appeared to increase aggression. In human situations, the possibility of facilitation, or, at best, no suppression of the aggressive response, would be of no value in its control. When only the most stringent punishment contingency (continuous punishment) is effective – and that is questionable (see above) – one might perhaps explore some other means of control.

4 When Subject 101 was punished for hose biting, but was allowed a similar, alternative, aggressive response, the total amount of aggression in-

creased greatly and the pattern of aggression was disrupted. Such a finding, were it to be shown to hold true for additional animals subjected to similar procedures, would appear to make the use of punishment even more inadvisable as a strategy for controlling aggression. In human situations, so many variables are typically not under the control of the behaviour modifier that the possibility of some form of enhanced aggression, perhaps directed at another individual, is a very serious consideration. This would be particularly true if the added aggression did not appear to be solely a function of the aversive stimulation received, but, as with Subject 101, an apparent function of the punishment schedule itself. Certainly much more research is needed to identify the facilitative effects of a punishment schedule on the phenomenon of aggression. The finding in relation to Subject 101, as well as the general results of the research reported in this paper, make this an area worthy of continued attention.

Sixth, when punishment is used to control non-aggressive operant behaviour, an increase in aggression can be expected as well as a perhaps unfortunate pairing of aggression-producing events with the operant response, even after punishment has been removed. The finding that when lever presses produced shock, the shock-produced aggression is not unique. The fact that lever presses soon came to produce aggression, even though no shock was delivered, can be explained by a possible classical conditioning of hose biting to lever pressing. It is unfortunate that our pilot subject died before we were able to determine this by prolonged exposure to respondent extinction.

There are two ways of looking at the implications of this experiment when extrapolating to human situations. When aversive stimuli are used in the suppression of some operant response in humans, the controller rarely considers a reversal phase a particularly favourable procedure. If a student is found cheating in class, punishment may be employed to suppress the rate of that behaviour. The teacher is probably not inclined to introduce purposely a reversal (hence, one of the reasons for multiple baseline procedures in applied projects instead of A-B-A designs). Even further, our society counts upon this type of pairing. We call it guilt. If the teacher is out of the room, the child may cheat. He may also feel guilty about it, which, in this case, is probably no more than the anticipation of possible punishment or aversive stimulation, which is the same behaviour our monkey exhibited. If we look at this situation, we might conclude that pairing aversive events with particular responses might be a favourable side effect of punishment.

Consider a different response, however. Humans are particularly complex organisms, very susceptible to pairings and complex relationships between environmental events. Suppose with our student and teacher interaction we look at a different response. Suppose we look at the going-to-school response, or at the interacting-with-teacher response, or at the working-on-school-work response. A pairing of these responses is not quite so favourable. If the child is punished by the teacher for cheating, the delivery of aversive stimulation has more than an effect upon rate of cheating behaviour. The child emits a lot of other non-aggressive operants that might be paired with the aversive events, including coming to school, interacting with teacher, and working on school work. Few children (or adults) feel guilty about going to school: They will often emit responses to avoid or escape it, however.

Perhaps the major implication of the aggression research cited in this paper is to point to areas of caution concerning the use of aversive control. This is not to say that aversive control should be totally eliminated. This would of course, constitute an impossible situation. It does indicate, however, the advisability of examining other methods of control. When aversive techniques must be employed, all the above conclusions and cautions should be seriously considered.

References and citation index

The bold face numbers at the end of each entry indicate the pages on which citation occurs.

Andersson, B. and Larsson, S. Water and food intake and the inhibitory effect of amphetamine on drinking and eating before and after 'prefontal lobotomy' in dogs. *Acta Physiologica Scandinavica*, 1957, 38, 22-30. **131**

Andrew, R.J. Some remarks on behaviour in conflict situations with special reference to Amberiza Spp. *British Journal of Animal Behaviour*, 1956, 4, 41-5. **146**

Anger, D. The role of temporal discriminations in the reinforcement of Sidman avoidance behavior. *Journal of the Experimental Analysis of Behavior*, 1963, 6, 477-506. **198**

Antal, J. and Kemeny, A. The rate of elaboration of alimentary and defensive reflexes in group conditioning. *Physiologia Bohemoslovencia*, 1964, 13, 110-15. **208**

Appel, J.B. Drugs, shock intensity and the CER. *Psychopharmacologia*, 1963, 4, 148-53. (a) **31**

Appel, J.B. Aversive aspects of a schedule of positive reinforcement. *Journal of the Experimental Analysis of Behavior*, 1963, 6, 423-8. (b) **174**

Armstrong, E.A. The nature and function of displacement activities. *Symposia of the Society for Experimental Biology*, 1950, 4, 361-84. **173**

Aull, J.C., Roberts, W.J., and Kinard, F.W. Rate of metabolism of ethanol in the rat. *American Journal of Physiology*, 1956, 186, 380-2. **126**

Azrin, N.H. Time-out from positive reinforcement. *Science*, 1961, 133, 382-3. **35, 152, 155, 159-60, 163, 174**

Azrin, N.H. Aggression. Paper read at Meeting of the American Psychological Association, Los Angeles, September, 1964. **162**

Azrin, N.H. and Hake, D.F. Positive conditioned suppression: conditioned suppression using positive reinforcers as the unconditioned stimuli. *Journal of the Experimental Analysis of Behavior*, 1969, 12, 167-73. **12, 23**

Azrin, N.H., Hake, D.F., and Hutchinson, R.R. Elicitation of aggression by a physical blow. *Journal of the Experimental Analysis of Behavior*, 1965, 8, 55-7. **206, 208**

Azrin, N.H. and Holz, W.C. Punishment. In W.K. Honig (ed.), *Operant behavior: areas of research and application*. New York: Appleton-Century-Crofts, 1966, pp. 380-447. **13, 235**

Azrin, N.H., Hutchinson, R.R., and Hake, D.F. Pain-induced fighting in the squirrel monkey. *Journal of the Experimental Analysis of Behavior*, 1963, 6, 620. **206**

Azrin, N.H., Hutchinson, R.R., and Hake, D.F. Extinction-induced aggression. *Journal of the Experimental Analysis of Behavior*, 1966, 9, 191-204. **130, 151, 157-61, 165, 175, 212**

Azrin, N.H., Hutchinson, R.R., and Hake, D.F. Attack, avoidance, and escape reactions to aversive shock. *Journal of the Experimental Analysis of Behavior*, 1967, 10, 131-48. **175, 213-16, 218-19**

Azrin, N.H., Hutchinson, R.R., and McLaughlin, R. The opportunity for aggression as an operant reinforcer during aversive stimulation. *Journal of the Experimental Analysis of Behavior*, 1965, 8, 171-80. **209**

Azrin, N.H., Hutchinson, R.R., and Sallery, R.D. Pain-aggression toward inanimate objects. *Journal of the Experimental Analysis of Behavior*, 1964, 7, 223-8. **206-7**

Azrin, N.H., Rubin, H.B., and Hutchinson, R.R. Biting attack by rats in response to aversive shock. *Journal of the Experimental Analysis of Behavior*, 1968, 11, 633-9. **206-7, 209**

Azrin, N.H., Ulrich, R.E., Hutchinson, R.R., and Norman, D.G. Effect of shock duration on shock-induced fighting. *Journal of the Experimental Analysis of Behavior*, 1964, 7, 9-11. **207**

Baenninger, R. and Grossman, J.C. Some effects of punishment on pain-elicited aggression. *Journal of the Experimental Analysis of Behavior*, 1969, 12, 1017-22. **205, 221**

Blackman, D.E. Response rate and conditioned suppression. *Psychological Reports*, 1966, 19, 687-93. **32**

Blackman, D.E. Effects of response pacing on conditioned suppression. *Quarterly Journal of Experimental Psychology*, 1967, 19, 170-4. **32**

Blackman, D.E. Conditioned suppression or facilitation as a function of the behavioural baseline. *Journal of the Experimental Analysis of Behavior*, 1968, 11, 53-61. (a) **35, 39**

Blackman, D.E. Response rate, reinforcement frequency and conditioned suppression. *Journal of the Experimental Analysis of Behavior*, 1968, 11, 503-16. (b) **33**

Blackman, D.E. Effects of a pre-shock stimulus on temporal control of behavior. *Journal of the Experimental Analysis of Behavior*, 1970, 14, 313-19. (a) **36-9**

Blackman, D.E. Conditioned suppression of avoidance behaviour in rats. *Quarterly Journal of Experimental Psychology*, 1970, 22, 547-53. (b) **40-4**

Boe, E.E. and Church R.M. (eds.). *Punishment: issues and experiments.* New York: Appleton-Century-Crofts, 1968. **235**

Bolles, R.C. Species-specific defense reactions and avoidance learning. *Psychological Review*, 1970, 77, 32-48. **77, 79**

Brady, J.V. Extinction of a conditioned 'fear' response as a function of reinforcement schedules for competing behavior. *Journal of Psychology*, 1955, 40, 25-34. **30-3**

Brady, J.V. Assessment of drug effects of emotional behavior. *Science*, 1956, 123, 1033. **30-2, 48**

Brady, J.V. and Hunt, H.F. The effect of electro-convulsive shock on a conditioned emotional response: a control for impaired hearing. *Journal of Comparative and Physiological Psychology*, 1952, 45, 180-2. **29**

Brady, J.V., Kelly, D., and Plumlee, L. Autonomic and behavioral responses of the rhesus monkey to emotional conditioning. *Annals of the New York Academy of Sciences*, 1969, 159, 959-75. **47**

Breland, K. and Breland, M. The misbehavior of organisms. *American Psychologist*, 1961, 16, 681-4. **68, 79**

Breland, K. and Breland, M. *Animal behavior.* New York: Macmillan, 1966. **68, 79**

Brown, P.L. and Jenkins, H.M. Auto-shaping of the pigeon's key-peck. *Journal of the Experimental Analysis of Behavior*, 1968, 11, 1-8. **201**

Burt, C. The concept of consciousness. *British Journal of Psychology*, 1962, 53, 329-42. **67**

Byrd, L.D. Responding in the cat maintained under response-independent electric shock. *Journal of the Experimental Analysis of Behavior*, 1969, 12, 1-10. **13, 23, 24, 198**

Caggiula, A.R. and Eibergen, R. Copulation of virgin male rats evoked by painful peripheral stimulation. *Journal of Comparative and Physiological Psychology*, 1969, 69, 414-19. **164**

Catania, A.C. (ed.). *Contemporary research in operant behavior.* Glenview, Illinois: Scott, Foresman, 1968. **172**

Catania, A.C. and Reynolds, G.S. A quantitative analysis of the responding maintained by interval schedules of reinforcement. *Journal of the Experimental Analysis of Behavior*, 1968, 11, 327-83. **103**

Chapman, H.W. Oropharyngeal determinants of non-regulatory drinking in the rat. Unpublished Ph.D. dissertation, University of Pennsylvania, 1969. **165**

Church, R.M. The varied effects of punishment on behavior. *Psychological Review*, 1963, 70, 369-402. **13**

Clark, F.C. Some observations on the adventitious reinforcement of drinking under food reinforcement. *Journal of the Experimental Analysis of Behavior*, 1962, 5, 61-3. **83, 95-6, 104, 130**

Clark, F.C. and Steele, B.J. Effects of d-amphetamine on performance under a multiple schedule in the rat. *Psychopharmacologia*, 1956, 9, 157-69. **136**

Colasacco, A.P. Schedule effects on escape behavior of individual and paired albino rats. Unpublished M.A. thesis, Western Michigan University, 1970. **217-18, 224**

Colotla, V.A., Keehn, J.D., and Gardner, L.L. Control of schedule-induced drink durations by interpellet intervals. *Psychonomic Science*, 1970, 21, 137-9. **93, 130, 145**

Cook, L. and Catania, A.C. Effects of drugs on avoidance and escape behavior. *Federation Proceedings*, 1964, 23, 818-35. **6**

Coons, E.E., Anderson, N.H., and Myers, A.K. Disappearance of avoidance responding during continued training. *Journal of Comparative and Physiological Psychology*, 1960, 53, 290-2. **70**

Coulson, G.E. Positive reinforcement as an increase in the availability of food. Unpublished Ph. D. thesis, York University, 1970. **73-7, 94**

Creer, T.L., Hitzing, E.W., and Schaeffer, R.W. Classical conditioning of reflexive fighting. *Psychonomic Science*, 1966, 4, 89-90. **210**

Daniel, W.J. An experimental note on the O'Kelly-Steckle reaction. *Journal of Comparative Psychology*, 1943, 35, 267-8. **203-4**

Davis, H. Conditioned suppression: a survey of the literature. *Psychonomic Monograph Supplements*, 1968, 2, 283-91. **28, 31, 40**

Davis, J.D. and Keehn, J.D. Magnitude of reinforcement and consummatory behavior. *Science*, 1959, 130, 269-71. **83**

Dews, P.B. Studies on behavior: IV. Stimulant actions of methamphetamine. *Journal of Pharmacology and Experimental Therapeutics*, 1958, 122, 137-47. **6, 131**

Dews, P.B. Drugs in psychology. A commentary on Travis Thompson and Charles R. Schuster's *Behavioral pharmacology*. *Journal of the Experimental Analysis of Behavior*, 1970, 13, 395-406. **23**

Dews, P.B. and Morse, W.H. Behavioral pharmacology. *Annual Review of Pharmacology*, 1961, 1, 145-74. **4**

Dinsmoor, J.A. Escape from shock as a conditioning technique. In M.R. Jones (ed.), *Miami symposium on the prediction of behavior, 1967: Aversive stimulation*. Coral Gables, Fla: University of Miami Press, 1968. **79**

Dinsmoor, J.A. and Hughes, L.H. Training rats to press a bar to turn off shock. *Journal of Comparative and Physiological Psychology*, 1956, 49, 235-8. **77**

Eibl-Eibesfeldt, I. The fighting behavior of animals. *Scientific American*, 1961, 203, 112-22. **205**

Emley, G.S. and Hutchinson, R.R. Modification of shock-induced biting attack by certain stimulant and depressant drugs. In preparation, 1970. **195**

Epstein, A.N. Suppression of eating and drinking by amphetamine and other drugs in normal and hyperphagic rats. *Journal of Comparative and Physiological Psychology*, 1959, 52, 37-45. **131**

Essig, C.F. and Lam, R.C. Convulsions and hallucinatory behavior following alcohol withdrawal in the dog. *Archives of Neurology and Psychiatry*, 1968, 18, 626-32. **128**

Estes, W.K. Outline of a theory of punishment. In B.A. Campbell and R.M. Church (eds.), *Punishment and aversive behavior*. New York: Appleton-Century-Crofts, 1969. **28**

Estes, W.K. and Skinner, B.F. Some quantitative properties of anxiety. *Journal of Experimental Psychology*, 1941, 29, 390-400. **11, 26-8, 46-7**

Everett, P.B. and King, R.A. Schedule-induced alcohol ingestion. *Psychonomic Science*, 1970, 18, 278-9. **115**

Falk, J.L. Production of polydipsia in normal rats by an intermittent food schedule. *Science*, 1961, 133, 195-6. (a) **51, 80, 95-7, 109, 113, 129, 148**

Falk, J.L. The behavioral regulation of water-electrolyte balance. *Nebraska Symposium on Motivation, 1961*. Lincoln: University of Nebraska Press, 1961, 1-33. (b) **106, 159, 161**

Falk, J.L. Studies on schedule-induced polydipsia. In M.J. Wayner (ed.), *Thirst: First international symposium on thirst in the regulation of body water*. New York: Pergamon Press, 1964, 95-116. **80, 132, 158, 172**

Falk, J.L. The motivational properties of schedule-induced polydipsia. *Journal of the Experimental Analysis of Behavior*, 1966, 9, 19-25. (a) **85, 150, 162, 165**

Falk, J.L. Schedule-induced polydipsia as a function of fixed-interval length. *Journal of the Experimental Analysis of Behavior*, 1966, 9, 37-9. (b) **85, 96-103, 150, 153, 159**

Falk, J.L. Analysis of water and NaCl solution acceptance by schedule-induced polydipsia. *Journal of the Experimental Analysis of Behavior*, 1966, 9, 111-18. (c) **90, 172**

Falk, J.L. Control of schedule-induced polydipsia: type, size and spacing of meals. *Journal of the Experimental Analysis of Behavior*, 1967, 10, 199-206. **90, 101, 104-6, 109-10, 155, 165**

Falk, J.L. Conditions producing psychogenic polydipsia in animals. *Annals of the New York Academy of Sciences*, 1969, 157, 569-93. **80, 94, 95, 102, 106, 130, 146, 150, 154-7, 160-1, 165-6**

Fantino, E. Conditioned reinforcement, choice, and the psychological distance to reward. In D.P. Hendry (ed.), *Conditioned reinforcement*. Homewood: The Dorsey Press, 1969. **35**

Feldman, R.S. and Bremner, F.J. A method for rapid conditioning of stable avoidance bar pressing behavior. *Journal of the Experimental Analysis of Behavior*, 1963, 6, 393-4. **78-9**

Ferster, C.B. Control of behavior in chimpanzees and pigeons by time out from positive reinforcement. *Psychological Monographs*, 1958, 72 (Whole No 461), 1-38. **151, 174**

Ferster, C.B. and Skinner, B.F. *Schedules of reinforcement*. New York: Appleton-Century-Crofts, 1957. **33, 50, 67-8, 131, 133, 145**

Finocchio, D. Changes in temporally-spaced responding as a measure of conditioned emotional behavior. Paper read to Eastern Psychological Association, 1963. (Cited by Migler and Brady, 1964.) **35, 39**

Flory, R.K. Attack behavior as a function of minimum inter-food interval. *Journal of the Experimental Analysis of Behavior*, 1969, 12, 825-8. (a) **152, 155, 158, 160-1**

Flory, R.K. Attack behavior in a multiple fixed-ratio schedule of reinforcement. *Psychonomic Science*, 1969, 16, 156-7. (b) **155, 163**

Flory, R.K. The control of schedule-induced polydipsia: frequency and magnitude of reinforcement. Unpublished Ph.D. dissertation, Arizona State University, 1969. (c) **154-5**

Flory, R.K., Ulrich, R.E., and Wolff, P.C. The effects of visual impairment on aggressive behavior. *Psychological Record*, 1965, 15, 185-90. **208**

Freed, E.X. and Hymowitz, N. A fortuitous observation regarding 'psychogenic' polydipsia. *Psychological Reports*, 1969, 24, 224-6. **163**

Freed, E.X. and Lester, D. Schedule-induced consumption of ethanol: calories or chemotherapy. *Physiology and Behavior*, 1970, 5, 555-60. **115**

Gentry, W.D. Fixed-ratio schedule-induced aggression. *Journal of the Experimental Analysis of Behavior*, 1968, 11, 813-17. **152, 159-60, 163, 165**

Giarman, N.J. Antidepressant drugs. In J.R. Di Palma (ed.), *Drill's pharmacology in medicine*. New York: McGraw-Hill, 1965. **131**

Gilbert, R.M. and Sherman, I.P. Palatability-induced polydipsia: saccharin, sucrose, and water intake in rats, with and without food deprivation. *Psychological Reports*, 1970, 27, 319-25. **82**

Goy, R.W. and Hunt, H.F. The resistance of an instrumental response to suppression by conditioned fear. *American Psychologist*, 1953, 8, 509. **29**

Hake, D.F. and Azrin, N.H. An apparatus for delivering pain shock to monkeys. *Journal of the Experimental Analysis of Behavior*, 1963, 6, 297-8. **177, 206**

Hawkins, T.D. Pellet frequency: effects on schedule-induced polydipsia and variable-interval bar-press performance. Paper read at Psychonomic Science Meeting, Chicago, 1967. **154**

Hearst. E. Stress-induced breakdown of an appetitive discrimination. Journal of the *Experimental Analysis of Behavior*, 1965, 8, 135-46. **39**

Hendry, D.P. and Rasche, R.H. Analysis of a new nonnutritive positive reinforcer based on thirst. *Journal of Comparative and Physiological Psychology*, 1961, 54, 477-83. **165**

Herrnstein, R.J. Superstition: A corollary of the principles of operant conditioning. In W.K. Honig (ed.), *Operant behavior: areas of research and application*. New York: Appleton-Century-Crofts, 1966. **109**

Herrnstein, R.J. Method and theory in the study of avoidance. *Psychological Review*, 1969, 76, 49-69. **26**

Herrnstein, R.J. On the law of effect. *Journal of the Experimental Analysis of Behavior*, 1970, 13, 243-66. **94, 162**

Herrnstein, R.J. and Hineline, P.N. Negative reinforcement as shock frequency reduction. *Journal of the Experimental Analysis of Behavior*, 1966, 9, 421-30. **73**

Herrnstein, R.J. and Morse, W.H. Some effects of response-independent positive reinforcement on maintained operant behavior. *Journal of Comparative and Physiological Psychology*, 1957, 50, 461-7. **12**

Herrnstein, R.J. and Sidman, M. Avoidance conditioning as a factor in the effects of unavoidable shocks on food-reinforced behavior. *Journal of Comparative and Physiological Psychology*, 1958, 51, 380-5. **40**

Hinde, R.A. *Animal behaviour*. New York: McGraw-Hill, 1966. **130**

Hitzig, E.W. Schedule-induced polydipsia: a reinforcement analysis. Unpublished Ph.D. dissertation, Florida State University, 1968. **106**

Hodos, W. and Kalman, G. Effects of increment size and reinforcer volume on progressive ratio performance. *Journal of the Experimental Analysis of Behavior*, 1963, 6, 387-92. **113**

Hoffman, H.S. The analysis of discriminated avoidance. In W.K. Honig (ed.), *Operant behavior: areas of research and application*. New York: Appleton-Century-Crofts, 1966, 499-530. **77, 198**

Hoffman, H.S., Fleshler, M. and Chorny, H. Discriminated bar-press avoidance. *Journal of the Experimental Analysis of Behavior*, 1961, 4, 309-16. **197-8**

Holland, J. and Skinner, B.F. *Analysis of behavior*. New York: McGraw-Hill, 1961. **73**

Holman, R.B. and Myers, R.D. Ethanol consumption under conditions of psychogenic polydipsia. *Physiology and Behavior*, 1968, 3, 369-71. **115**

Holz, W.C. and Azrin, N.H. Discriminative properties of punishment. *Journal of the Experimental Analysis of Behavior*, 1961, 4, 225-32. **13**

Hull, C.L. *Principles of behavior*. New York: Appleton-Century-Crofts, 1943. **66**

Hunt, H.F. Some effects of drugs on classical (type S) conditioning. *Annals of the New York Academy of Sciences*, 1956, 65, 258-67. **30**

Hunt, H.F. Some effects of meprobamate on conditioned fear and emotional behavior. *Annals of the New York Academy of Sciences*, 1957, 67, 712-22. **30**

Hunt, H.F. and Brady, J.V. Some effects of electro-convulsive shock on a conditioned emotional response ('anxiety'). *Journal of Comparative and Physiological Psychology*, 1951, 44, 88-98. **29**

Hurwitz, H.M.B. and Roberts, A.E. Conditioned suppression of an avoidance response. Unpublished manuscript, 1970. **46**

Hutchinson, R.R., Azrin, N.H., and Hake, D.F. An automatic method for the study of aggression in squirrel monkeys. *Journal of the Experimental Analysis of Behavior*, 1966, 9, 233-7. **178, 206, 209**

Hutchinson, R.R., Azrin, N.H., and Hunt, G.M. Attack produced by intermittent reinforcement of a concurrent operant response. *Journal*

nal of the Experimental Analysis of Behavior, 1968, 11, 485-95. **152, 155, 159, 175**

Hutchinson, R.R., Azrin, N.H., and Renfrew, J.W. Effects of shock intensity and duration on the frequency of biting attack by squirrel monkeys. *Journal of the Experimental Analysis of Behavior*, 1968, 11, 83-8. **178-9, 207-8**

Hutchinson, R.R. and Emley, G.S. Effects of opportunity to attack on pre-shock manipulative responses. In preparation, 1971. **194**

Hutchinson, R.R., Renfrew, J.W., and Young, G.A. Effects of long-term shock and associated stimuli on aggressive and manual responses. *Journal of the Experimental Analysis of Behavior*, 1971, 15, 141-66. **23, 24, 182-3, 198**

Hutchinson, R.R., Ulrich, R.E., and Azrin, N.H. Effects of age and related factors on the pain-aggression reaction. *Journal of Comparative and Physiological Psychology*, 1965, 59, 365-9. **208-9**

Kamin, L.J. Temporal and intensity characteristics of the conditioned stimulus. In W.F. Prokasy (ed.), *Classical conditioning: a symposium.* New York: Appleton-Century-Crofts, 1965, 118-47. **28, 47**

Keehn, J.D. A reversal effect with pauses on mixed schedules of reinforcement. *Nature*, 1963, 200, 1124-5. **132**

Keehn, J.D. Double discrimination bar-press and bar-release avoidance. *Psychonomic Science*, 1967, 8, 189-90. (a) **79**

Keehn, J.D. Is bar-holding with negative reinforcement preparatory or perseverative? *Journal of the Experimental Analysis of Behavior*, 1967, 10, 461-5. (b) **79**

Keehn, J.D. Running and bar pressing as avoidance responses. *Psychological Reports*, 1967, 20, 591-602. (c) **78-9**

Keehn, J.D. Double discrimination avoidance with a single stimulus. *Journal of the Experimental Analysis of Behavior*, 1968, 11, 467-72. **79**

Keehn, J.D. Consciousness, discrimination and the stimulus control of behaviour. In R.M. Gilbert and N.S. Sutherland (eds.), *Animal discrimination learning.* London: Academic Press, 1969. (a) **65**

Keehn, J.D. Translating behavioral research into practical terms for alcoholism. *Canadian Psychologist*, 1969, 10, 438-46. (b) **67, 94**

Keehn, J.D. Schedule-induced licking and polydipsia. *Psychological Reports*, 1970, 26, 155-61. **82-4**

Keehn, J.D. and Chaudrey, S. Superstitious escape behavior during Sidman avoidance training. *Journal of the Experimental Analysis of Behavior*, 1964, 7, 26. **77-8**

Keehn, J.D. and Colotla, V.A. Predictability of schedule-induced drink durations. *Psychonomic Science*, 1970, 18, 297-8. (a) **85, 87, 145**

Keehn, J.D. and Colotla, V.A. Prediction and control of schedule-induced drink durations. *Psychonomic Science*, 1970, 21, 147-8. (b) **91, 144**

Keehn, J.D. and Colotla, V.A. Stimulus and subject control of schedule-induced drinking. *Journal of the Experimental Analysis of Behavior*, 1971, 16, 257-62. **92**

Keehn, J.D., Colotla, V.A., and Beaton, J.M. Palatability as a factor in the pattern and duration of schedule-induced drinking. *Psychological Record*, 1970, 20, 433-42. **88-90**

Keehn, J.D. and Nagai, M. Attenuation of schedule-induced polydipsia by trihexyphenidyl. *Psychonomic Science*, 1969, 15, 61-2. **80**

Keehn, J.D. and Sabbagh, U. Conditioned inhibition and avoidance learning. *Psychological Reports*, 1958, 4, 547-52. **70**

Keehn, J.D. and Walsh, M.G. Bar-holding with negative reinforcement as a function of press- and release-shock intervals. *Learning and Motivation*, 1970, 1, 36-43. **79, 82**

Keehn, J.D. and Webster, C.D. Discriminated Sidman avoidance behavior by guinea pigs. *Psychonomic Science*, 1967, 7, 315-6. **69-71, 79**

Kelleher, R. T. Chaining and conditioned reinforcement. In W.K. Honig (ed.), *Operant behavior: areas of research and application*. New York: Appleton-Century-Crofts, 1966, 160-212. **132**

Kelleher, R.T. and Morse, W.H. Escape behavior and punished behavior. *Federation Proceedings*, 1964, 23, 808-17. **6-8.**

Kelleher, R.T. and Morse, W.H. Determinants of the specificity of the behavioral effects of drugs. *Ergebnisse der Physiologie*, 1968, 60, 1-56. (a) **4-6, 9, 131, 136**

Kelleher, R.T. and Morse, W.H. Schedules using noxious stimuli, III. Responding maintained with response-produced electric shocks. *Journal of the Experimental Analysis of Behavior*, 1968, 11, 819-38. (b) **13, 14, 22, 23, 198**

Kelleher, R.T., Riddle, W.C., and Cook, L. Persistent behavior maintained by unavoidable shocks. *Journal of the Experimental Analysis of Behavior*, 1963, 6, 507-17. **12, 13, 198**

Killeen, P. Response rate as a factor in choice. *Psychonomic Science*, 1968, 12, 34. **162**

Kimble, G.A. *Hilgard and Marquis' conditioning and learning*. New York: Appleton-Century-Crofts, 1961. **144**

Kinnard, W.J., Aceto, M.D.G., and Buckley, J.P. The effects of certain psychotropic agents on the conditioned emotional response behavior pattern of the rat. *Psychopharmacologia*, 1962, 3, 227-30. **31**

Kissileff, H.R. Oropharyngeal control of prandial drinking. *Journal of Comparative and Physiological Psychology*, 1969, 67, 309-19. **166**

Knutson, J.F. Aggression during the fixed-ratio and extinction components of a multiple schedule of reinforcement. *Journal of the Experimental Analysis of Behavior*, 1970, 13, 221-31. **160-1, 163, 172**

Kortlandt, A. De uitdrukkingsbewegungen en-geluiden van Phalacocorax carbo sineusis (Shaw and Nodder). *Ardea*, 1938, 27, 1-40. **145**

Kuhn, T.S. *The structure of scientific revolutions*. Chicago: University of Chicago Press, 1962. **65, 67**

Lester, D. Self-maintenance of intoxication in the rat. *Quarterly Journal of Studies on Alcohol*, 1961, 22, 223-31. **51, 114**

Levitsky, D. and Collier, G. Schedule-induced wheel running. *Physiology and Behavior*, 1968, 3, 571-3. **83, 130, 152, 159-60, 163, 165**

Leyhausen, P. Theoretische Überlegungen zur Kritik des Begriffes der Übersprungbewegungen (1952). In K. Lorenz and P. Leyhausen, *Antriebe tierischen und menschlichen Verhaltens*. Munich: R. Pieper u. Co. Verlag, 1968, 77-88. **145**

Lindsley, O.R. Direct measurement and prosthesis of retarded behavior. *Journal of Education*, 1964, 147, 62-81. **171**

Lorenz, K. *On aggression*. New York: Harcourt, Brace and World, Inc., 1966. **205**

Lyon, D.O. Frequency of reinforcement as a parameter of conditioned suppression. *Journal of the Experimental Analysis of Behavior*, 1963, 7, 289-91. **33**

Lyon, D.O. Conditioned suppression: operant variables and aversive control. *Psychological Record,* 1968, 18, 317-38. **28**

Matsunaga, M. and Keehn, J.D. Attenuation of palatability-induced polydipsia by biperiden hydrochloride. *Psychonomic Science*, 1969, 17, 9-10. **82**

McFarland, D.J. On the causal and functional significance of displacement activities. *Zeitschrift für Tierpsychologie*, 1966, 23, 217-35. **147**

McKearney, J.W. Maintenance of responding under a fixed-interval schedule of electric shock presentation. *Science*, 1968, 160, 1249-51. **13, 14, 15, 23, 164, 198**

McKearney, J.W. Fixed-interval schedules of electric shock presentation: Extinction and recovery of performance under different shock intensities and fixed-interval durations. *Journal of the Experimental Analysis of Behavior*, 1969, 12, 301-13. **13, 16-17, 23, 198**

McKearney, J.W. Responding under fixed-ratio and multiple fixed-interval fixed-ratio schedules of electric shock presentation. *Journal of the Experimental Analysis of Behavior*, 1970, 14, 1-6. (a) **19, 20, 23**

McKearney, J.W. Rate-dependent effects of drugs: modification by discriminative stimuli of the effects of amobarbital on schedule-controlled behavior. *Journal of the Experimental Analysis of Behavior*, 1970, 14, 167-75. (b) **9**

McMillan, D.E. The effects of sympathomimetic amines on schedule-controlled behavior in the pigeon. *Journal of Pharmacology and Experimental Therapeutics*, 1968, 160, 315-25. **9**

Meisch, R.A. Self-administration of pentobarbital by means of schedule-induced polydipsia. *Psychonomic Science*, 1969, 16, 16-17. **51**

Meisch, R., Anderson, W., and Thompson, T. Water deprivation, food deprivation and reinforcement schedule determinants of oral ethanol self-administration by rats. Reported to the Committee on Problems of Drug Dependence, 1970. **53-5, 57-9**

Meisch, R. and Pickens, R.   A new technique for oral self-administration of drugs by animals. Reported to the Committee on Problems of Drug Dependence, 1968. **51-3, 61**

Mello, N.K.   Some aspects of the behavioral pharmacology of alcohol. In D.H. Efron *et al.* (eds.), *Pharmacology: A review of progress, 1957-1967.* (PHS Publ. No 1836) Washington, DC., United States Government Printing Office, 1968. **128**

Meltzer, D. and Brahlek, J.A.   Conditioned suppression and conditioned enhancement with the same positive UCS: an effect of CS duration. *Journal of the Experimental Analysis of Behavior,* 1970, 13, 67-73. **12**

Mendelson, J. and Chillag, D.   Schedule-induced air licking in rats. *Physiology and Behavior,* 1970, 5, 535-7. **130, 153, 160, 162**

Migler, B.   Bar-holding during escape conditioning. *Journal of the Experimental Analysis of Behavior,* 1963, 6, 65-72. (a) **77**

Migler, B.   Experimental self-punishment and superstitious escape behavior. *Journal of the Experimental Analysis of Behavior,* 1963, 6, 371-85. (b) **77**

Migler, B. and Brady, J.V.   Timing behavior and conditioned fear. *Journal of the Experimental Analysis of Behavior,* 1964, 7, 247-51. **38**

Millenson, J.R.   *Principles of behavioral analysis.* New York: Macmillan, 1967. **12**

Millenson, J.R. and Hurwitz, H.M.B.   Some temporal and sequential properties of behavior during conditioning and extinction. *Journal of the Experimental Analysis of Behavior,* 1961, 4, 97-106. **79**

Miller, N.E.   Theory and experiment relating psychoanalytic displacement to stimulus generalization. *Journal of Abnormal and Social Psychology,* 1948, 43, 155-78. **203**

Morris, D.   The reproductive behavior of the Zebra finch *(Poephila guttata)* with special reference to pseudofemale behavior and displacement activities. *Behaviour,* 1954, 6, 271-322. **168**

Morse, W.H. and Kelleher, R.T.   Schedules using noxious stimuli, I. Multiple fixed-ratio and fixed-interval termination of schedule complexes. *Journal of the Experimental Analysis of Behavior,* 1966, 9, 267-90. **198**

Morse, W.H. and Kelleher, R.T.   Schedules as fundamental determinants of behavior. In W.N. Schoenfeld (ed.), *The theory of reinforcement schedules.* New York: Appleton-Century-Crofts, 1970, 139-85. **22, 24-5**

Morse, W.H., Mead, R.N., and Kelleher, R.T.   Modulation of elicited behavior by a fixed-interval schedule of electric shock presentation. *Science,* 1967, 157, 215-17. **16, 22, 23, 161, 164**

Mowrer, O.H. and Miller, N.E.   A multi-purpose learning-demonstration apparatus. *Journal of Experimental Psychology,* 1942, 31, 163-70. **71**

Moynihan, M.   Some displacement activities of the Black-headed Gull. *Behaviour,* 1953, 5, 58-80. **167-8**

O'Kelly, L.E. and Steckle, L.C. A note on long-enduring emotional responses in the rat. *Journal of Psychology*, 1939, 8, 125-31. **203-4, 209**

Orr, J.L. A semicircular bite-hose assembly. In preparation. **231**

Pickens, R. and Harris, W. Self-administration of d-amphetamine by rats. *Psychopharmacologia*, 1968, 12, 158-63. **55**

Pickens, R., Meisch, R., and McGuire, L.E. Methamphetamine reinforcement in rats. *Psychonomic Science*, 1967, 8, 371-2. **55**

Pickens, R. and Thompson, T. Cocaine-reinforced behavior in rats: Effects of reinforcement magnitude and fixed-ratio size. *Journal of Pharmacology and Experimental Therapeutics*, 1968, 161, 122-9. **55, 63**

Pickens, R. and Thompson, T. Characteristics of stimulant drug reinforcement. In T. Thompson and R. Pickens (eds.), *Stimulus functions of drugs*. New York: Appleton-Century-Crofts, 1971. **50, 56-7, 64**

Pickens, R., Thompson, T., and Yokel, R.A. Self-administration of amphetamines by animals. Symposium on 'Current Research on Amphetamine and Behavior,' Duke University, June 1970. **50**

Pomerleau, O.F. The effects of stimuli followed by response-independent shock on shock-avoidance behavior. *Journal of the Experimental Analysis of Behavior*, 1970, 14, 11-21. **46**

Rachlin, H. Autoshaping of key pecking in pigeons with negative reinforcement. *Journal of the Experimental Analysis of Behavior*, 1969, 12, 521-31. **70**

Rachman, S. and Teasdale, J. *Aversion therapy and behavior disorders*. Coral Gables, Fla.: University of Miami Press, 1969. **239**

Ray, O.S. Tranquilizer effects as a function of experimental anxiety procedures. *Archives Internationales de Pharmacodynamie et de Therapie*, 1964, 153, 49-68. **31**

Rescorla, R. and Solomon, R. Two-process learning theory: relationships between Pavlovian conditioning and instrumental learning. *Psychological Review*, 1967, 74, 151-82. **47**

Reynierse, J.H. Excessive drinking in rats as a function of number of meals. *Canadian Journal of Psychology*, 1966, 20, 82-6. **97**

Reynierse, J.H. and Spanier, D. Excessive drinking in rats' adaptation to the schedule of feeding. *Psychonomic Science*, 1968, 10, 95-6. **150**

Reynierse, J.H., Zerbolio, D.J., and Denny, M.R. Avoidance decrement: replication and further analysis. *Psychonomic Science*, 1964, 1, 401-2. **70**

Reynolds, G.S. *A primer of operant conditioning*. Glenview: Scott, Foresman, 1968. **73**

Reynolds, G.S., Catania, A.C., and Skinner, B.F. Conditioned and unconditioned aggression in pigeons. *Journal of the Experimental Analysis of Behavior*, 1963, 1, 73-4. **211-12, 224, 239**

Riddle, W.C., Rednick, A.B., Catania, A.C., and Tucker, S.J. Complete squirrel monkey diet in tablet form. *Journal of the Experimental Analysis of Behavior*, 1966, 9, 670. **133**

Rilling, M., Askew, H.R., Ahlskog, J.E., and Kramer, T.J. Aversive properties of the negative stimulus in a successive discrimination. *Journal of the Experimental Analysis of Behavior*, 1969, 12, 917-32. **155, 160**

Risley, T.R. The effects and side effects of punishing the autistic behaviors of a defiant child. *Journal of Applied Behavior Analysis*, 1968, 1, 21-34. **239**

Roberts, A.E. and Hurwitz, H.M.B. The effect of a pre-shock signal on a free-operant avoidance response. *Journal of the Experimental Analysis of Behavior*, 1970, 14, 331-40. **12**

Rosenblith, J.Z. Polydipsia induced in the rat by a second-order schedule. *Journal of the Experimental Analysis of Behavior*, 1970, 14, 139-44. **106, 132, 144, 146, 166**

Rowell, C.H.F. Displacement grooming in the chaffinch. *Animal Behaviour*, 1961, 9, 38-63. **168**

Sansone, M. and Bovet, D. Effects of amphetamine on the decrement of performance in avoidance conditioning of guinea pigs. *Psychopharmacologia*, 1969, 16, 234-9. **70**

Schaeffer, R.W., Diehl, J.C., and Salzberg, C.L. An application of Premack's theory to behaviours associated with a FFI food schedule. *Psychonomic Science*, 1966, 6, 405-6. **130**

Schneider, B.A. A two-state analysis of fixed-interval responding in the pigeon. *Journal of the Experimental Analysis of Behavior,* 1969, 12, 677-87. **145**

Schoenfeld, W.N. An experimental approach to anxiety, escape, and avoidance behavior. In P.H. Hoch and J. Zubin (eds.), *Anxiety*. New York: Grune and Stratton, 1950. **47**

Schuster, C.R. and Thompson, T. Self-administration of and behavioral dependence on drugs. *Annual Review of Pharmacology*, 1969, 9, 483-502. **50**

Schuster, C.R. and Woods, J.H. Schedule-induced polydipsia in the rhesus monkey. *Psychological Reports*, 1966, 19, 823-8. **129, 148, 163**

Scobie, S.R. Shock intensity and conditioned suppression or acceleration of avoidance in rats. *Proceedings 77th Annual Convention, American Psychological Association*, 1969, 99-100. **46**

Scott, J.P. Incomplete adjustment caused by frustration of untrained mice. *Journal of Comparative Psychology*, 1946, 39, 379-90. **204**

Scott, J.P. and Fredrickson, E. The causes of fighting in mice and rats. *Psychological Zoology*, 1951, 24, 273-309. **204**

Segal, E.F. The interaction of psychogenic polydipsia with wheel running in rats. *Psychonomic Science*, 1969, 14, 141-4. (a) **83**

Segal, E.F. Transformation of polydipsic drinking into operant drinking: a paradigm? *Psychonomic Science*, 1969, 16, 133-5. (b) **161**

Segal, E.F. and Deadwyler, S.A. Water drinking patterns under several dry food reinforcement schedules. *Psychonomic Science*, 1965, 1, 271-2. **103**

Segal, E.F. and Holloway, S.M. Timing behavior in rats with water drinking as a mediator. *Science*, 1963, 140, 888-9. **96**

Segal, E.F., Oden, D.L., and Deadwyler, S.A. Determinants of polydipsia: IV. Free-reinforcement schedules. *Psychonomic Science*, 1965, 3, 11-12. **97, 161**

Senter, R.J. and Sinclair, J.D. Self-maintenance of intoxication in the rat: a modified replication. *Psychonomic Science,* 1967, 9, 291-2. **51**

Sevenster, P. A causal analysis of a displacement activity (Fanning in *Gasteroteus aculeatus* L.). *Behaviour Supplements*, 1961, 9, 1-170. **168**

Shanab, M.E. and Peterson, J.L. Polydipsia in the pigeon. *Psychonomic Science*, 1969, 15, 51-2. **148, 163**

Sidman, M. Avoidance conditioning with brief shock and no exteroceptive warning signal. *Science*, 1953, 118, 157-8. **14, 40, 77**

Sidman, M. Technique for assessing the effects of drugs on timing behavior. *Science*, 1955, 122, 925. **36**

Sidman, M. By-products of aversive control. *Journal of the Experimental Analysis of Behavior*, 1958, 1, 265-80. **13**

Sidman, M. Normal sources of pathological behavior. *Science*, 1960, 132, 61-8. **40-1, 68, 150, 198**

Sidman, M. Anxiety. *Proceedings of the American Philosophical Society*, 1964, 108, 478-81. **26**

Sidman, M. Avoidance behavior. In W.K. Honig (ed.), *Operant behavior: areas of research and application.* New York: Appleton-Century-Crofts, 1966, 448-98. **198**

Sidman, M., Herrnstein, R.J., and Conrad, D.G. Maintenance of avoidance behavior by unavoidable shocks. *Journal of Comparative and Physiological Psychology*, 1957, 50, 553-7. **12, 13, 40, 198**

Skinner, B.F. *The behavior of organisms.* New York: Appleton-Century, 1938. **11, 65, 67, 73**

Skinner, B.F. The operational analysis of psychological terms. *Psychological Review*, 1945, 52, 270-8. **67**

Skinner, B.F. 'Superstition' in the pigeon. *Journal of Experimental Psychology*, 1948, 38, 168-72. **130**

Skinner, B.F. Are theories of learning necessary? *Psychological Review*, 1950, 57, 193-216. **66**

Skinner, B.F. The phylogeny and ontogeny of behavior. *Science*, 1966, 153, 1205-13. **77, 165**

Stachnik, T.J., Ulrich, R.E., and Mabry, J.H. Reinforcement of intra-
and inter-species aggression with intracranial stimulation. *American
Zoologist*, 1966, 6, 663-8. **212**

Staddon, J.E.R. and Simmelhag, V.L. The 'superstition' experiment: A
reexamination of its implications for the principles of adaptive behavior. *Psychological Review*, 1971, 78, 3-43. **130, 146-7**

Stein, L. Excessive drinking in the rat: superstition or thirst? *Journal
of Comparative and Physiological Psychology*, 1964, 58, 237-42.
83, 95-6, 109-110, 112

Stretch, R. Development and maintenance of responding under schedules of electric-shock presentation. In R.M. Gilbert and J.R. Millenson (eds.), *Reinforcement: Behavioral analyses*. New York: Academic Press, 1972, in press. **13**

Stretch, R., Orloff, E.R., and Dalrymple, S.D. Maintenance of responding by fixed-interval schedule of electric shock presentation in squirrel monkeys. *Science*, 1968, 162, 583-6. **164**

Stricker, E.M. and Adair, E.R. Body fluid balance, taste, and post-prandial factors in schedule-induced polydipsia. *Journal of Comparative
and Physiological Psychology*, 1966, 62, 449-54. **95-6, 109-110, 112**

Taylor, D.B. and Lester, D. Schedule-induced nitrogen drinking in the
rat. *Psychonomic Science*, 1969, 15, 17-18. **130**

Teitelbaum, P. and Derks, P. The effects of amphetamine on forced
drinking in the rat. *Journal of Comparative and Physiological Psychology*, 1958, 51, 801-10. **131-32**

Thompson, D.M. Escape from S[D] associated with fixed-ratio reinforcement. *Journal of the Experimental Analysis of Behavior*, 1964, 7,
1-8. **152, 155, 159, 162, 174**

Thompson, D.M. Punishment by S[D] associated with fixed-ratio reinforcement. *Journal of the Experimental Analysis of Behavior*, 1965,
8, 189-94. **160, 174**

Thompson, T., Bigelow, G., and Pickens, R. Factors influencing self-
administration by unrestrained monkeys in a complex programmed
environment. Presented to the Committee on Problems of Drug Dependence, 1969. **50, 55-7, 63**

Thompson, T. and Pickens, R. Drug dependence and conditioning. In
H. Steinberg (ed.), *Scientific basis of drug dependence*. London: J.A.
Churchill, 1969. **50**

Thompson, T. and Pickens, R. Stimulant self-administration by animals:
Some comparisons with opiate self-administration. *Federation Proceedings*, 1970, 29, 6-12. **50-1, 55**

Thompson, T. and Pickens, R. (eds.), *Stimulus functions of drugs*. New
York: Appleton-Century-Crofts, 1971. **50, 60**

Thompson, T. and Schuster, C.R. Morphine self-administration, food-
reinforced and avoidance behaviors in rhesus monkeys. *Psychopharmacologia*, 1964, 5, 87-94. **57, 62**

Thompson, T. and Schuster, C.R. *Behavioral pharmacology*. Englewood Cliffs, NJ: Prentice Hall, 1968. **50, 171**

Thorndike, E.L. *Animal intelligence*. New York: Macmillan, 1911. **65**

Tinbergen, N. Die Ubersprungbewegung. *Zeitschrift für Tierpsychologie*, 1940, 4, 1-40. **145**

Tinbergen, N. 'Derived' activities: their causation, biological significance, origin, and emancipation during evolution. *Quarterly Review of Biology*, 1952, 27, 1-32. **167-8**

Tinbergen, N. and VanIersel, J.J.A. 'Displacement reactions' in the three-spined stickleback. *Behaviour*, 1947, 1, 56-63. **168**

Ulrich, R.E. Pain as a cause of aggression. *American Zoologist*, 1966, 6, 643-62. **204**

Ulrich, R.E. Interaction between reflexive fighting and cooperative escape. *Journal of the Experimental Analysis of Behavior*, 1967, 10, 311-17. (a) **213, 215-17**

Ulrich, R.E. Unconditioned and conditioned aggression and its relation to pain. *Activas Nervosa Superior*, 1967, 9, 80-91. (b) **224**

Ulrich, R.E. and Azrin, N.H. Reflexive fighting in response to aversive stimulation. *Journal of the Experimental Analysis of Behavior*, 1962, 5, 511-20. **151, 164, 175, 178, 204, 206-8, 210**

Ulrich, R.E. and Craine, W.H. Behavior: Persistence of shock-induced aggression. *Science*, 1964, 143, 971-3. **213**

Ulrich, R.E., Holz, W.C., and Azrin, W.H. Stimulus control of avoidance behavior. *Journal of the Experimental Analysis of Behavior*, 1964, 7, 129-33. **40**

Ulrich, R.E., Hutchinson, R.R., and Azrin, N.H. Pain-elicited aggression. *Psychological Record*, 1965, 15, 111-26. **205, 209**

Ulrich, R.E., Johnston, M., Richardson, J., and Wolff, P.C. The operant conditioning of fighting in rats. *Psychological Record*, 1963, 13, 465-70. **211-12, 239**

Ulrich, R.E., Stachnik, T.J., Brierton, G.R., and Mabry, J.H. Fighting and avoidance in response to aversive stimulation. *Behaviour*, 1966, 26, 124-9. **214-15, 224**

Ulrich, R.E., Wolfe, M., and Dulaney, S.J. Punishment of shock-induced aggression. *Journal of the Experimental Analysis of Behavior*, 1969, 12, 1009-15. **221-31, 235, 240**

Ulrich, R.E., Wolff, P.C., and Azrin, N.H. Shock as an elcitor of intra- and inter-species fighting behaviour. *Animal Behaviour*, 1964, 12, 14-15. **206-8**

Valenstein, E.S., Cox, V.C., and Kakolewski, J.W. Modification of motivated behavior elicited by electrical stimulation of the hypothalamus. *Science*, 1968, 159, 1119-21. **163-4**

Verhave, T. The effect of methamphetamine on operant level and avoidance behavior. *Journal of the Experimental Analysis of Behavior*, 1958, 1, 207-19. **9**

Vernon, W. and Ulrich, R.E. Classical conditioning of pain-elicited aggression. *Science*, 1966, 152, 668-9. **210, 238**

Villarreal, J.E. Schedule-induced pica. Paper read at Meeting of Eastern Psychological Association, Boston, April 1967. **130, 152, 159-60, 162-3, 165**

Waller, M.B. and Waller, P.F. The effects of unavoidable shocks on a multiple schedule having an avoidance component. *Journal of the Experimental Analysis of Behavior*, 1963, 6, 29-37. **12, 13**

Walsh, M.G. and Keehn, J.D. Avoidance behavior in a bar-pressing situation as a function of release-shock intervals. *Psychological Reports*, 1969, 24, 511-18. **79-80**

Walters, G.C. and Glazer, R.D. Punishment of instinctive behavior in the Mongolian gerbil. *Journal of Comparative and Physiological Psychology*, 1971, 75, 331-40. **13**

Weeks, J. Experimental morphine addiction: Method for automatic intravenous injections in unrestrained rats: *Science*, 1962, 138, 143-4. **55**

Weiskrantz, L. Emotion. In L. Weiskrantz (ed.), *Analysis of behavioral change*. New York: Harper and Row, 1968. **47**

Woods, J. and Schuster, C.R. Opiates as reinforcing stimuli. In T. Thompson and R. Pickens (eds.), *Stimulus functions of drugs*. New York: Appleton-Century-Crofts, 1971. **57**

Wuttke, W. The effects of d-amphetamine on schedule-controlled water licking in the squirrel monkey. *Psychopharmacologia* (Berl.), 1970, 17, 70-82. **132**

Yanagita, T., Deneau, G.A., and Seevers, M.H. Evaluation of pharmacologic agents in monkey by long term intravenous self or programmed administration. Abstract No 66, 23rd International Congress of Physiological Sciences, Tokyo, 1965, p. 48. **128**

Subject index